Surgeons' Lives

Surgeons' Lives

Royal College of Surgeons of Edinburgh
An Anthology of College Fellows over 500 years

Edited by Iain Macintyre and Iain MacLaren

First published in Great Britain June 2005
by the Royal College of Surgeons of Edinburgh
Nicolson Street
Edinburgh EH8 9DW

ISBN 0-9503620-9-3

A catalogue record of this book is available from the British Library

Designed and typeset by Pax Consulting, Edinburgh
Printed by Arc Colourprint, Edinburgh

Preface by HRH Prince Philip, Patron of the College

PALACE OF HOLYROODHOUSE

In the course of its 500 years of teaching surgery, any number of aspiring surgeons has passed through its lecture halls. All have eventually given valuable service to the community, but some have had outstanding careers in different parts of the world, and many have introduced innovations in techniques and skills. This book contains short biographies of some 200 of these exceptional Fellows and contains many illustrations dating from the 16th century to the present day.

'Surgeons' Lives' makes an interesting companion to the history of the College in the volume 'A Famous and Flourishing Society'.

Contents

Acknowledgements

The publication of this book was made possible by the generosity of the President and Council of the Royal College of Surgeons of Edinburgh, who agreed that it should be written as part of the College's Quincentenary celebration.

Many people have contributed to the making of this book and the editors would like to thank the following: Marianne Smith, the College Librarian, without whose enthusiastic help, guidance and support the book would not have been possible. The College Library provided invaluable help in obtaining source material and in scanning images. In particular Steven Kerr, David Collier and Simon Johnston were always willing to find essential source material at short notice.

The College Archivist, Dr Alistair Masson, gave his blessing to the project and provided expert guidance. Many of the earlier biographies were the result of his original research. The list of Fellows from 1505 to the present day, which was compiled by him and the Library staff, facilitated the otherwise time-consuming task of selecting Fellows and ascribing their roll numbers.

Dr Helen Dingwall, who wrote the history of the College, gave advice throughout and provided a concise historical account for this book.

The onerous task of checking the proofs was taken on by Helen Dingwall, Dawn Kemp, Mathew Kaufman and Marianne Smith and we wish to record our thanks to them.

We are grateful to the many secretaries who typed the original manuscripts. In particular Alexis Wood, Irene MacDonald, Emma Cook, Ashleigh Kennedy, Nicola McLennan, Moira Britton, Sarah Kirkland and Lyndsey Houston.

The College Publications Department supplied advice and stimulus from the start. Jennifer Clarke initially guided the project, which was brought to fruition by Mark Baillie. Ann Vinnicombe, the copy-editor, ensured that editorial standards were maintained. Carrie Young and Zoe Meredew provided valuable support.

David Eccles and Lindsay Snedden of Pax Consulting were responsible for the design of the cover, the layout of the book and gave invaluable advice about all aspects of the project. Andrew Connell, in the College Museum, supplied photographs and other source material and Max McKenzie took most of the original photographs.

Librarians and archivists from around the world willingly supplied source documents and images. While the institutions concerned have been acknowledged in the illustrations list, the editors would like to thank: Iain Milne and the Library staff at the Royal College of Physicians of Edinburgh; Valerie McLure and the Library staff of the Royal College of Physicians and Surgeons of Glasgow; Lucy Reid, Royal College of Obstetricians and Gynaecologists; Tina Craig, Royal College of Surgeons of England; Alison Gardner, Lothian Health Services Archive; Captain (retd) P. H. Starling, Army Medical Services Museum, Aldershot; Roderick Stewart of Toronto, who generously provided photographs of Norman Bethune; Mrs M. Pierce Moulton, Librarian, Liverpool Medical Institution; Mr A. W. Beasley, who corrected the manuscripts of the New Zealand biographies.

Finally we thank Tessa and Fiona for their patience and help throughout.

COLLEGIUM REGIUM CHIRURGORUM EDINENSE, MM.

College Photograph, 2000

To mark the Millennium the College commissioned a portrait of current and former Office Bearers and Council members in the style of the painting of the 1889 Meeting of Fellows (see pages 136–137).

To try to reproduce that portrait as accurately as possible the positions of the subjects and even the papers scattered on the floor were faithfully copied from the original group portrait.

1. A. G. D. Maran *President 1997–2000*
2. J. A. R. Smith *Vice President*
3. W. A. Wallace *Vice President*
4. D. Morcom *Head College Officer*
5. A. S. Campbell *Secretary*
6. I. M. C. Macintyre *Council*
7. A. B. MacGregor *Treasurer*
8. O. Eremin *Editor of the Journal*
9. I. D. Learmonth *Council*
10. M. F. Macnicol *Former Treasurer*
11. M. Bean *Former Clerk*
12. A. C. H. Watson *Former Treasurer*
13. L. D. Finch *Past Dean*
14. J. Walker *Former College Officer*
15. A. Watson *Deputy College Officer*
16. A. A. Gunn *Former Honorary Librarian*
17. L. H. Allan *Bursar*

18. D. L. Gardner *Former Conservator*
19. A. H. B Masson *Honorary Archivist*
20. J. F. Gould *Past Dean*
21. W. D. MacLennan *Past Dean*
22. J. H. Steyn *Former Treasurer*
23. S. P. F. Hughes *Former Vice President*
24. I. F. MacLaren *Regent inter alia*
25. A. C. B. Dean *Former Secretary*
26. I. B. Macleod *Former Secretary*
27. A. N. Smith *Former Wade Professor inter alia*
28. P. Edmond *Former Vice President*
29. W. A. Thomson *Former Clerk*
30. J. St C. McCormick *Vice President Elect*
31. D. Lee *Council*
32. Sir Alfred Cuschieri *Former Council*
33. J. D. Orr *Council*
34. M. Khan *Council*
35. C. M. Evans *Council*

36. J. E. Newsam *Former Council*
37. J. A. Wilson *Council*
38. J. R. C. Foster *Chief Executive*
39. D. A. D. Macleod *Vice President Elect*
40. K. Chockalingam *Council*
41. R. W. Porter *Former Council*
42. J. G. Temple *President Elect*
43. D. J. Wheatley *Council*
44. C. J. L. Strachan *Council*
45. C. M. Doig *Council*
46. J. R. C. Logie *Council*
47. R. M. Gibson *Chairman, Faculty of Pre Hospital Care inter alia*
48. Sir Robert Shields *Past President*
49. P. S. Boulter *Past President*
50. M. C. Meikle *Dean*
51. F. J. Gillingham *Past President*
52. Rev Gilleasbuig Macmillan *Chaplain*

Foreword by the President

The Royal College of Surgeons of Edinburgh has grown impressively over the last century. At the time of our 400th anniversary celebrations in 1905, only 1,811 individuals in total had been admitted to the Fellowship. At our Quincentenary we have approximately 16,000 Fellows and Members who live and work in over 90 countries in the world.

The task of selecting only 200 Fellows for inclusion in this book was a daunting one. Iain Macintyre and Iain MacLaren have

The original Surgeons' Hall opened in 1697.
The painting is based on an engraving
by Paul Sandby c. 1750, and all of the figures,
most of whom are surgeons or physicians,
have been copied from Kay's *Portraits* (1837–8).

chosen wisely, and, while many of us may have particular favourites, there is little doubt that the 200 Fellows they have chosen are entirely appropriate for special acknowledgement at the time of our Quincentenary celebrations. The authors are to be congratulated on these biographies, on the superb illustrations which accompany them, and on the quality of this publication. At this milestone in the history of the College, this book provides glimpses into the lives of some of the surgeons who made the College successful over the years.

It makes fascinating reading, will be a valuable reference source, and further enhances our knowledge of collegiate history.

J. A. R. Smith
2005

Biographies

The 20th Century

Introduction

This commemorative volume was commissioned by the College Council to honour, in the Quincentennial year, the memory of some of the many Fellows over the past 500 years whose characters, personalities and achievements have won for the College the prestige and influence which it enjoys in the 21st century.

To be entrusted with its production was, for the editors, a very great honour and an equally great challenge; we did not undertake the task lightly, but its fulfilment has been for us a labour of love.

It was decided that the book would contain a maximum of 200 biographical sketches and that it would be illustrated as lavishly as possible. Obviously this presented us with the problem of selecting, from the College's roll of 31,500 Fellows, 200 names particularly worthy of Quincentennial remembrance. For that selection we are ready to accept censure for sins of omission, but we believe ourselves to be free of sins of commission. We appreciate that there are many names whose absence from this biographical collection will inevitably incur criticism, but we are convinced that none of the Fellows of whom we have written is unworthy of inclusion.

Except for Lord Lister, who was, of course, an ordinary Fellow, we omitted from our selection the 354 distinguished persons upon whom, since 1670, the College has conferred its Honorary Fellowship or Honorary Fellowship in Dental Surgery. Lister is the only ordinary Fellow to have been made an Honorary Fellow and it is unlikely that there will ever be another.

Among the 200 Fellows commemorated in this book are some who made major contributions to the advancement of surgical science and to the relief of human suffering. There are others who in their own lifetimes were recognised internationally as master-surgeons, but professional and academic distinction have not been the only criteria for inclusion. Some have been chosen because of their outstanding services to the College or to their universities, and both sporting prowess and distinguished military service have been used as selection factors.

There are others who owe their places in the book to unusual non-surgical achievements or to their remarkable personal qualities and idiosyncrasies, and we have not regarded either eccentricity or notoriety as a bar to inclusion.

The Ionic columns at the entrance to the Playfair building.

Many of the 200 chosen Fellows were of such distinction that even the most abbreviated accounts of their careers could fill several pages (or, in some cases, several books) and we are very conscious that what we have been able to write about them may seem inadequate.

We also regret deeply that we have been obliged to omit several eminently worthy names because of scarcity of biographical material, and this has been particularly disappointing in respect of certain famous overseas Fellows.

Ultimately, we take full responsibility for the selection of Fellows commemorated in this book. Our choice has been arbitrary, and perhaps in certain instances may even have been capricious and influenced by personal foibles. We hope that the result of our efforts, however, might be regarded as a useful and possibly entertaining adjunct to Dr Helen Dingwall's splendid, definitive Quincentennial history of the College, *A Famous and Flourishing Society*.

We are indebted to the many people whose support and advice made this book possible. If our list of acknowledgements has omitted any of these, we take full responsibility. We would particularly like to thank those who contributed individual chapters, namely Helen Dingwall, John Cook, Matthew Kaufman, Dugald Gardner, Sir David Mason, John Blair (Vice–President, International Society for the History of Medicine), Colin Strachan, Geoffrey Millar, Adam Smith, A. W. Beasley, Arnold Maran, George Parks, Fraser McCord, Paul Geissler, John Chalmers, Howard Moody and Jonathan Sandy. In collecting the many illustrations, we received help from people and institutions throughout the world. We have sought to obtain permission to publish each of these, but if omissions have been made we will redress these in any future reprinting.

Finally, if those who read this book derive from it even a fraction of the interest and pleasure which its production has given to us, we shall feel that our aim has been achieved.

I. M. C. Macintyre

I. F. MacLaren

Above: The 1897 stained-glass window on the main staircase of the College.

Left: *Hinc Sanitas*. Sculpted in bronze by Denys Mitchell, 1994.

The Royal College of Surgeons of Edinburgh: A Short History

On 1 July 1505 the Town Council of Edinburgh granted a charter of incorporation, or Seal of Cause, to the barbers and surgeons of the burgh. This gave them not only exclusive rights to practise surgery in and around Edinburgh but also a monopoly on the distilling of aquavite. The Seal of Cause was ratified on 13 October 1506 by James IV, a monarch who had a particular interest in medical and scientific matters. The Seal of Cause confirmed the usual craft demarcation rights, but it was much more. It contained clauses not found in other craft charters, and these set the foundations for the efforts to promote the highest possible surgical standards, which have continued ever since.

The Seal of Cause stated that apprentices must be able to 'baith wryte and read', and two further clauses may be seen as establishing the essence of the College. First, it was stipulated that 'euery man aucht to knaw the nature and substance of euery thing that he werkis, or ellis he is negligent; and that we may have anis in the yeir any condampnit [condemned] man efter he be deid to mak anatomell off, quhairthraw [so that] we may haif experience, ilk ane [each one] to instrict vtheris, and we sall do suffrage for the soule'. There was, therefore, early emphasis on teaching and learning anatomy (and on the astrological signs). Second, it was ordained that 'na maner of persoun occupie nor vse ony poyntis of our saidis craftis of Surregenie or Barbour craft within this burgh bott gif he be first frieman and burges of the saymn, and that he be worthy and expert in all the poyntis belangand the saidis craftis diligentlie and avysitlie examinit and admittit be the maisters of the said craft for the honorabill seruying of oure Souerane Lord his lieges and nychtbouris of this burgh'. This clause set in train the examinations which would test the competence of surgical apprentices. Teaching and examining have been the core activities of the College over the ensuing 500 years, though their form, content and application have evolved in parallel with progress in anatomical knowledge and surgical techniques.

The written records of the College are continuous from 1581 and demonstrate clearly the implementation of the Seal of Cause in practical terms. This was not always easy. The changing and complex social, political and economic context in which the College operated had a significant influence on internal matters, and its existence was threatened on a number of occasions, from plague in the 17th century, to economic difficulties in the 18th and political pressures in the 19th, in the period before the passing of the Medical Act in 1858.

In the early years the Incorporation of Surgeons and Barbers had no permanent home, and meetings were held in the deacon's house or occasionally in St Giles' Kirk, where in pre-Reformation times the Incorporation had maintained an altar dedicated to St Mungo. The main concerns were with establishing and maintaining discipline at meetings, ensuring that apprentices were properly trained, that entrant masters were 'diligently and avisitly examinit', and that unauthorised surgical practice was prevented as far as possible. It was also crucial for the Incorporation to maintain its contacts with royalty and the nobility, and many Edinburgh surgeons served royal houses and armies. In 1567 Mary, Queen of Scots granted the Incorporation exemption from bearing arms

---

The Seal of Cause
A translation of some of the clauses

Item, that no manner of person employ nor use any points of our said crafts of surgery or barber craft within this burgh unless he is first a freeman and burgess of the same; and that he be worthy and expert in all subjects belonging to the said crafts, diligently and knowlegeably examined and admitted by the masters of the said craft ... be examined and approved in these following points, that is to say, that he know anatomy, the nature and complexion of every member of the human body, and likewise that he know all the veins of the same, that he may perform phlebotomy in due time ... for every man ought to know the nature and substance of every thing with which he deals or else he is negligent; and that we may have once a year a condemned man after death to perform anatomy on, whereby we may have experience, each one to instruct others, and we shall do sufferage for the soul ...and that no barber, master nor servant, within this practice, use nor exercise the craft of Surgery without he be expert and know perfectly the things described above ... that no masters of the said craft will take an apprentice unless he can both write and read ... we have appended our common seal of cause, at Edinburgh, the first day of the month of July, the year of God one thousand five hundred and five years.

Detail from the 1505 Seal of Cause held in the City of Edinburgh Archive.

in conflict, provided that the surgeons treated the wounded of all sides impartially. The Letter of Exemption stated that 'cunyng men of the occupatioun and craft of chyrurgianrie ar als necessar to be within this realme as in vthir partis', and also that excusal would give them the opportunity to 'studie the perfection of the said craft and occupatioun to the vttermost of their ingynis'.

In terms of fulfilling the Seal of Cause, the early entrance examinations took the form of a general session in which all the available masters participated. If the apprentice was successful, he had to produce his burgess ticket, pay the appropriate fee and provide a dinner for the masters. By 1696 this latter requirement was relaxed because of alleged overindulgence, and it was stipulated that in future 'examinators be allowed every one of them a pynt of wine and the intrant a pynt of wine and no more'. More formal examination regulations appeared in 1647 – coincidentally at the same time as the first rented meeting rooms in Dickson's Close were obtained – and three distinct sessions were stipulated, including a test on anatomy 'by ocular inspection'. In 1723 tests on botany and materia medica were added, and by this time a rota for elected examiners was in operation.

The turn of the 18th century found the Incorporation flourishing. In 1697 it moved from Curryhill House (which had been acquired in 1656) to a newly built hall and anatomy theatre, which expanded possible activities, including public anatomical dissections. After a period of bitter conflicts with the new Royal College of Physicians over pharmacy and supervision of the apothecaries, the Incorporation's rights and privileges had been confirmed by King William and Queen Mary in 1695. Apprentices and masters had access to physic gardens, and a library and museum collection had been instituted in 1699, in keeping with the Incorporation's strong desire to be viewed as a learned society rather than a manual craft. The award of Honorary Freedoms to high-status individuals was introduced in the 1670s, as this was considered politically useful and in keeping with the ethos of the 'famous and flourishing society'.

The period of the Enlightenment brought new challenges and new opportunities. The medical school was established at Edinburgh University in 1726, and the surgeon John Monro played a part, not least in ensuring that in 1720 his son, Alexander Monro *primus*, would gain the Chair of Anatomy which had been established extra-murally by the Town Council in 1705. The medical school had both positive and negative effects on the Incorporation. Anatomical teaching was available to apprentices, but there was growing resentment at the domination of the succeeding Monros, *secundus* and *tertius*, both of whom were physicians who maintained a monopoly on the teaching of surgery as a pendicle of the anatomy course. Although Monro *secundus* in particular made significant contributions to anatomical description and elucidation of the structure and function of the body, university anatomy was increasingly seen inappropriate for practical surgery. This was to prove a major stimulus to the growth of extra-mural teaching from the late 18th century, an area which would be important to the continuing influence of the College. Indeed, the College established its own Professorship of Surgery in 1804, the first incumbent being John Thomson (q.v.), and continued to provide teaching in surgery until the University established a surgical chair in 1831.

The Surgeon by David Teniers the younger. Teniers' masterpiece provides an insight into the work of the 17th-century surgeon. In the foreground the surgeon is lancing a boil, his assistant on the right, ready with a dressing. In the background another patient is being prepared for blood-letting.

'cunyng men of the occupatioun and craft of chyrurgianrie ar als necessar to be within this realme as in vthir partis'

'studie the perfection of the said craft and occupatioun to the vttermost of their ingynis'

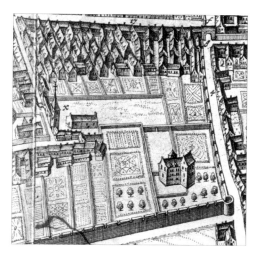

Map (1647) showing Curryhill House inside the south-east corner of the Flodden Wall.

Model of the Surgeons' Hall of 1697.

A Victorian artist's impression of the Playfair Building.

The most significant event in the 18th century for the College was the granting of a Royal Charter by George III in 1778. This redesignated the Incorporation as the Royal College of Surgeons of the City of Edinburgh, and established a contributory Widows' Fund. Masters were known thereafter as Fellows and the Deacon as President. Though it owed its existence and early survival to the Town Council, this municipal connection had come to be regarded as a disadvantage. Yet it would not be until a further charter was granted by Queen Victoria in 1851 that the link with the Town Council would be severed finally and the designation of Royal College of Surgeons of Edinburgh applied.

In addition to increasing opportunities for clinical teaching at the Royal Infirmary, the introduction of the College diploma examination from the 1770s was significant and would prove to be economically beneficial. It was introduced initially for a single occasion at the request of the War Office to examine a potential army surgeon, but very quickly developed as a subordinate qualification sought after by candidates from all over the world, including medical students, surgical apprentices, army and navy surgeons and – controversially – slave-ship surgeons. By 1815 the various diplomas were amalgamated into a single diploma, and holders henceforth designated Licentiates. The curriculum for this examination was reviewed frequently and by the 1830s it was very similar to that in operation for the MD degree at the University.

By the time that the debate on medical reform (in which College representatives played a full part) was in full swing, the College had consolidated its status with an elegant new building, designed by Playfair and opened in 1832. This provided strong visual symbolism of the gravitas which it considered that it had achieved as a Royal College. The Licentiate qualification was increasingly popular, although the requirements for the Fellowship examination were diluted from the 1820s. (Indeed, for a short period from 1850 to 1885 there was no additional examination for the Fellowship – possession of the Licentiateship and ballot of the Fellows were sufficient. The Fellowship examination was rapidly re-introduced in 1885 in the light of outside criticism.)

In the Victorian period the College Fellows had to deal with the effects of government legislation, in particular the Medical Act of 1858 and the foundation of the General Medical Council (GMC). It was necessary for the College to comply with GMC requirements if it were to remain as one of the designated entry portals for basic qualification, and the ability to do this meant co-operation with the other Scottish Colleges, with the introduction of the Double Qualification examination with the Royal College of Physicians of Edinburgh in 1859 and the Triple Qualification, incorporating the Faculty of Physicians and Surgeons of Glasgow, in 1884. The School of Medicine of the Royal Colleges was established in 1895 and lasted until 1948, providing an alternative to university medical education. Many Fellows acted as lecturers, including some of the most famous names of the day – James Syme (q.v.), Robert Liston (q.v.), Henry Littlejohn (q.v.) and John Chiene (q.v.). In parallel, though, were the great surgical opportunities brought about by the advent of anaesthetics and antiseptics and the growth of hospital medicine. College Fellows were also to make significant contributions in this area.

The first half of the 20th century was punctuated by the two world wars. Many College Fellows and Licentiates served in the forces with distinction and made lasting contributions to the surgery of war, but it was a period of relative inactivity for the College in terms of new corporate initiatives or different directions – though there was participation in the early activities of the Edinburgh Postgraduate Board for Medicine, which began classes in 1905. During the Second World War a Polish School of Medicine in exile was established in Edinburgh University and this had the active support of the College.

By the end of the Second World War and the advent of the National Health Service, it was felt that the Fellowship examination had to be revised in the light of the importance of basic sciences and the great strides which had taken place in the laboratory sciences, and in 1948 a Primary FRCS examination was introduced to cover these aspects. In the more recent past the modifications to the examination system have mirrored the extensive specialisation which has taken place in surgery, such that even general surgery is now a specialty in its own right, with its own subspecialities becoming ever more clearly defined. The other Royal Surgical Colleges in the British Isles held their own Fellowship examinations, and it was hoped that the new Specialty Fellowship might be intercollegiate, but negotiations failed. Unable to secure intercollegiate co-operation initially, the College brought in its own Specialty Fellowships in the early 1980s, initially in surgical neurology and orthopaedics. Since then, these and most of the subsequent specialty examinations have become intercollegiate. The final diet of the original Fellowship examination took place in 2003, and examinations now take place at two stages in surgical training – the new Membership (MRCS) examination (intercollegiate from 2004) at the end of basic training and the appropriate Specialty Fellowship towards the end of Higher Surgical Training, which culminates in the award of the Certificate of Completion of Higher Surgical Training. Innovative courses and examinations in areas such as sports medicine, immediate care and health informatics, including distributed learning packages and surgical masterclasses, have enabled the College to keep a high profile in the area of modern surgical education. In addition to these developments in surgery, the Dental Faculty of the College (founded as the Dental Council in 1954 and given faculty status in 1982) has taken very similar action in developing the range of its examinations and specialty examinations in areas such as orthodontics and paediatric dentistry. This proliferation in examinations has stimulated an equal proliferation in the numbers and types of training courses on offer, to cater for the requirements of modern, technological surgery, in areas such as minimal access surgery. These teaching activities will be expanded, wil be expanded within the College campus, using a new clinical skills facility to be opened during the Quincentenary celebration.

The School of Medicine of the Royal Colleges, 1905.

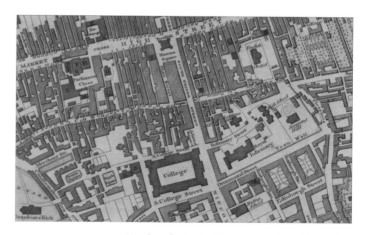

Map (1805) showing the Old Quad of the University ('labelled College'), the old Royal Infirmary in Infirmary Street and Surgeons' Square.

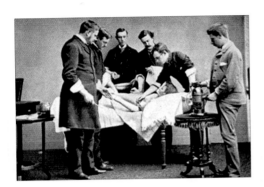

A surgical operation using Lister's carbolic spray.

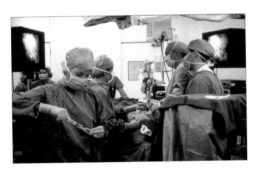

A surgical operation in the 21st century.

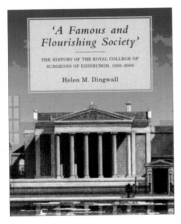

A Famous and Flourishing Society.
The history of the College written by
Dr Helen Dingwall as part of the
Quincentennial celebration.

As well as all of these home developments, a major feature of the College's outreach has been its overseas contacts and examinations. The first overseas examination was held in Hong Kong in 1965, and from that time the geographical coverage has spread to include Bangladesh, Malaysia, Saudi Arabia, Kuwait, Oman, Syria, Nepal, India, Singapore and Myanmar. A Clinical and Scientific Meeting is held furth of the United Kingdom during each presidency – the first was held in Cairo and Alexandria in 1976. These activities have maintained the presence and influence of the College world wide, and have attracted large numbers of examination candidates. The majority of the 16,000 Fellows and Members of the College are located overseas, and an Indian Chapter of the College was founded in 1976. The Overseas Doctors' Training Scheme has allowed many sponsored overseas candidates to train in Scotland before taking the College examinations.

Over the last five hundred years, then, the College has grown from a small trade incorporation with limited, local vision and horizons, to a major surgical institution with worldwide contact and influence. Throughout its history it has attempted to follow the rules set out in the Seal of Cause. Its ability to do this successfully has depended on its willingness to adapt to change and the pressure of external circumstances. The training requirements of modern surgeons are determined by government-appointed boards and, latterly, European legislation. In order to remain distinctive and attract candidates who take standard examinations, the College must continue to anticipate and react to change in teaching and assessment methods and in new specialties. The College aims to enlarge its heritage dimension in order to utilise its long history, its elegant listed building and extensive museum and archive collections, and all of these activities should help to ensure its continued success. College Fellows have in very different ways carried out the 'honorabill seruying of oure Souerane Lord his lieges and nychtbouris'. The 'honorabill seruying' may be very different in 2005 from what it was in 1505, but the aims and intentions are very similar.

Helen M. Dingwall

16th Century

The years following the granting of the Seal of Cause to the Edinburgh surgeons in 1505 saw greater changes in art and religion than had been seen for several centuries.

In a century dominated in Europe by the Renaissance and the Reformation, medicine began to emerge from the Dark Ages towards an understanding of the human body and the nature of disease based on reason. The Swiss doctor Paracelsus (1493–1541) derided witchcraft and superstition, and for the first time questioned the theories of Galen and the Greek theory of humours. His observations on the natural history of wounds and of wound infections were among the first rational studies of the topic. The French surgeon Ambroise Paré (1510–90) greatly improved the treatment of gunshot wounds by his knowledge of anatomy, his rediscovery of the vascular ligature and his observation that an emollient cream would speed the healing of battle wounds compared to the traditional boiling oil.

The influence of the anatomist Andreas Vesalius (1514–64) was profound. He produced meticulous dissections and the detailed etchings derived from them illustrated his book *De Humani Corporis Fabrica*, published in 1543.

In England the Company of Barber-Surgeons was given a Royal Charter by King Henry VIII in 1540. Thomas Vicary (1495–1561), the first master of that company and surgeon to the King, was the first surgeon to write in English on anatomy and surgery. Thomas Gale (1507–87), the best-known English surgeon of his day, wrote extensively in English and furthered the understanding of the treatment of gunshot wounds.

The privileges and responsibilities vested in the Edinburgh Barber Surgeons by their Seal of Cause were confirmed in 1506 by a Royal Charter granted to them by James IV, King of Scots, a true prince of the Renaissance and arguably the most interesting and attractive personality of the entire Stuart dynasty. Although only 15 years old when he succeeded to the throne, he was in full control of his kingdom within a few years and soon showed himself to be a strong, vigorous and wise ruler. He brought law and order to his realm along with impartial justice

Paracelsus (1493–1541).

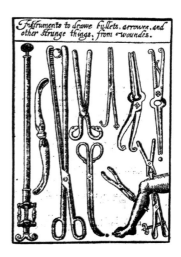

Illustration of 16th-century surgical instruments from Peter Lowe's textbook *A Discourse on the Whole Art of Chyrurgerie.*

Henry VIII and the Barber-Surgeons in 1540. Henry is depicted handing a document to his serjeant surgeon, Thomas Vickery.

Maister Peter Lowe (c. 1550–1610).

to all his subjects and the stability thus secured made it possible for trade and commerce to flourish. The King's ambitious building projects and the brilliance of his court are indications of the nation's relative prosperity during his reign as was also his development of the Scottish navy and the launching of the *Great Michael,* which was in its time one of the largest and most powerful warships in the world.

James IV's reign was for Scotland a cultural 'golden age' which produced great poets in William Dunbar, Robert Henryson and Gavin Douglas along with several others of scarcely lesser fame. It also saw the foundation in 1495 of Scotland's third university at Aberdeen, the promulgation in 1496 of an Education Act for the compulsory attendance at grammar school of the sons of barons and freeholders and in 1507 the establishment of the first Scottish printing press.

The King naturally endowed with a keen intellect and an inquiring mind was well educated and could speak seven languages including Gaelic, which endeared him to his Highland subjects. He had an intense interest in literature and the arts as well as in learning and scholarship of all kinds. He was particularly fascinated by what would now be called the natural sciences, but became obsessed to some extent with alchemy. Medicine, surgery and dentistry were among his greatest enthusiasms, and it is known that he carried out procedures such as blood-letting, the setting of fractures and dental extraction on patients to whom he made payments for letting him do so.

In 1503 James married the Princess Margaret Tudor, daughter of King Henry VII of England, and this inspired William Dunbar to write his famous celebratory poem 'The Thistle and the Rose'. Hopes that his marriage might ensure lasting peace between Scotland and England were blighted by James' rash involvement in the Anglo-French power struggle as an ally of France against England – ruled since 1509 by his brother-in-law King Henry VIII. In 1513, James IV, along with most of the Scottish nobility and nearly 10,000 of the army he had led into England, perished on 'Flodden's fatal field' in Scotland's worst military disaster. It was a tragic end to the reign of a charismatic monarch, who in his 25 years upon the Scottish throne had worthily won the respect, admiration and affection of his people.

The success with which the Barber Surgeons of Edinburgh fulfilled the obligations of their Seal of Cause in promoting and maintaining the highest standards of training and practice owed much to James IV's royal patronage and to the Charter which he granted to them.

The major figure in Scottish medicine in the latter years of the 16th century was Maister Peter Lowe, who learned his skills in Europe, particularly in France, and who, with Robert Hamilton, established the Faculty of Physicians and Surgeons of Glasgow. He was author of a significant textbook *A Discourse of the Whole Art of Chyrurgerie* in 1597.

King James IV of Scotland.

Gilbert Primrose (1535–1615)

The early references to the Incorporation of Surgeons and Barbers of Edinburgh appear in the Burgh records. These records describe the granting of the Seal of Cause by the Town Council in 1505, a Charter which was endorsed by King James IV the following year. The earliest Minutes of the Incorporation date from 1581, since when the proceedings of the surgeons have been continuously recorded.

While the names of many of the earliest members of the craft appear in the College records, roll numbers have been assigned from 1580, when the Deacon of the Incorporation was Gilbert Primrose. To him has been ascribed the honour of being first in the Roll of Fellows, which has continued in an uninterrupted sequence to this day. Robert Henrysoun was a founder member of the Incorporation and Primrose was his apprentice. The name Gilbert Primrose first appears in 1558 when Scotland was threatened by an invasion from 'the auld inemies of Ingland'. The craft guilds were required to list those men who could be mustered in the event of an attack and Gilbert Primrose was one of the 27 nominated by the Incorporation of Surgeons and Barbers. He was subsequently elected Deacon of the Incorporation on no fewer than five occasions. While he was Deacon in 1581, the Surgeon-Barbers became first in the order of precedence of the 14 crafts of the City of Edinburgh.

Gilbert Primrose was born, it is thought, in 1535, a member of the Perthshire family from which the current Earl of Rosebery is descended. He went to St Andrews University, where he graduated with a Master of Arts degree. On 6 June 1558 he was admitted to the Incorporation as apprentice to Robert Henrysoun, and went on to become Surgeon to King James VI of Scotland. He was a friend of Maister Peter Lowe, the founder of the Faculty of Physicians and Surgeons of Glasgow (now the Royal College of Physicians and Surgeons of Glasgow), who dedicated his masterly *Treatise on Chirurgery* to Gilbert Primrose. When he was elected Deacon for the third time in 1602 his status was such that he was able to impose considerable discipline on the Incorporation. Under his leadership all members of the Incorporation swore that they would uphold all aspects of the Seal of Cause and any violations were punished. Primrose was also responsible for passing new laws that sought to maintain even higher standards within the craft. Admission and examination fees were established and each member of the Incorporation was required to pay a subscription. The Incorporation thrived under his leadership.

As Serjeant-Surgeon, or principal surgeon to King James VI, he accompanied the Court to London on the Union of the Crowns, remaining Serjeant-Surgeon to the King, now James VI of Scotland and James I of England.

Gilbert Primrose died at Westminster in 1615 and was buried in Greyfriars Churchyard, Edinburgh, where his monument stands to this day. His grave carries the inscription: 'To Gilbert Primrose, Chief Surgeon to James and Anne, King and Queen of Great Britain, France and Ireland, his heirs erected this monument. He lived happily 80 years. To the end of his life he was Chief Surgeon to the King, and died, adorned with testimonials of public sorrow from Prince and people in the year of our Lord 1615.'

The tomb of Gilbert Primrose in Greyfriars Churchyard.

The replica of the mortar of Gilbert Primrose gifted to the College by his descendant, the Earl of Rosebury, on the occasion of the College's 400th anniversary.

Mural monument to John Naysmyth
in Greyfrairs burial ground, Edinburgh.
Above the recumbent effigy of Naysmyth
is the inscription 'O death where is thy sting?
O grave where is thy victory?'
The monument is thought to date
from 1613, the year of Naysmyth's death.

'O death
where is
thy sting?
O grave
where is
thy victory?'

The College Museum has an interesting exhibit labelled 'a replica of the mortar used by Gilbert Primrose, an ancestor of the Earl of Rosebery and a Deacon of the Chirurgeon-Barbers in 1581'. This mortar was presented to the College on the occasion of the opening of the new Hall of the College in December 1909 by the Earl of Rosebery, who had been Prime Minister from 1894 to 1895, and who was a descendant of Gilbert Primrose.

Roll number: 1

John Naysmyth (1556–1613)

In the 16th century and beyond, royal patronage was important for advancement in many walks of life, and surgery was no exception. The Incorporation as a body, and individual surgeons, valued such patronage, not only for the prestige which it carried, but also for the power that could enable them to overcome otherwise insurmountable political obstacles.

John Naysmyth was the younger son of Michael Naysmyth (or Nasmyth), Chamberlain to John Hamilton, the Archbishop of St Andrews. His early education was at St Mary's College, St Andrews, before he was apprenticed to Gilbert Primrose (q.v.). He was admitted to the Incorporation in 1588.

It is thought that he was a member of Lord Seton's party, a small select group who were entrusted to journey to England, ostensibly on a diplomatic visit to Queen Elizabeth I, but in reality to smuggle letters to the imprisoned Mary, Queen of Scots, from the Regent. This was achieved successfully, and as a result of his part in this exploit Naysmyth found favour with King James VI. Later, however, he was suspected of involvement in a plot against the King by Francis, Earl of Bothwell, which resulted in his fleeing to France, where he became Chief Surgeon to the Scots Guards of the King of France.

Returning to Scotland in 1599, he appears to have been forgiven for his earlier infidelity, and was accepted back into the Royal Court. Gilbert Primrose, his surgical master, had by now been made Serjeant-Surgeon (or Chief Surgeon) to King James VI. Naysmyth became a surgeon to King James VI and, on the Union of the Crowns in 1603, he travelled with the Court to London. King James, now also King James I of England, made him Royal Herbalist for life. After his death in London he was buried in Greyfriars Churchyard in Edinburgh, where an elaborate monument marks his grave.

Roll number: 19

The 17th century in Europe saw a series of virtually continuous wars, many fought in the name of religion. In this, as in every other century, the battlefield was to prove a valuable training ground for the surgeon.

This century also saw remarkable advances in science. This was the century of Robert Boyle (1627–91) and Isaac Newton (1642–1727). Scientific societies took root throughout Europe and the advance of medical knowledge continued. William Harvey (1578–1657), the English physician, had demonstrated the circulation of the blood and in 1628 published his observations in *De Motu Cordis*, the first steps in the study of modern human physiology. The development of the microscope by Anthony van Leeuwenhoek (1632–1723) enabled anatomy and pathology to be studied for the first time at a cellular level.

In Edinburgh, the Incorporation of Surgeons continued to grow and to train and examine its apprentices. Whilst the Company of Barber-Surgeons in London, at this time, did not require its apprentices to learn Latin, this remained a requirement for apprentices of the Edinburgh Incorporation and undoubtedly enhanced their standards of literacy. Those who successfully fulfilled the terms of their indenture and passed the examination could aspire to become surgical masters. One of the masters was elected chairman for a variable period of time and took the title of 'Deacon'. The records of the Incorporation suggest that it took seriously its responsibilities to train the apprentices and maintained standards of discipline within its number.

William Harvey (1578–1657)
demonstrating to Charles I.

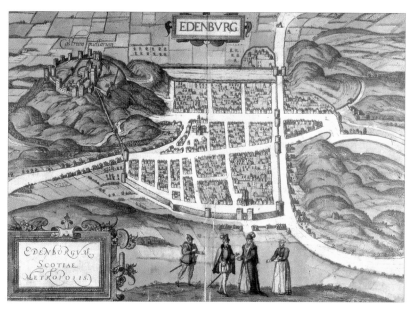

Map of Edinburgh, 1574–5.

Dickson's Close, meeting place of
the surgeons from 1647 to 1650.

The earliest meetings of the Incorporation had taken place in the Deacon's House and the High Kirk of St Giles. In 1647 they met in Dickson's Close in the High Street and some nine years later bought Curryhill House. There was increasing pressure to provide better accommodation which would allow anatomical dissection and teaching, and would house a library. The first Surgeons' Hall was opened in 1697.

In the last decade of the 17th century Sir John de Medina was commissioned to paint some thirty portraits of the members of the Incorporation at the time, and to include a few other notable figures such as James Douglas 4th Duke of Hamilton.

Sir John Baptiste de Medina (1659–1710)

Medina was a Spanish painter who was commissioned by the College to paint some thirty portraits of prominent Fellows of the College and prominent Scottish figures at the start of the 18th century. It is likely that this commission was to celebrate the opening of the new Surgeons' Hall in 1697.

The son of a captain in the Spanish army, Medina was born in Brussels in 1659. After early training in Belgium, where he studied under the Flemish portrait painter François Duchatel, he moved to London and from there he was persuaded to move to Scotland.

His patron in Scotland was the Earl of Leven, under whose patronage he set up a practice in Edinburgh, where he soon developed a reputation as a portrait painter, becoming known as the Kneller of the North.

During his time in Edinburgh, Medina produced a large number of portraits using apprentices to paint the draperies and adding the faces himself towards the end of the composition. One of his apprentices William Aikman continued the College series after Medina's death in 1710.

Medina was knighted in 1707, and was the last individual to receive a knighthood in Scotland before the Act of Union.

Alexander Pennycuik
of New Hall (1605–95)

In his *Historical Sketch of the College*, published in 1860, John Gairdner (q.v.) reckoned that around twenty of the first 150 members of the Incorporation were from landed families, many of whom took their name from that of their family estate. Alexander Pennycuik was one such. He joined the army of the Swedish King Gustavus Adolphus in the Thirty Years' War and went on to fight in the English Civil War. His son, in a fond posthumous tribute, described him as 'The oldest Aesculapian of his age ... who flattered not the rich nor scourged the poor.' He went on: 'From old forebears much worth he did inherit/ A gentleman by birth but more by merit.'

Alexander Pennycuik was a member of a landowning family that owned the estate of Penicuik, just south of Edinburgh. When he inherited the estate of Romanno, north of Peebles in 1647, he sold the family estate of Penicuik and bought that of New Hall on the southern borders of Midlothian. In the College records, therefore, he is often referred to as Alexander Pennycuik of New Hall.

Like many Scots, he felt drawn to serve in the Thirty Years' War. He was surgeon to General Baner, who led one of the armies of Queen Christina of Sweden. In 1640 he was admitted to the Incorporation of Surgeons and Barbers in consideration of his 'literature and qualifications' and on the payment of the sum of £200 Scots.

He spent much of his life as a military surgeon in Scotland and Ireland, becoming Surgeon General of the Scots Royalist forces in Ireland during the English Civil War. For these many years of service he claimed to have been paid a meagre £165 sterling. Furthermore, his loyalty to the Crown over this period had resulted in the loss of his land, which was plundered by the Parliamentarian Army. After the war, in 1663, he petitioned Parliament for £3,668 sterling, which he reckoned was the compensation due to him for services as a military surgeon, and the loss of his estate.

For all his involvement in conflict, he went on to live to the age of 90. His son Alexander achieved some fame as a poet and naturalist and his estate of New Hall became famous as the scene of *The Gentle Shepherd*, Allan Ramsay's celebrated pastoral poem.

Roll number: 55

James Borthwick of Stow (1615–75).

James Borthwick of Stow (1615–75)

The Seal of Cause of 1505 had required that every freeman of the Incorporation of Surgeons and Barbers must 'knaw anotomell, nature and complexion of euery member humanis bodie'. It had also made provision for anatomical dissection. The surgeons were to have 'anis in the yeir ane condampnit [condemned] man efter he be deid to mak antomell of, quhairthraw [so that] we may haif experience, ilk ane [each one] to instrict otheris, and we sall do suffrage for the soule'.

This vision of anatomical knowledge as the basis of surgical practice is all the more remarkable as it was written some thirty years before Vesalius began to teach anatomy in Padua. Indeed, Vesalius was not born until 1514. Yet it was almost 150 years before the Incorporation appointed what was in effect its first teacher of anatomy.

James Borthwick, an apothecary who had served as a surgeon overseas along with Alexander Pennycuik (q.v.), was unusual in being admitted to the Incorporation of Surgeons and Barbers without first having served an apprenticeship. This was probably because the membership of the Incorporation had been reduced by the plague. It seems likely that his admission was facilitated by Pennycuik, who was Deacon of the Incorporation at the time. Borthwick was admitted in 1645 with a particular responsibility – he was to perform anatomical dissections for the instruction of apprentices.

He was responsible, jointly, with Thomas Kincaid (q.v.) for the Act of the Town Council, which, in 1657, brought the surgeon-apothecary into being in Edinburgh. Up until then, the surgeons and apothecaries had different areas of practice, the surgeons being responsible for treating tumours, wounds, ulcers and fractures while the apothecaries were involved in dispensing medicines. After the 1657 Act it became possible to combine these skills as a surgeon-apothecary. Borthwick's original mortar used for preparing medications is in the National Museum of Scotland.

James Borthwick was Deacon of the Incorporation from 1638 to 1641 and again from 1659 to 1661. He owned the estate of Stow, south of Edinburgh, and was a member of the Scottish Parliament representing Edinburgh.

He was buried in Greyfriars Churchyard, Edinburgh, where an impressive mural monument to his memory stands to this day.

Roll number: 62

Bronze mortar used by
James Borthwick, dated 1668.

Detail from James Borthwick's mural monument in Greyfriars Churchyard. The central panel depicts the King of Terrors armed with the scythe of Father Time, representing death and immortality respectively.

Thomas Kincaid (1619–91)

The completion of Surgeons' Hall in 1697 gave the Incorporation the opportunity to expand its library. Rules were established for that library – there was, for example, to be no eating or drinking. Books (and surgical instruments) could be borrowed by members of the Incorporation – with fines for late returns – and books could be consulted by apprentices. In 1697 they advertised in the *Edinburgh Gazette* for books for the library, demonstrating their desire to have a collection that would include a wide range of subjects other than medical. Thomas Kincaid's son, in 1709, donated his collection of books to the College. While this was not as large as the collections of his contemporaries, Archibald Pitcairne (q.v.) or those of Robert Sibbald and Andrew Balfour, founders of the Edinburgh Physic Garden, it offers valuable insight into the books which were read by 17th-century surgeons.

Little is know about the early career of Thomas Kincaid. He was commissioned in 1644 into the Scots Covenanting army and was known to be active in the Covenanting government which ruled Scotland for 11 years. He was admitted into the Incorporation in 1646, served as treasurer from 1652 to 1655 and then became Deacon. His time in office saw a period of educational reform which resulted in apprentices being trained as surgeon-apothecaries, learning chemistry, botany and herbal cures so becoming thereby more roundly educated.

A selection of books from Thomas Kincaid's library.

Thomas Kincaid practised as a surgeon-apothecary in Edinburgh for 45 years, died in 1691 at the age of 72, and was buried in Greyfriars Churchyard, Edinburgh.

In 1709 his son Thomas (q.v.) donated his father's collection of some 230 books to the College. This was not as large as those of several of his contemporaries, such as Archibald Pitcairne who had, of course, trained as a physician and been Professor of Physic in Leiden before joining the Incorporation. Andrew Balfour, another contemporary physician, had a collection of some 3,500 books, while Robert Sibbald, the physician with whom he had founded the Physic Garden, had a library of over 5,000 books.

Kincaid's library was a comprehensive collection of major 16th- and 17th-century texts, which is probably typical of a working practitioner and surgeon of that time. It included several books in 'question and answer' format for surgical apprentices. In addition to the classical works of Celsus, Galen and Fabricius, there were many books from the Leiden School. Books in French included the works of Ambroise Paré, and Paracelsus, the Swiss physician.

Roll number: 63

Christopher Irvine of Bonshaw (1620–93)

Surgeons in Scotland in the 16th and 17th centuries had one important advantage over physicians. The aspiring surgeon could be apprenticed to a member of the Incorporation, pass the necessary examinations, pay the fee and become a legitimate surgical practitioner. Until the establishment of the Faculty of Medicine in Edinburgh in 1726, the pathway for the aspiring physician was much more difficult. Obtaining a medical degree meant first taking a general degree in the arts (or, for a few, in medicine) at a Scottish university, then for most attending a medical school in continental Europe, with most Scots choosing Rheims or Leyden. Christopher Irvine was the first medical graduate to be admitted to the Incorporation and went on to become physician to King James VII of Scotland and James II of England.

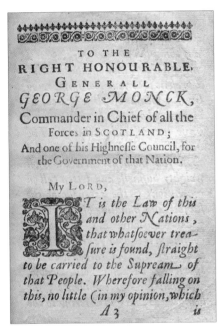

Medicina Magnetica, which Christopher Irvine dedicated to General George Monk.

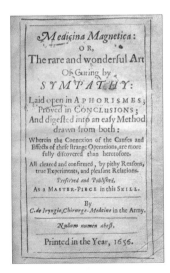

Irvine was admitted to the Incorporation in 1658. He appears to have graduated in medicine some years before, since in the list of graduates in arts from the University of Edinburgh in 1645 he is designated 'Medicinae Doctor' and would therefore probably have obtained a medical degree from a university in continental Europe.

By the standards of the day he was a prolific author. He published *Bellum Grammaticale* (1650), a Latin drama designed to help teach the principles of Latin grammar. Another publication explained the derivation of Scots names and place names, which he dedicated to the Duke of York, who became James VII of Scotland. Irvine had cause to be grateful to King James in later years. When he fell upon hard times with the combined loss of the family estate in Ireland and of his teaching position at Edinburgh University as a result of having signed the National Covenant, James VII and II compensated him for these losses by making him Physician to the royal household.

This was a time of vacillating loyalties. In 1656 Irvine published a medical textbook, *Medicinae Magnetica*, which he dedicated to General George Monk, in whose army he had served. Monk, who had distinguished himself at the defeat of the Covenanting army at the Battle of Dunbar, was made commander-in-chief of Cromwell's army in Scotland, and waged a fierce campaign against the Scottish Highlanders. He was later to become a Royalist and was largely responsible for the restoration of Charles ll to the throne. Irvine, too, seems to have changed allegiance – initially a supporter of the National Covenant, then a supporter of Cromwell, and latterly prepared to accept royal patronage again from James VII and II.

While the Seal of Cause had set out educational standards for the surgeons' apprentices at the beginning of the 16th century, these appear to have fallen by the start of the 17th century. Christopher Irvine in 1661 was instrumental in reinforcing educational discipline, so that apprentices who failed to satisfy the examiners were not allowed to proceed.

He appears to have taken umbrage at the establishment of the Royal College of Physicians in 1681, setting the tone for future frictions between physicians and surgeons. He petitioned the Privy Council, setting out his education, degrees and army service, and asking that his practice in medicine should not be demeaned by the new College, which in his view was composed of men altogether his 'junior in the studies of philosophy and the practice of physick'. This was granted by the Privy Council and confirmed by an Act of the Scottish Parliament in 1685, enabling him to continue in practice as a physician to the King until the accession of King William.

Roll number: 78

Hugh Broun (dates not known)

Hugh Broun (or Brown) was admitted to the Incorporation of Surgeons and Barbers in 1665 at which time it met in Curriehill House just inside Edinburgh's Flodden Wall. The records show that he was one of a number of members who pledged £100 towards the building of a new convening house. This was to become the first Surgeons' Hall and was completed in 1697.

Little of substance is known about Broun although he was a Roman Catholic and was appointed Chirurgeon Apothecary to King James VII of Scotland and II of England in 1688. James VII had enthusiastically supported Roman Catholicism and had offered patronage to Catholics whenever he could. This did not protect Broun from becoming a victim of the religious intolerance which was widespread in Scotland at the time. In 1695 he was rebuked by the government for simply attending a Roman Catholic mass. Broun and his son James were required to give an assurance 'of their doing nothing offensive to the Government in future, or else to be kept in prison'.

Broun's name and that of his son are included in a list, published in 1704, of 'Papists and children under papists within the bounds of the Presbytery of Edinburgh', a further indication of the religious intolerance of the period.

Roll number: 87

Hugh Broun depicted by Sir John Medina.

William Borthwick of Pilmuir (1641–89)

William Borthwick was probably the first to bring an international perspective to the Incorporation.

After studying at two of the great European medical centres, Padua in Italy in 1666, and Leiden in Holland, where he matriculated the following year, William Borthwick was apprenticed to his father-in-law, James Borthwick (q.v.). He went on to become Deacon of the Incorporation of Surgeons and Barbers from 1675 to 1677 and again from 1681 to 1683. In 1679 he became Chirurgeon Major of his Majesty's Forces in Scotland.

Impressed by his experience of the quality of medical teaching in Europe, he was to encourage one of his apprentices, John Monro (q.v.) to study in Leiden. Monro duly did so and returned to Scotland, inspired and determined to set up a similar faculty in Edinburgh. His vision led to the establishment in Edinburgh of a Seminary of Medical Education, based on the Leiden model, with his own brilliant son, Alexander Monro (q.v.) the Professor of Anatomy. So began the Monro dynasty, which was to bring Edinburgh medicine to pre-eminence on the world stage.

Borthwick owned the Pilmuir estate in East Lothian. His country home, Pilmuir House, was built in 1627. Some 300 years later it was bought by Sir Henry Wade (q.v.), under the terms of whose will a trust for its maintenance was set up, from which the College derives educational income.

Roll number: 88

William Borthwick of Pilmuir (1641–89).

Pilmuir House.

Robert Clerk (1664–1720).

Robert Clerk (1664–1720)

The Incorporation of Surgeons and Barbers of Edinburgh had its origins as a craft guild. From the early days, unlike most other guilds, it attracted members who owned landed property. Robert Clerk was one such.

Robert Clerk was the fifth and youngest son of the first man to hold the Barony of 'Pennycuick', or Penicuik, a small town a few miles south of Edinburgh. He was apprentice to Hugh Broun (q.v.) and married Margaret, one of Broun's daughters. Clerk was admitted to the Incorporation in 1689 having studied 'at home and abroad'. In that year he attended his nephew John (later Sir John) Clerk when the latter was 13 years old. Sir John later wrote: 'had it not been for the extraordinary care of Mr Robert Clerk, my unckle, who was a very expert Chyrurgeon, I must have lost my leg'. Robert Clerk also attended his uncle's wife at her first labour and Sir John was later to give this graphic description of the event. 'We had called for one of the chief physitians in Town, one doctor Hackete and two of the chief Chyrurgeons, my unckle Robert Clerk, and one Mr Hamilton, a man much emploied in Midwifery. They took all the pains about her they cou'd think of, but I'm afraid they were too hasty in their operations by which she lost a vast deal of blood. The placenta it seems was adhering to the uterus, and this they thought themselves oblidged to bring away by force.' Unfortunately, Lady Clerk died.

In 1701 Robert Clerk was elected Deacon but he declined office, alleging that he was not qualified according to the law. He was prohibited from attending meetings and suspended from all voting, until he changed his mind. When a new Deacon was elected, however, all his forfeited privileges were restored. The following year he demonstrated 'the skeleton in general with the head' on the sixth day of the first public anatomical demonstration at Surgeons' Hall in 1702.

His son, Dr John Clerk, became President of the Royal College of Physicians of Edinburgh in 1740.

Roll number: 109

Gideon Eliot (1644–1713)

Like some other members of the Incorporation towards the end of the 17th century, Gideon Eliot had obtained his initial medical degree in continental Europe. Much of his surgical experience was gained as a military surgeon in an era dominated by conflict.

Gideon Eliot studied medicine at Leiden, matriculating in 1686, and was admitted to the Incorporation three years later.

In 1689 he also became Surgeon to the 26th Regiment of Foot (The Cameronians). This regiment had been raised in May 1689, largely to protect the Covenanters, Scottish Presbyterians who supported the National Covenant of 1638. This Covenant had been signed by many Scots opposed to Charles II's intention to impose an episcopal system of religion in Scotland, with the King effectively as its head. In 1685 Covenanting was declared to be treason, punishable by death, and the Covenanters were forced to hold outdoor services in secret – hence the need for protection by soldiers.

In his capacity as Surgeon to the Cameronians, Eliot attended to the wounded at the Battle of Dunkeld, the first action for the new regiment. During this battle, they defeated the much larger army of Stuart sympathisers, marking the end of what was effectively the first Jacobite uprising.

Eliot was elected Deacon of the Incorporation in 1694 and in 1695. On 3 April that year he was asked by King William, together with the physician Sir Thomas Burnett, to visit the Earl of Home, who was under house arrest at The Hirsel near Coldstream, seat of the Earls of Home to this day. They were required to report on whether the Earl was fit to be transferred for imprisonment in Edinburgh Castle. For this service Sir Thomas, as the King's Physician received £200 Scots, while Eliot, a surgeon with no such royal appointment, received only £100 Scots.

Like Robert Clerk (q.v.) he was elected to the office of Deacon and then turned it down. His reasons for this are not clear, but this action displeased the Town Council, which fined him 300 merks, with the threat of imprisonment. This sentence was clearly effective – when he was elected Deacon two years later in 1699, he happily accepted office.

Roll number: 111

Gideon Eliot (1644–1713).

An archstone from the original 1697 Surgeons' Hall preserved within the present College building.

Alexander Monteith of Auldcathie (1660–1713)

The closing years of the 17th century were important in the history of the College. Increasingly, aspiring surgeons took a formal medical qualification, enhancing both their status and that of the Incorporation. When Dr Archibald Pitcairne (q.v.), perhaps the greatest physician of his day, returned to Edinburgh from the Chair of Medicine in Leiden in 1693, he joined the Incorporation, further establishing surgery as a respectable branch of medical practice in Edinburgh. The following year the Incorporation obtained permission from the Town Council to receive for anatomical dissection the bodies of prisoners dying in jail. In 1697 the original Surgeons' Hall was completed. Alexander Monteith presided over much of this change as Deacon in 1695, 1699 and 1701, and appears to have played the central role at an important time in the College's history.

Alexander Monteith was apprenticed to William Borthwick of Pilmuir (q.v.). As Borthwick had studied at two of the great European medical centres, Padua and Leiden, it was natural that he should have inspired his apprentice to do the same and Monteith spent several years studying on the continent. After admission to the Incorporation in 1691, he negotiated with the Town Council to obtain anatomical subjects to be used for dissection and the teaching of anatomy, and for a room dedicated to dissection.

He was elected Deacon of the Incorporation in 1695 and again in 1699, but on the latter occasion was deposed. This was almost certainly because he was a Jacobite and the Incorporation had a strong Presbyterian tradition – all of the surgeons had signed the National Covenant in 1638. Like his friend Archibald Pitcairne, also an enthusiastic Jacobite, he seems to have had the strength of character to overcome this setback and he was again elected Deacon in 1701.

The original Surgeons' Hall, 1697.

Monteith was therefore Deacon at an important time in the history of the Incorporation. In 1695 the Incorporation was granted a new charter by William and Mary. This confirmed the sole rights to practise surgery in south-east Scotland to members of the Incorporation, and also its responsibility for the teaching of anatomy. Two years later in 1697 the Surgeons' Hall was completed. This was the first meeting place which had been purpose-built for the surgeons, and contained a room for anatomical dissection. This Surgeons' Hall, with its dissection theatre, allowed public dissections to take place and Monteith was involved in the first of these in 1702, as was his friend, Archibald Pitcairne.

Monteith is also noteworthy because in 1700 he asked the Scottish Parliament in a petition: 'That the art discovered by him to draw spirits from malt equal in goodness to true French brandy may be declared a manufactory with the same privileges and immunities as are granted to other manufactories.' This was effectively asking for a patent to distil his own brand of malt whisky!

Roll number: 114

During the 18th century, Britain was intermittently at war with France and because of colonial rivalry most of their conflict took place on the sea, in the West Indies, in America and in India. A series of British victories led to the Peace of Paris in 1763 under the terms of which Britain acquired a considerable amount of colonial territory, and became established as an imperial power, but her pride was humbled by the successful revolt of her American colonies 12–18 years later.

For Scotland the first important event of the 18th century was the 1701 Act of Settlement, which ensured that Queen Anne, who had no surviving children, would be succeeded on the throne of Britain by the Protestant Elector of Hanover.

Under the terms of the Treaty of Union of 1707 the Parliaments of Scotland and England were united to form the Parliament of Great Britain, a momentous historical landmark which James Ogilvie, Earl of Seafield, Secretary of State for Scotland and Lord High Chancellor of Scotland, declared to be 'the end of an auld sang'.

The failed Jacobite risings of 1715 and 1745 resulted in the destruction of the Highland clan system and the denigration and neglect of Scotland's Gaelic heritage. Scotland increasingly became North Britain, but if it seemed to be losing its national identity substantial compensation was gained from a Scottish cultural pre-eminence which was recognised and admired throughout Europe and in the Americas.

There may possibly have been a hint of satire but undoubtedly there was also a very large measure of truth in Voltaire's famous comment made in 1762 that 'it is from Scotland that we now receive rules of taste in all the arts from the epic poem to gardening'. Regardless of the spirit in which it may have been made, this remark attests the brilliance of that extraordinary period of cultural, academic and scientific achievement in the second half of the 18th century known today as the Scottish Enlightenment.

Its time-span is disputed and many theories have been advanced regarding the causes of what was an astonishing outburst of intellectual activity occurring in a small poor country on the fringe of Europe. There is, however, no argument about the genius of the great thinkers of the Scottish Enlightenment or the magnitude of their contributions to the advancement of man's understanding of himself and of the world in which he lives.

A simple list of its most illustrious names would fill many pages and to place them in some sort of order of merit would be an impossible and a pointless task. Four who would certainly be amongst the leaders of such a list are David Hume (1711–76), one of the greatest European philosophers; Adam Smith (1723–90), founder of the science of economics and author of *The wealth of Nations*; James Hutton (1726–97), the father of modern Geology; and Joseph Black (1728–99), physician, physiologist and chemist, the discoverer of carbon dioxide and of the phenomenon of latent heat.

18th Century

James Ogilvie, first Earl of Seafield, Secretary of State for Scotland and Lord High Chancellor of Scotland, who signed the Act of Union in 1707.

Joseph Black (1728–99).

John Hunter (1728–93).

Among many others worthy of a place among the greatest names of the Scottish Enlightenment are Scotland's beloved national poet Robert Burns (1759–96); James Boswell (1740–95), the greatest of all biographers; the architects Robert Adam (1728–92) and James Craig (1744–95), designer and planner of Edinburgh's New Town; the artists Henry Raeburn (1756–1823) and David Allan (1744–96); and the brilliant engineer James Watt (1736–1819), whose improvements to the steam engine revolutionised transport and manufacturing and thereby changed the world.

Sir Walter Scott (1771–1832), poet, novelist, historian and fervent patriot, born during the Enlightenment is one of the greatest Scotsmen of all time. His historical novels are a towering literary achievement and the image of Scotland which they created fascinated and delighted his readers throughout the civilised world as well as helping to restore a sense of Scottish national identity. So also did his rediscovery of the honours of Scotland, the Scottish Crown Jewels, which had not been publicly displayed for 150 years and this could be regarded as the start of a process which led eventually to the restoration of the Scottish Parliament in 1999.

The Scottish Enlightenment has its monuments, among which are the *Encyclopaedia Britannica,* first published in Edinburgh in 1768, the granting of the Charter to the Royal Society of Edinburgh in 1783, and perhaps also the Royal Charter granted by King George III in 1778 to the Incorporation of Surgeons whereby it became the Royal College of Surgeons of the City of Edinburgh.

Alexander Monro *primus* (1697–1767) (q.v.) and his son Alexander Monro *secundus* (1733–1817), who succeeded him as Professor of Anatomy in Edinburgh University, are the two most distinguished medical figures of the Scottish Enlightenment and the Edinburgh physicians William Cullen and John Gregory also achieved international fame. The surgeon Benjamin Bell (1749–1806) (q.v.), a prolific writer whose books were read throughout Europe, was also a product of the Scottish Enlightenment but major advances in surgical practice had to await the advent of anaesthesia and antisepsis in the middle of the next century.

The 18th century was the era of classification and scientific order as exemplified by the taxonomy of the Swedish botanist Linnaeus (1707–78). In surgery William Hunter and his younger brother, John, born in Lanarkshire, became the most famous surgeon-anatomists of their day in London. John Hunter (1728–93) in particular was one of the most influential surgeons.

Archibald Pitcairne (1652–1713)

In 17th-century Europe, Leiden and Rheims had become the two major centres for Scots seeking university medical education. Leiden was to play an important role in the development of medicine and surgery in Edinburgh and Archibald Pitcairne was to provide the most important link between the two centres.

Pitcairne was one of the most brilliant doctors of his day. A true polymath, he had studied divinity and law before medicine, he wrote poetry and drama, including *The Assembly,* the only Scottish Restoration comedy. He was also well versed in mathematics and astronomy and corresponded with Sir Isaac Newton. His reputation was such that he was invited by the University of Leiden, arguably the leading European medical school at that time, to serve as Professor of Medicine. After his return to Edinburgh, an internal dispute resulted in his leaving the Royal College of Physicians of Edinburgh to join the Incorporation of Surgeons, where he studied and taught anatomy.

Archibald Pitcairne (1652–1713).

Archibald Pitcairne was born in Edinburgh, the son of a merchant. He studied initially at Edinburgh University, graduating MA in 1671. His studies had included divinity, but his father intended that he should become a lawyer and he was sent to Paris to study law. There he developed an interest in medicine and after further studies at Padua, he graduated MD from Rheims in 1680 before returning to Edinburgh and medical practice. Within a year he had become the youngest of the original Fellows of the newly founded Royal College of Physicians of Edinburgh.

Whilst he excelled as a physician, he also had a particular aptitude for mathematics. He was friendly with David Gregory, who was to become Professor of Mathematics at Edinburgh University and, thereafter, Professor of Astronomy at Oxford. This mathematical background led to Pitcairne championing what became known as the iatro-mechanical theory of physiology. This hypothesis was based on the assumption that bodily functions such as the circulation were determined by mechanical factors rather than by the ebb and flow of humours. Pitcairne's enthusiasm for this highly controversial subject led to his publishing *Solutio Problematis de historicis, seu inventoribus* (1688). This was largely responsible for his being appointed (jointly with Robert Sibbald and James Halket) Professor of Medicine in the Town's College (later to become the University). In this position he became one of the more eminent protagonists of the iatro-mechanical theory and in 1692 he was invited to the Chair of Medicine in the University of Leiden. On the journey there, he visited Sir Isaac Newton in Cambridge.

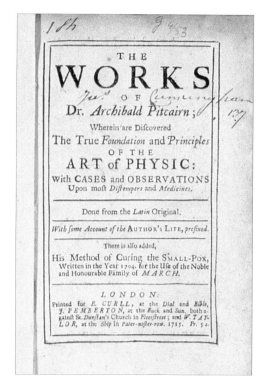

The title page from Archibald Pitcairne's
*The True Foundation and Principles
of the Art of Physic* (1715).

Dissection by Archibald Pitcairne, performed 1702, on display in the College Museum.

His pupils at Leiden included several who were later to achieve fame in their own right, including Hermann Boerhaave and Richard Mead.

Pitcairne's stay at Leiden was short because his future wife did not wish to settle there. Returning to Edinburgh he was again plunged into controversy. He had supported the ideas of Thomas Sydenham about the treatment of fevers, a view not shared by the Edinburgh physicians of the day. A devoted Episcopalian and Jacobite, he was scathing in his criticism of all things Presbyterian. These and other views resulted in the 'riot in the College', as a consequence of which he was excluded from the Royal College of Physicians of Edinburgh. His reputation as a scholar was further enhanced, however, by the publication of his *Dissertationes Medicae* in Rotterdam in 1701. In that year he was admitted to the Incorporation of Surgeons, where he promoted the study and teaching of anatomy. He provided the epilogue at the first two successful public demonstrations of anatomical dissection performed in the 'new' Surgeons' Hall and one of his dissections from 1702 remains on display in the College Museum. Pitcairne was, by contemporary account, the most distinguished member of the Incorporation, and his efforts led to the appointment of Robert Elliot as public dissector to the Incorporation.

Pitcairne remained a fervent Jacobite to the end. Before his death in 1713 he left instructions that some of his best wine was to be set aside to be drunk on the restoration of the Stuart dynasty to the throne. This, of course, never came about, but in 1800 on the occasion of the restoration of Pitcairne's tombstone in Greyfriars Churchyard, and with the agreement of Pitcairne's granddaughter, Lady Ann Erskine, a large gathering of Edinburgh doctors liberally interpreted the terms of his will and drank to his memory. The wine proved to be Malmsey, still apparently in excellent condition after more than 85 years!

The large library which Pitcairne had amassed during his life was purchased in 1718 for the Czar of Russia by Robert Erskine, a Scottish physician who had known Pitcairne in Edinburgh and had been physician to Peter the Great. That library is preserved to this day in the Academy of Sciences in St Petersburg.

His son, Andrew, a committed Jacobite like his father, was arrested after the Jacobite defeat of 1715. Imprisoned in the Tower of London, he obtained his release after the intervention of Richard Mead, whom his father had taught in Leiden and who had gone on to become Physician to King George II.

Archibald Pitcairne may rightly be viewed as the most celebrated Scottish doctor of his day.

Roll number: 133

John Monro (1670–1740)

John Monro was the progenitor of a celebrated dynasty of anatomists who occupied the Edinburgh University Chair of Anatomy for 126 years. His greatest monument, however, is the University's Faculty of Medicine, which was established in 1726 largely through his foresight, energy and single-minded determination.

John Monro was the younger son of Sir Alexander Monro of Bearscroft, the Commissary of Supply for Stirling. When he was aged 13, his father was arrested on suspicion of complicity in the Rye House Plot and accused of treason, but no prosecution took place and he was pardoned one year later. Little is known about John Monro's education or of the factors which influenced his decision to become a surgeon, but in 1687 he was apprenticed to William Borthwick (q.v.), a well-known Edinburgh surgeon who had served two terms as Deacon (President) of the Incorporation of Surgeons and Barbers. Borthwick already had an apprentice under his tutelage and in taking on another he was contravening the rules of the Incorporation, but this difficulty was resolved by the nominal transfer of Monro's apprenticeship from Borthwick to Dr Christopher Irvine (q.v.), who has the distinction of being the very first member of the Incorporation to hold a university degree in medicine. In fact, Monro continued to receive most of his surgical training from William Borthwick, but this was interrupted in 1690 by a period of military service as surgeon's mate in Viscount Kenmure's regiment. Nevertheless, he completed his apprenticeship in 1692 and in that same year he matriculated as a student at the University of Leiden, then the most renowned medical school in Europe. One of his teachers there was Archibald Pitcairne (q.v.), the Professor of Medicine, and among his fellow students was Hermann Boerhaave, later to occupy the Leiden Chair of Medicine and to become the most famous European physician of the first half of the 18th century. Leiden made a profound impression on John Monro and the quality of the teaching he experienced there inspired in him the ambition to establish in Scotland a medical school of comparable excellence.

He returned to Edinburgh in 1694 and, in the following year, he joined the army as Surgeon to the 22nd Regiment of Foot (later to become the Cheshire Regiment). Almost immediately, the regiment proceeded to Flanders as part of the Allied army under the personal command of King William III and Monro saw action at the siege and capture of Namur.

John Monro (1670–1740).

The University of Leiden.

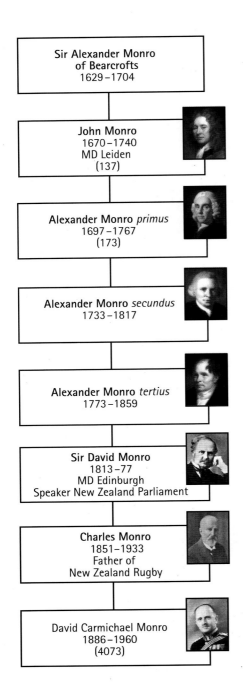

Sir Alexander Monro
of Bearcrofts
1629–1704

John Monro
1670–1740
MD Leiden
(137)

Alexander Monro *primus*
1697–1767
(173)

Alexander Monro *secundus*
1733–1817

Alexander Monro *tertius*
1773–1859

Sir David Monro
1813–77
MD Edinburgh
Speaker New Zealand Parliament

Charles Monro
1851–1933
Father of
New Zealand Rugby

David Carmichael Monro
1886–1960
(4073)

The Monro lineage
(numbers in parentheses
are College roll numbers).

From 1696 to 1700 Monro was stationed in England and in Ireland but he appears to have been given lengthy periods of leave which enabled him to set up house with his wife in London, and it was there that his son, Alexander (q.v.), was born in 1697. He left the army in 1700 and returned to Edinburgh, where he opened an apothecary's shop but did not immediately engage in surgical practice. Three years later, having become a Burgess of the City, an essential preliminary qualification, he presented for examination, as a result of which he was admitted a Freeman of the Incorporation of Surgeons and Barbers. From then, John Monro gradually built up a large surgical practice and in 1708 he was appointed Boxmaster (Treasurer) of the Incorporation. Four years later he was elected Deacon, and *ex officio* had a seat upon the Town Council of Edinburgh. Soon afterwards he was elected Deacon Convenor of the Trades of Edinburgh and in the following year was re-elected to these offices. He was also appointed one of the city's representatives on the Convention of the Royal Burghs of Scotland.

Towards the end of John Monro's second term of office as Deacon of the Incorporation, Queen Anne died. Having declared his support for the Hanoverian succession, he was present in his official robes along with other civic dignitaries at the proclamation of George I as King of Great Britain, France and Ireland at the Mercat Cross on 5 August 1714. During the Jacobite rising of 1715 his previous military experience stood him in good stead when he attended casualties from both sides after the Battle of Sheriffmuir.

Having established himself in Edinburgh as a man of influence and authority in professional and civic affairs, John Monro set about the fulfilment of his long-cherished ambition of founding in the city a 'Seminary of Medical Education' modelled on the medical school of the University of Leiden. In 1720 he produced a plan which was favourably received by the Town Council, the University and the two medical corporations of the city. The key to its success was the appointment to the University Chair of Anatomy of John Monro's brilliant son, Alexander, whose education and training had been planned with this specific objective.

Over the next six years, it was the influence of the Monros, father and son, which brought about the appointment of Professors Rutherford, St Clair, Plummer, Innes and Gibson, who, together with Alexander Monro, formed the original medical faculty of Edinburgh University.

The realisation of his dream, largely through the agency of his son, entitles John Monro to be saluted by posterity as one of the founding fathers of the Edinburgh medical school and he could not have had a more gratifying reward than the international reputation which it and his son acquired during his lifetime.

Roll number: 137

Adam Drummond (1679–1758)

In 1657 an Act of the Edinburgh Town Council enabled the Incorporation of Surgeons and Barbers to recognise the surgeon-apothecary with the establishment of the Fraternity of Surgeons and Surgeon-apothecaries. This led eventually to the demise of the barber-surgeon and the rise of a new generation of surgeons, knowledgeable about medical therapies. Adam Drummond was one of the most prominent.

Adam Drummond was the third son of Adam Drummond of Megginch, a member of the Scottish Parliament and a Privy Councillor of Scotland. His father, a prominent Scottish lawyer and politician, was appointed in 1692 as one of the commissioners into the inquiry about the massacre at Glencoe. Born on the family estate at Megginch in Perthshire, Adam the younger went to the local school in Errol before graduating from St Andrews University. The route to a surgical career at that time was through apprenticeship and he was apprentice to Thomas Edgar (roll number: 97), who had been Deacon of the Incorporation from 1685 to 1687.

Adam Drummond (1679–1758).

On completion of his apprenticeship he went, as was the custom of the day, for further education in a continental university. *En route* to the continent he took a course of anatomy in London before continuing his studies in Leiden.

On his return to Edinburgh, Drummond was admitted to the Incorporation in 1707. Having established a practice as a surgeon-apothecary in the Lawnmarket in Edinburgh, he was appointed as the joint Professor of Anatomy to the Town's College (which became the University of Edinburgh in 1708). He held the post jointly with Robert Elliot, the first incumbent, and the first Professor of Anatomy in Britain. In 1720 he resigned and recommended Alexander Monro *primus* (q.v.) as his successor, thereby paving the way for the famous dynasty.

Drummond's practice as a surgeon-apothecary flourished and he dispensed remedies prescribed by the most eminent physicians of the day. This successful practice attracted many apprentices. These included John Campbell (roll number: 218), who, from evidence of prescriptions written at the time, must have visited the Edinburgh Physic Garden to collect herbal remedies like rosemary, St John's Wort, mint and sage.

The Drummond family were staunch Hanoverians. In the 1745 Jacobite uprising the Young Pretender's army of Highlanders, having marched through Edinburgh, defeated a government army under the command of General Sir John Cope at the Battle of Prestonpans. (The Jacobite song 'Hey, Johnnie Cope' celebrates this victory.) After the battle, surgeons from Edinburgh came to dress the wounded. Among these was Colin Simpson, one of Drummond's apprentices, whose loyalty to the government was such that he was entrusted to deliver 400 guineas to another of Drummond's nephews, Captain Adam Drummond, paymaster to a Hanoverian regiment.

Drummond had been librarian to the Incorporation of Surgeons from 1706 to 1709 and was made Deacon of the Incorporation between 1748 and 1750.

Roll number: 144

Thomas Kincaid (the Younger)

(1661–1726)

Extract from the diary of Thomas Kincaid the Younger.

Diarists who record every detail of their daily experiences, no matter how mundane, and who share thoughts and ideas with the diary, offer a unique window into their life and times. Thomas Kincaid the younger wrote such a diary for the years 1687 and 1688 during his medical studies. The diaries outline his activities, the books he read and his thoughts on an almost bewildering variety of topics but their prime historical significance lies in the fact that they provide the first known account of how the game of golf should be played. Kincaid's detailed description of the grip, the address, the stance and the swing have won him a place in history as providing the first written account of these all-important aspects of the game.

Thomas Kincaid's diaries are held in the National Library of Scotland (adv.MS.32.7.7) and cover the period January 1687 to 31 December 1688. These were turbulent years in Scotland. In 1685 the Catholic King James VII of Scotland and II of England succeeded to the throne and announced a general religious amnesty. It was during these years of official religious tolerance that Kincaid wrote his diary, a time when the influence of the Covenanters was declining. The year after the diary ended, the English Parliament asked James II's Protestant daughter, Mary, and her husband, William of Orange, to become joint rulers. This 'Glorious Revolution' in England was a bloodless accession, but, in 1689, the beginnings of the Jacobite movement to restore a Catholic to the throne of Britain resulted in continued fighting in Scotland. The diaries were therefore written during a relative lull in a half-century of conflict.

Thomas Kincaid's father, Thomas Kincaid the elder (q.v.), had been a member of the Incorporation and went on to become Deacon. It seems likely that he wished his son to follow this career path. It is thought that Thomas junior was intending to take a medical degree in Europe, probably in Leiden, as he describes his studies of French and Dutch, and, indeed, his brother James had already studied in Holland.

Kincaid's choice of medical books included works by Thomas Willis (1621–75), who, in addition to gaining eponymous fame by describing the circle of Willis, defined the features and courses of several common illnesses. He also read the works of the physician Thomas Sydenham (1624–89), and of Nicholas Culpeper, the English apothecary whose book on herbal medicine was to become the standard work for the next two centuries. Like any student, his reading also included non-medical books like Sir Thomas Hope's *The Scots Fencing Master* (1687) and Johann Neander's treatise on tobacco, published in 1622, and, of course, he read novels.

Like most of his contemporaries in Scotland, he was religious, and the diary records his regular attendance at the Tron, the parish church, but from July 1687 he begins to attend the Magdalene Chapel, which had been a meeting place for Coventicles, suggesting that he was a Presbyterian who sympathised with the Covenanters. Only one of that religious persuasion would be likely to read the Westminster Confession of Faith and the works of Calvin.

Translation of Diary Entry
20 January 1687

... after dinner I went to the Golve with Hen. Leggat [his friend and companion Henry Leggat]. I found that the only way of playing at the Golve is to stand as you do at fencing with the small sword, bending your legs a little and holding the muscles of your legs and back and armes exceeding bent or fixt or stiffe and not at all slackning them in the time you are bringing down the stroak (which you readily doe), the ball must be straight before your breast, a little towards the left foot. Your left foot must stand but a little before the right, or rather it must be even with it, and at a convenient distance from it. Ye most lean most to the right foot. But all the turning about of your body must be only ... upon your legs holding them as stiffe as ye can ...

Although he had a serious side he had a variety of worldly interests. There is an almost daily entry in the diary 'I thought upon…', and, indeed, the topics he thought about were many and varied. For the month of January 1687 his thoughts included the principle of 'Chymien' (chemistry), fighting robbers, different 'humours', how to play at golf, the best posture for throwing a stone, and voting in Parliament. Other thoughts in this remarkably diverse series include ways of shooting at the butts, billiards, building a meeting house, the best way of making a smith's vice and breeding horses to run swiftly.

He had an inventive mind and loved to experiment. He made plaster of Paris moulds of the face of his brother and his friend Henry Leggat, but one of his favourite topics, and one to which he constantly returns, is golf. On 20 January after reading *Chirurgia* till lunchtime, he analysed the stance, the address and swing which he reckoned would produce the best result, writing: '1. Stand as you do at fencing … bending your legs a little and holding the muscles of your legs and back and arms exceedingly bent but fixed and stiff. 2. The ball must be straight before your breast a little towards the left foot. 3. Your left foot must stand but a little before the right or rather it must be even with it and at a convenient distance from it.' He goes on in 13 such notes to describe the detail of the swing, the best type of club and the best type of ball. He clearly thought long and hard about this topic and the following day arose at four in the morning to write about some detailed modifications, including: 'the ball must lie upon a line that is perpendicular to that line that passeth between the one foot and the other'. With Henry Leggat he played golf on Leith Links, and probably also nearer home on Bruntsfield Links.

In the summer archery began to take up more of his time. Like his father, he became a member of the Royal Company of Archers, taking part in many competitions, including the official contests at Leith and Musselburgh. Archery provided the opportunity for socialising, as the butts where they practised were always close to a tavern. After shooting they would go to a tavern for the evening and he mentions no fewer than twelve of these in the two years of the diary.

The latter pages of the diary are missing and little detail is known about his later life. We do, however, know that in 1709 he donated his late father's very large library to the Incorporation. The following year Thomas Kincaid was admitted to the Incorporation, probably the first to be admitted without examination. The admission note in the Fellows' register reads that he was admitted: 'In regard of good deeds done by him … without payment of any upsett [entrance] money.'

He does not ever seem to have practised as a surgeon but rather became a gentleman of leisure. In later life he is frequently mentioned in the Minutes of the Royal Company of Archers, on one occasion winning the Silver Arrow. His poems, both in English and in Latin, published in later life, won him a degree of contemporary fame.

Roll number: 147

Another Early Golfing Enthusiasist in Edinburgh

From Kay's *Portraits*.

ALEXANDER M'KELLAR, the 'Cock o' the Green' (whom the Print represents as about to strike the ball) was probably one of the most enthusiastic golf-players that ever handled a club. When the weather would at all permit, he generally spent the whole day on Bruntsfield Links; and he was frequently to be found engaged at the 'short holes' by lamp light. Even in winter, if the snow was sufficiently frozen, he might be seen enjoying his favourite exercise alone, or with any one he could persuade to join him in the pastime. M'Kellar thus became well known in the neighbourhood of the green; and his almost insane devotion to golf was a matter of much amusement to his acquaintances … and, notwithstanding his incessant practice, he was by no means considered a dexterous player … He had contrived to save a little money; and he and his wife, on their coming to Edinburgh, opened a small tavern in the New Town. M'Kellar had thus ample leisure for the indulgence of his fancy. His all-absorbing predilection for golf was a source of much vexation to his managing partner in life, on whom devolved the whole duty of attending to the affairs of the tavern … So provoked at length was the good dame that she abhorred the very name of golf, as well as all who practised it; and to her customers, if they were her husband's associates on the green, even a regard for her own interest could scarcely induce her to extend to them the common civilities of the tavern.

The Incorporation and the Early History of Golf

Before the 15th century, games involving hitting a ball with a stick were played throughout Europe. In Scotland the game of golf as we know it today began, and several members of the Incorporation were closely associated with its origins.

In 1457 the Scottish Parliament decreed that golf should not be played on Sundays and that instead the people should practise archery. In an age of conflict when the bow and arrow was a principal weapon, archery had a serious purpose and a further Act enforcing the ban was passed in 1471. The very need for such Acts of Parliament suggests that the game was popular among the general population. This game has come to be known as the short game and was often played in churchyards.

Another variant of the game was enjoyed by the nobility, who played golf on parkland or stretches of open ground near the shores of the east coast of Scotland, known as links.

James IV, who ratified the Seal of Cause in 1506, was known to play golf. His accounts show that in 1505 he paid the sum of 14 shillings to the Bower (bowmaker) at St Johnston (Perth) for golf clubs. Subsequent entries show expenditure on golf balls and 'to play at the golf with the Earl of Bothwell', suggesting that the King had lost a wager on the match. By the 17th century, golf seems to have been played regularly at Leith Links and legend has it that it was here while playing golf that Charles I received the news of the Irish rebellion in 1641.

It is to **Thomas Kincaid the Younger** (q.v.), that we owe the first detailed description of the stance and the swing. In his diary, written between 1687 and 1688, Kincaid describes his preferences for clubs and their repair, for balls and even an early handicapping system.

By the middle of the next century golf was well established in Leith Links and records show that it was also played on Bruntsfield Links, at Musselburgh and elsewhere in Scotland. The first golf club in the world, the Company of Gentlemen Golfers, which later became the Honourable Company of Edinburgh Golfers, was founded in 1744, several years before the Royal and Ancient Golf Club of St Andrews.

John Rattray (q.v.), the Edinburgh surgeon, was a leading member of the Company and played regularly with Duncan Forbes of Culloden, Lord President of the Council, an eminent Scottish judge. The first rules of golf were written and signed by John Rattray in 1744.

Rattray was unusual among the surgeons in his Jacobite allegiance as the Incorporation awarded the Duke of Cumberland an Honorary Fellowship, albeit before the Battle of Culloden!

Rattray's contemporary, **William Inglis** (q.v.), was another prominent member of the Company of Gentlemen Golfers. Magnificent portraits by two of the leading Scottish artists of the day, David Allan and Sir Henry Raeburn, have assured him a place in golfing history.

The Edinburgh surgeons, and indeed surgeons everywhere, have maintained links with golf over the centuries. It seems appropriate, therefore, that the biography of John Rattray for this book should have been written by Colin Strachan, who also combined a career in surgery with golfing distinction, as a Scottish amateur and member of the Royal and Ancient Championship Committee.

John McGill (?–1735)

The origins of systematic anatomy teaching in Edinburgh date from the mid-17th century. In 1705 Robert Elliot, a leading member of the Incorporation, was appointed Teacher of Anatomy to the apprentices of the Freemen of the Incorporation. Later that year, he received a salaried appointment from the Town's College – subsequently to become the University of Edinburgh. Although not given the title, he was *de facto* the first Professor of Anatomy in Edinburgh. When he died in 1717, John McGill and Adam Drummond (q.v.) were jointly appointed to succeed him.

John McGill had begun his career as an apprentice to Henry Hamilton, a surgeon-apothecary, and was admitted into the Incorporation in 1710. His appointment, jointly with Adam Drummond, as Professor of Anatomy did not last long as they both resigned after three years 'as the state of their health and business were such that they could not duly attend the said Professorships'. It is likely, however, that this was the result of political pressure, probably from John Monro, who had been grooming his son Alexander for the post.

McGill rose to become Deacon of the Incorporation in 1716 and again in 1732. He was appointed Apothecary in Scotland to King George I and, thereafter, to King George II. With the opening of the hospital at the top of Robertson's Close in 1729 (which in 1736 was to become the Royal Infirmary), McGill appears to have been one of the first surgeons to be appointed.

When he resigned as joint Professor of Anatomy in 1720, he was succeeded by Alexander Monro *primus* (q.v.), a move which ushered in the start of the golden age of the Edinburgh medical school.

Roll number: 148

John McGill (d. 1735).

Alexander Monro *primus* (1697–1767)

The Monro dynasty occupied the Chair of Anatomy in the Edinburgh University medical school for more than 120 years. The inspiration to establish a new Seminary for Medical Education had come from John Monro, who prepared his son Alexander to be one of the early teachers. The brilliance of Alexander Monro exceeded the expectations of even his father.

Alexander, the only surviving child of John Monro (q.v.), was born in London in 1697. At that time, his father was an army surgeon, but three years later he resigned his commission and settled with his family in Edinburgh, where he served his surgical apprenticeship and was admitted to the Incorporation in 1703.

Young Alexander Monro was given a very comprehensive education, which, in addition to the Classics, included French, philosophy, mathematics and book-keeping, but there is no record of him having attended any school in Edinburgh and it is presumed that he was taught entirely by private tutors. As if all this was not enough, we know from his autobiography that his father also put him under qualified masters to be instructed in fencing, dancing, music and designing.

John Monro was determined that his son would follow in his own professional footsteps and in 1712, having been elected Deacon of the Incorporation, he took on Alexander as his apprentice. In this capacity Alexander studied anatomy intensively and attended dissections carried out at Surgeons' Hall by the joint professors of anatomy, Adam Drummond (q.v.) and John McGill (q.v.). He attended university classes in botany and chemistry and through his father's influence he assisted certain Edinburgh physicians from time to time, thereby gaining some knowledge of medicine at an early stage in his career. As assistant to his father, he helped with the treatment of casualties from the Battle of Sheriffmuir in 1715 and this gave him valuable experience of traumatic surgery.

In 1717, having completed his apprenticeship, Alexander Monro went for further training to London, where he attended lectures and demonstrations given by the famous surgeon and anatomist William Cheselden. After a year in London, he went on to Paris, where he studied botany, chemistry, anatomy, operative surgery and obstetrics, but, before leaving, he sent home to his father some dissected specimens which he had prepared himself without supervision. John Monro used these to demonstrate his son's ability by presenting some to the Royal College of Physicians and some to the Incorporation of Surgeons and Barbers. These were very favourably received and Adam Drummond declared that he would be happy to relinquish his portion of the joint Chair of Anatomy to the younger Monro when the latter returned to Edinburgh. After Paris, Alexander spent a year in Leiden, where he was profoundly impressed by the teaching of the famous Professor of Medicine Hermann Boerhaave, who had been his father's fellow student 15 years previously.

He returned home in 1719 and later that year, having passed the necessary examination, he was admitted a Freeman of the Incorporation of Surgeons and Barbers. Normally the examination was taken in four stages conducted at monthly intervals, but Alexander Monro managed to combine the third and fourth stages and thereby expedited his admission to the Incorporation. Soon after this the joint professors of anatomy, Adam Drummond and John McGill, both resigned and the

Alexander Monro *primus* (1697–1767).

'... he launches out into all the branches of physick where his remarks are new and useful ... he is not only a skilful physician but an able orator ...'

Oliver Goldsmith on Alexander Monro *primus*.

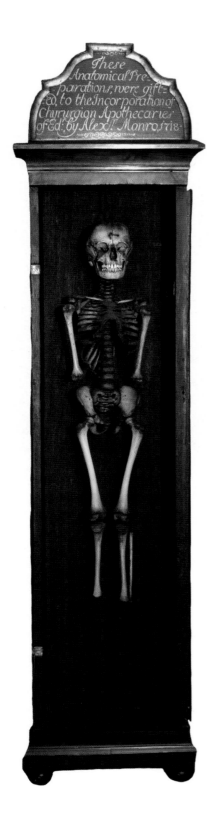

Human skeleton from a dissection by
Alexander Monro *primus* in the College Museum.

Incorporation recommended to the Town Council that Alexander Monro be appointed sole Professor of Anatomy in their places. This recommendation was accepted and forthwith the new professor, aged 23, embarked on his illustrious teaching career. He immediately departed from tradition by lecturing in English rather than in Latin, which, together with his scholarship and intellectual brilliance, made him a very popular teacher and the number of students attending his classes increased rapidly. In addition to anatomy, he also taught operative surgery and bandaging, and he seems also to have maintained quite an extensive private surgical practice.

A regular supply of cadavers for dissection was essential for the continuing success of Monro's anatomy course and this was a situation which grave robbers, also known as 'resurrectionists' or 'body-snatchers' were not slow to exploit. The Incorporation of Surgeons and Barbers and Professor Monro publicly condemned the abhorrent crime of grave robbery and offered rewards for information leading to the apprehension and conviction of resurrectionists, but this did not exempt them from vilification. Public outrage was so strong that in 1725 riots occurred which were serious enough to endanger the Professor of Anatomy and his collection of anatomical specimens housed in the unprotected Surgeons' Hall. For greater safety, Monro petitioned the Town Council as patrons of the University to allow him the use of a theatre for dissection within its walls. His request was granted and the Chair of Anatomy was thus moved from the Incorporation of Surgeons and Barbers and became part of the University.

John Monro hoped that his son would teach medicine and chemistry as well as anatomy, but Alexander wisely recognised that such a task would be beyond his powers and urged that these additional commitments be assigned to four doctors well known to both him and his father. Thus it was that, in 1726, these four were appointed professors by the University and, together with Alexander Monro and John Gibson, the world's first Professor of Midwifery, they formed the original medical faculty of Edinburgh University.

Under Alexander Monro's leadership the Edinburgh medical school acquired an international reputation for the excellence of its teaching and nowhere more than in the British North American colonies. In a letter written while he was a medical student in Edinburgh, Oliver Goldsmith (1728–74) said of Professor Monro that 'he has brought the science which he teaches to such perfection as he is capable of and not content with teaching anatomy he launches out into all the branches of physick where all his remarks are new and useful. Tis he, I may venture to say that, draws hither such a number of students from most parts of the world, even from Russia; he is not only a skilful physician, but an able orator and delivers things in their nature abstruse in so easy a manner that the most unlearned may understand him.'

Alexander Monro *primus* was also a man of exceptional energy and organising ability and together with his friend, the famous Lord Provost George Drummond, he played a key role in the establishment of the Edinburgh Royal Infirmary. Like his father, Alexander Monro *primus* was a staunch Hanoverian, but during the 1745 Jacobite rising he attended the wounded of both sides on the battlefield of Prestonpans, and arranged the admission of many of them to the Royal Infirmary.

Although trained as a surgeon, he became progressively more interested in medicine and was awarded its MD degree by the University in 1756. Later in the same year he was elected a Fellow of the Royal College of Physicians of Edinburgh and from 1757 he started to teach clinical medicine as well as anatomy and operative surgery, but one year later he handed over all the teaching in the two latter subjects to his son, Alexander Monro *secundus*, who had been appointed joint professor with him in 1754.

Alexander Monro *primus* was undoubtedly a man of genius who was recognised in his own lifetime as one of Europe's greatest medical scientists and his memory is justly celebrated because of his remarkable achievements as anatomist, surgeon, teacher and educational statesman. His name is among the most illustrious in the history of Scottish medicine and the continuing fame of the Edinburgh medical school, in the foundation of which he played such a notable part, is his greatest monument.

Roll number: 173

George Drummond (1687–1766), Lord Provost of Edinburgh, who played a crucial role in the establishment of the Royal Infirmary of Edinburgh.

John Rattray (1707–71)

It was a cliché of the 20th century that the best opportunities for business contacts and professional advancement could be found on the golf course. For one 18th-century Edinburgh surgeon, however, it was his golfing connections which literally saved his life. John Rattray, who produced the first written rules of golf, and was personal physician to Prince Charles Edward Stuart during the 1745 Jacobite uprising, was famously saved from execution after the Battle of Culloden through the intervention of Scotland's most senior judge, his golfing partner.

Rattray's father, chief of the Clan Rattray, was an Episcopalian and became Bishop of Brechin, then Bishop of Dunkeld and finally Primus of Scotland. His son John began his surgical training by apprenticeship to John Semple, an Edinburgh surgeon. After completing the apprenticeship in 1735, he applied for a 'Petition of Freedom' asking to be examined to become a Freeman of the Incorporation. Examiners were appointed and the dates for the examinations, or 'lessons', were set. He successfully passed the four-part examination for admission to the Incorporation of Surgeons and Barbers of Edinburgh in 1740 and was admitted.

Rattray was a keen sportsman and one of the few surgeons of that era for whom records of sporting achievements are available. In 1731 he joined the Royal Company of Archers, the sovereign's bodyguard in Scotland. He won the Archer's Silver Bowl on four occasions. On two further occasions in 1735 and 1744 he won the Silver Arrow, defeating the best archers in Scotland. Rattray was also a skilled golfer and this was acknowledged in the first-ever poem devoted to golf – Mathison's *The Goff* in 1743.

In one of the earliest historical references to golf, the accounts of King James IV of Scotland (who had ratified the Seal of Cause of the Incorporation in 1506) record that he purchased golf clubs at Perth in 1502 and golf balls in1503 at Stirling. Yet 240 years later in 1744, there were still no rules.

This portrait in the possession of the Rattray family is believed by them to be that of John Rattray, but other authorities are not convinced of this.

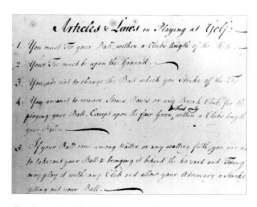

The first rules of golf drawn up by John Rattray in 1744.

Duncan Forbes of Culloden,
Lord President of the Court
of Session, who played golf
regularly with John Rattray.

Jacobite Risings of the 18th Century

In modern times the aura of romance and heroic idealism that surrounds the Jacobite risings of 1715 and 1745 still tends to obscure the fact that both were tragic episodes in Scottish history. Families were divided against themselves and all manner of friendships and associations were sundered by the bitterness of the dynastic power-struggle between those who sought restoration of the Royal House of Stuart to the British throne and those who were equally determined to maintain the Hanoverian succession.

The citizens of Edinburgh were mostly Hanoverian in sympathy, and it would seem that a majority of the members of the Incorporation of Surgeons were also of this persuasion, which is presumably why, on 25 March 1746, they honoured HRH the Duke of Cumberland by making him an honorary Freeman of the Incorporation. All the other Edinburgh city incorporations did likewise.

The Duke, a younger son of King George II, was commander-in-chief of the government forces and had recently passed through Edinburgh on his way to meet and defeat Prince Charles Edward Stuart's Highland army at Culloden Moor on 16 April 1746. Cumberland was blamed for the savage atrocities committed by the Hanoverian army after the Battle of Culloden, which earned for him the shameful sobriquet of 'Butcher' by which he is still remembered. One may hope retrospectively that, after Culloden, any proposal to honour him would have been firmly rejected by the Edinburgh Incorporations, and especially by the surgeons, but regrettably this would have been very far from certain.

It is pleasing to record that the professional conduct of the small number of members of the Incorporation who served as army surgeons during the risings, or who attended battle casualties as civilian surgeons, was entirely honourable and totally free from factional partiality.

The Incorporation was reputed, after the 1745 rising and the final defeat of the Jacobites, to have commissioned a portrait of the Duke of Cumberland which hung in Old Surgeons' Hall for several years. There is no historical evidence for this but latter-day Jacobites (of which there are a few!) may take satisfaction from the end of the story which is that the portrait was stolen by a person or persons unknown and never seen again.

By the middle of the 18th century golf was regularly played on Leith Links. (The diaries of Thomas Kincaid the younger (q.v.) record this in some detail.) Many of the regular golfers were also members of the Royal Company of Archers and wanted to establish an annual golfing competition similar to the annual competitions which were (and still are) the high point of the Archers' year. The players on Leith Links asked Edinburgh Town Council to present a silver club for open competition. This was agreed with the stipulation that it had to be played to rules similar to those used in the Company of Archers' contests, playing for a silver club rather than the silver arrow, and so the original rules of golf emerged. Twelve rules (and one local rule, specific to Leith Links) were devised and signed off by Rattray in 1744, after he had won the Silver Club.

It was the tradition after the golf for competitors to retreat to Mrs Clephan's, or Straiton's Tavern, near the Links to relive their games over jugs of claret. Today's Open Golf Championship trophy is a silver claret jug.

Like most Scottish Episcopalians, the Rattray family had a Jacobite tendency. After the victory at Prestonpans, when the Jacobite army marched into Edinburgh, Rattray and George Lauder, the Incorporation's Deacon, were dragged out of their beds in the Canongate in September 1745 and press-ganged into Jacobite service. By the time of the Battle of Culloden in April 1746, Rattray had become personal physician to the Prince. After the defeat he surrendered to the government forces and was imprisoned in Inverness Church. It was at this time that his golfing association arguably saved his life.

One of his regular golfing partners at Leith, Duncan Forbes, Lord President of the Court of Session, interceded on Rattray's behalf and secured his reprieve from execution, the fate of many Jacobite officers. He was re-impeached by the Hanoverians in Edinburgh and sent to languish under house arrest in London to await the gallows on Tower Hill until in the spring of 1747, when, after signing an Oath of Obedience procured by one of his patients, Lord Milton, the Lord Justice Clerk, he was released along with Lauder.

Thereafter he returned to life in Edinburgh, practising as a surgeon, playing golf as before with Duncan Forbes, and winning the Silver Club of the Honourable Company of Edinburgh Golfers in 1751. He passed on his surgical practice to 'Lang Sandy' Wood (q.v.) and he died at his home in Leith Walk, Edinburgh, in 1771.

Author: Colin Strachan

Roll number: 212

William Inglis (1712–92)

Golf has been and remains a favourite leisure activity for surgeons. Two Fellows have been closely associated with the early days of the sport from its origins in East Lothian. John Rattray (q.v.) was the first to write down the rules of golf, and William Inglis achieved lasting fame by being the subject of one of the best-known portraits of the early history of golf. He was Deacon of the Incorporation of Surgeons and Barbers on three occasions and was one of the earliest captains of the Honourable Company of Edinburgh Golfers.

Little is known about Inglis' early life. After serving his surgical apprenticeship, he applied on 5 August 1743 to sit the examination which would enable him to be elected a Fellow. Four examiners were appointed and the examination was held in four parts over the next three months. At the initial sitting he was examined on surgery in general, after which he gave a discourse and was examined on the topic of 'fistula'. The subject for his second examination was 'the brain and its membranes'. On his third appearance he was examined on botany, materia medica and 'reading and explaining receipts', as the surgeons of the day were required to demonstrate that they were competent in simple drug recipes or pharmacy in addition to surgery. His final examination was on an operation for empyema and the composition of various unctions. Having successfully passed these examinations, he paid the Incorporation the sum of £8 6 shillings and 8 pence and was admitted a Fellow on 7 October 1743.

He was also a proficient golfer. His famous portrait by David Allan depicts him in the red livery of the Honourable Company of Edinburgh Golfers, of which he was captain between 1782 and 1784. In the portrait by Raeburn he is seated with the Silver Club, the trophy presented to the champion golfer.

Roll number: 217

William Inglis on Leith Links, 1787. This famous portrait by David Allan portrays Inglis wearing the uniform of the Honourable Company of Edinburgh Golfers. In the background on the right of the picture can be seen the procession of the Silver Club, the prize in the annual competition of the Honourable Company.

William Inglis. In this portrait by Sir Henry Raeburn the Silver Club can be seen on the table to his right.

James Rae with Dr William Laing and Dr James Hay.

John Rae, James Rae's son, as depicted in one of Kay's *Portraits*. Rae is the figure on the left carrying the bottle. The scene depicted is a walking race from Edinburgh to Musselburgh, the home of the fishwives shown on the right. The central figure is Mr Hamilton Bell WS who is carrying a Vintners boy on his back as a handicap. John Rae is in attendance with the bottle as the race was conducted on a hot summer's day.

James Rae (1716–91)

Edinburgh's pre-eminence as a medical school reached its height in the 19th century, at which time its reputation for teaching medicine was recognised throughout the world. The origins of this reputation arguably date from the Seal of Cause and the establishment of two Royal Colleges. Much of the credit for the introduction of formal teaching in the 18th century belongs to James Rae, who established systematic clinical teaching and the first planned course of lectures in surgery.

James Rae was born in Edinburgh. He became an apprentice surgeon in the Incorporation of Surgeons and Barbers of Edinburgh, first to Robert Hope and then to George Lauder. In the summer of 1747 he was examined for admission to the Incorporation and the details of his examination are set out in the College Minutes. He sat a total of five examinations, roughly one month apart. The topics for his first examination included general questions in surgery and anatomy. He was then examined on the detailed anatomy of the pleura and mediastinum and at the next examination on the contents of the thoracic cavity. A month later he was examined on botany and materia medica, and was required to give an explanation of billing and receipts. His final examination was on 'the operation of amputation with the proper dressings'.

As a Freeman of the Incorporation he served as Treasurer and Librarian. In 1764 he was elected Deacon and in 1766 was appointed Surgeon in Ordinary to the Royal Infirmary of Edinburgh.

It was at this time that he began regular clinical teaching on the patients under his care and gave a lecture course on surgery in Surgeons' Hall in High School Yards. This clinical teaching and lecture course was well received and in 1776, just at the time when the Incorporation was about to become a Royal College, it raised a proposal that a chair of surgery be established in the University. However, this proposal was blocked by Monro *secundus*, who had succeeded his father in the Chair of Anatomy. He was able to persuade the medical faculty to oppose this and went on to make a counter-proposal that his Chair should be renamed the Chair of Anatomy and Surgery, despite the fact that he, himself, was not a surgeon.

Despite this setback, James Rae continued with his successful teaching courses and established a large practice. His elder son, William Rae, who died young, also a member of the Incorporation (roll number: 262), established himself in practice in London, and in 1785 began to give lectures on teeth in John Hunter's house. His younger son, John Rae (1749–1808), could be regarded as one of the first Fellows of the Royal College of Surgeons of Edinburgh (roll number: 264). Under the terms of the 1778 Royal Charter the Incorporation became a Royal College and members became Fellows. Like his father and brother, he confined himself largely to dental practice.

James Rae was buried in Greyfriars Churchyard, Edinburgh.

Roll number: 222

Nathaniel Spens (1728–1815)

The magnificent portrait by Raeburn showing Nathaniel Spens in the livery of the Royal Company of Archers hangs in Archers' Hall in Edinburgh. The records of the Royal Company of Archers show that Spens was a skilled and enthusiastic archer, and indeed more is known of his accomplishments as a bowman than as a surgeon.

Nathaniel Spens came from a family who owned the estate of Lathallan in Fife. He was admitted into the Incorporation in July 1751, and served as Librarian from 1757 to 1760. After practising as a surgeon in Edinburgh, he became increasingly interested in the practice of physic, becoming a Licentiate of the Royal College of Physicians of Edinburgh in 1773 and Fellow the following year. He went on to become Treasurer of that College and its President in 1794.

Today, he is more remembered as a member of the Royal Company of Archers than as a physician or surgeon. The Royal Company of Archers began as a private club in 1676 obtaining its Royal Charter from Queen Anne in 1704. It is based, to this day, in Archers' Hall in Edinburgh, which was built in 1776 and extended in 1900 by Balfour Paul, the architect who was also responsible for the extension to the Hall of the College. Since the visit of George IV to Scotland in 1822 the Royal Company have acted as the sovereign's bodyguard in Scotland. Among the prizes for which the archers compete to this day is the Spens Medal. His yew bow, which was presented by his son, is still on display in Archers' Hall.

His son, Thomas Spens, was, like his father, a member of the Royal Company of Archers and Treasurer and President of the Royal College of Physicians of Edinburgh. Dr Thomas Spens is credited with the first description of a case of heart block in Britain. (See Wood/Spens family tree on page 71.)

Roll number: 229

Nathaniel Spens (1728–1815). Portrayed in the livery of the Royal Company of Archers.

Archery in Scotland and the Royal Company of Archers

Archery was practised widely in Scotland from medieval times. In the 15th century, when it had a major military significance, King James I encouraged the practice by a decree that all those over 12 years of age were to practise archery and persons not practising were to be fined.

James II went further during his reign. Football and golf were to be 'utterly cried down and not to be used' and shooting at the butts was to be practised every Sunday from Easter to Allhallowmas, each man having to shoot six shots at least under a fine of two pence.

By the 17th century archery competitions were held in many Scottish towns, and prizes given for proficiency among the competitors. The records of the Royal Company of Archers date back to 1676 when 'Archers and Bowmen residing within and about the City of Edinburgh' resolved to 'enter a particular Society and Company for Archery and Shutting [shooting] with Bows and Arrows, to be called His Majestie's Company of Archers'. Butts were to be erected, and a prize of a silver arrow, or other piece of plate, was to be shot for annually.

Even in the early days of the Company, while arrows and bowstrings were imported from abroad – principally from Ghent – bows were made at home, from native wood, by the Company's own bowmaker.

In 1822, during the visit of George IV to Edinburgh, the Royal Company offered its services as bodyguard. This offer was accepted, and the Company occupied a conspicuous position in the various ceremonials which then took place. Since that time the Royal Company has been the sovereign's bodyguard in Scotland.

Since its foundation, the Royal Company has held shooting competitions, many of which continue to this day. The Musselburgh Silver Arrow (dating from at least 1603), the Peebles arrow (first shot for in 1628), and the Corporation of Edinburgh arrow, presented in 1709, are among the prizes for which today's archers still compete.

Alexander Wood (1725–1807).
(See the Wood/Spens family tree on page 71.)

Alexander Wood (1725–1807)

An English visitor to Edinburgh in 1776, at the apogee of that remarkable period known as the 'Scottish Enlightenment', wrote 'Here I stand at the Cross of Edinburgh and can, within a few minutes, take fifty men of learning and genius by the hand.' Almost certainly this visitor would, sooner or later, also have seen, and possibly taken by the hand, the surgeon Mr Alexander Wood, who, although no genius, was undoubtedly one of Edinburgh's most extraordinary citizens at that time and whose amiable eccentricities became, in his own lifetime, part of the city's folklore.

Alexander Wood was the son of Thomas Wood, a farmer on the outskirts of Edinburgh. On account of his lean, lanky physique, he was better known to his contemporaries and to posterity as 'Lang Sandy' Wood. Little is known of his education or of what inspired him to become a surgeon and we have no details of his surgical apprenticeship.

He became a Freeman of the Incorporation of Surgeons and Barbers in 1756 and rapidly gained a reputation as a skilled and safe operator. Having built up a large surgical practice and been appointed to the staff of the new Royal Infirmary, he was elected Deacon (President) of the Incorporation in 1762 and held office for two years. By this time, 'Lang Sandy' had become a well-known and universally popular figure in Edinburgh, but, although a highly competent, practical surgeon, he made no contributions to the advancement of surgical knowledge and he became, and remains to this day, famous because of his character and personality.

He was a genial extrovert whose affability, bonhomie and kindliness enriched the Edinburgh social scene and endeared him not just to a narrow coterie of friends and colleagues, but to the citizenry at large. 'Lang Sandy' was an enthusiastic supporter of many dining clubs and convivial societies and a founder member of two medico-social fraternities which flourish to this day – the Aesculapian Club, founded in 1773, and the Harveian Society, founded in 1778. He was the chief instigator of the Gymnastic Club, founded in 1786, the members of which met annually at Leith to celebrate the 'Ludi Apollinaris' and to compete with each other at 'Gowfing, Bowling and Swimming'. At all of these Sandy Wood was a notable performer and especially at 'Gowf', which he continued to play energetically and with no little skill when past his 80th birthday. The Gymnastic Club disbanded in 1811, but its memorabilia still adorn the table at dinners of the Aesculapian Club, to which they were bequeathed.

Nothing in all his life gave Lang Sandy greater pleasure than the diploma of 'Doctor of Mirth', which his fellow Aesculapians conferred upon him in 1803.

In an age when personal idiosyncrasy was often deliberately cultivated and no one was diffident about expressing his individuality, Sandy Wood stood out among his fellow citizens. Wherever he went, including domiciliary visits to his patients, he was accompanied by his two pets – a tame sheep which trotted along beside him and a raven which perched on his shoulder – and he caused a considerable stir by being the first person in Edinburgh to own and use an umbrella.

When Robert Burns first came to Edinburgh in 1787 he sustained a leg injury which incapacitated him for three or four weeks. During this time he was treated by 'Lang Sandy', of whom the poet's patroness, Mrs Maclehose ('Clarinda'), herself a doctor's daughter, wrote: 'I am glad to hear Mr Wood attends you. He is a good soul and a safe surgeon. Do as he bids and I trust your leg will soon be quite well.' Lang Sandy and his famous patient became firm friends and there is no doubt that in his surgeon Burns found a man after his own heart. In two letters he refers to 'My very worthy respected friend, Mr Alexander Wood' and to 'one of the noblest men in God's world – Alexander Wood, Surgeon'. Sandy Wood was a subscriber to the first Edinburgh edition of Burns' poems and later it was upon his written recommendation that Burns was appointed to a post with the Commission of Excise.

There could be no more characteristic vignette of 'Lang Sandy' than the lines written by his friend and colleague Dr Andrew Duncan, after a memorably convivial meeting of the Gymnastic Club:

Alexander ('Lang Sandy') Wood
as depicted in Kay's *Portraits*.

Here lies Sandy Wood, a good honest fellow
Very wise when sober but wiser when mellow
At sensible nonsense by no man excelled
With wit and good humour dull care he repelled

But though now he's laid low we must not complain
For after a sleep, he'll be with us again
Shed no tears, my good friends, wear no garments of sable
Sandy Wood is not dead but laid under the table!

Roll number: 239

Kay's *Portraits*

John Kay became well known in Scotland as a caricaturist, and miniaturist, depicting not only the great and the good, but many of the characters who flourished in Edinburgh at the height of the Scottish Enlightenment.

He was born in 1742, near Dalkeith, outside Edinburgh. At the age of 13, he was apprenticed to a barber in Dalkeith, and, having served his apprenticeship, set up in practice in Edinburgh. At this time the barbers enjoyed status in society, despite having separated from the Incorporation of Surgeons and Barbers in 1722.

Kay's practice appears to have been a successful one, which involved dressing the wigs and trimming the heads and beards of his gentlemen clients each morning. From an early age he had had artistic talent andwhen it became apparent that this was where his true genius lay, he took up etching and painting professionally.

In 1784, he published his first caricature and from then until he was over 80 years of age he published a succession of caricatures of the people and the incidents that he saw each day on the streets of Edinburgh. He opened a shop in Parliament Square, where his caricatures and miniatures were displayed and sold.

During his career he etched almost nine hundred plates, which formed a unique and valuable record of the public characters, of all kinds, who made their mark in Edinburgh over what was arguably its most interesting half-century.

Kay died in 1826 at the age of 84, but after his death, the copper-plates of his works were purchased by Hugh Paton, who republished them in 1838 in two quarto volumes, under the title *A series of original portraits and caricature etchings by the late John Kay, Miniature Painter, Edinburgh; with biographical sketches and illustrative anecdotes.*

Alexander Hamilton (1739–1802).

Sedan Chairs in Edinburgh

In the latter half of the 18th century horse-drawn coaches remained the principal means of wheeled transport in Britain's cities. Edinburgh's Old Town was not well suited to the coach because of its steep hills and narrow closes, and so the sedan chair, when it was introduced for public hire in 1687, proved to be a particularly apt form of transport.

The door of the sedan chair was normally at the front, but most Edinburgh chairs had a door at the side to allow easier access from doorways in the narrow closes and wynds. Another Edinburgh adaptation was the pivoting seat that kept passengers in a horizontal position on the steep inclines in the Old Town.

The sedan chair reached the height of its popularity in the 18th century, so that by 1779 there were no fewer than 230 sedan chairs in Edinburgh, of which 50 were privately owned and the remainder for public hire. The main sedan-chair hire stance was at the Tron Kirk.

They proved to be a dignified method of transport, provided the passenger was not in a hurry and was travelling a short distance. They were not noted for their comfort, and it was common for the chairmen to 'set off at a plunging trot with their load, and as the carrying poles were quite pliant, the extreme bobbing up and down and swinging to and fro of the vehicle, produced an uneasy feeling in the passenger'.

The sedan chair continued to be used for all major Edinburgh social events well into the 19th century, but by that time most sedans were in the more affluent New Town. There were 101 sedan chairs in 1814, only 46 in 1827 and, by 1850, horse-drawn carriages had replaced this picturesque method of transport.

Alexander Hamilton (1739–1802)

As Professor of Midwifery, Alexander Hamilton was instrumental in the establishment of a lying-in hospital in Edinburgh and published several important textbooks on midwifery. During his term of office as Deacon, the Incorporation of Surgeons and Barbers was granted a Royal Charter from George III on 14 March 1778. Under the terms of this charter, the Incorporation became the Royal College of Surgeons of the City of Edinburgh, giving all members the status of Fellowship.

Alexander Hamilton was born in Kincardineshire, where his father, a retired army surgeon, was in practice. He became apprentice to John Straiton, a surgeon in Edinburgh, and was admitted as member of the Incorporation of Surgeons and Barbers in 1764. He went on to graduate MD from St Andrews University. It was Hamilton who made the case to the Edinburgh University Senate and Town Council that surgery should be taught by a separate professor in the University, but this proposal was opposed successfully by Monro *secundus*. In 1780 he was appointed joint Professor of Midwifery with Thomas Young and on Young's death in 1783, he became sole Professor of Midwifery. He was to make a major contribution in this area and was almost certainly the first Edinburgh Professor of Midwifery whose name was known to the outside world. Hamilton held strong views and was not afraid of promoting these. The 1792 pamphlet *A Guide for Gentlemen Studying Medicine at the University of Edinburgh* described in detail and was complimentary about the course of instruction in midwifery whilst criticising most of the other professors and their teaching. Although published under the pseudonym 'J. Johnson', it was widely believed that it had been written by Alexander Hamilton or his son, James Hamilton (q.v.), who followed him in the Chair.

His greatest contributions to midwifery were the production of successful textbooks of midwifery and the establishment of the lying-in hospital. The lying-in ward had been started by Dr Thomas Young, but it was Alexander Hamilton who planned and established the lying-in hospital, which was partially funded from his own pocket. He also published several important works on midwifery. His *Elements of the Practice of Midwifery* (1775) ran to several editions. He went on to write *A Treatise of Midwifery* (1780) and *Outlines of the Theory and Practice of Midwifery* (1784). Both of the latter were translated into German.

Hamilton had decided when his son, James, was very young that he should succeed him in the Chair of Midwifery, which he duly did in 1800.

Roll number: 242

Alexander Hamilton's sedan chair, in which he regularly travelled to visit patients.

John Aitken (d. 1790)

Two institutions, each founded in the late 18th century, the Royal Medical Society and the extra-mural School of Medicine, were to have a profound influence on standards of medical learning in Edinburgh over the next 200 years. John Aitken was involved in the establishment of both of these.

The Royal Medical Society provided for medical students and young doctors a platform for presentation of research work or theories, and a forum in which these and other medical topics could be debated. A Hall for the Society was built in 1775 close to Surgeons' Hall in Surgeons' Square, the foundation stone being laid by Dr William Cullen, then President of the Royal College of Physicians of Edinburgh.

The tradition of extra-mural teaching in Edinburgh began in the 17th century. In 1697, Surgeons' Hall and its anatomical theatre was built for the purposes of anatomy demonstrations and, just over a quarter of a century after this, in 1726, the Faculty of Medicine in the University of Edinburgh was established. Yet despite the establishment of these two bodies, dedicated to medical teaching, extra-mural education flourished. It was carried out by individuals or groups of teachers in various sites. In 1895, this became formally incorporated as the School of Medicine of the Royal Colleges, which continued until 1948.

John Aitken took medical classes in the University of Edinburgh from 1763, going on to become a Fellow of the Royal College of Surgeons of Edinburgh in 1770. The following year he joined the Royal Medical Society, becoming Senior President between 1774 and 1776. It was during his term of office as Senior President that the Royal Medical Society had its first meeting in their new hall, on land leased to it by the Royal College of Surgeons. The Society in its new premises clearly flourished and, in an attempt to enhance its status even further, applied for a Royal Charter. It was Aitken, aided by Dr Andrew Duncan (1744–1828), who acted for the Society, ensuring that their efforts were rewarded with the granting of a Royal Charter in 1778.

Aitken went on to become a surgeon in the Royal Infirmary in Edinburgh and, by the standards of the day, became a prolific author. He initially wrote books and pamphlets on surgery, later expanding this into the theory and practice of medicine, the principles and practice of midwifery and principles of anatomy and physiology. He will be best remembered, however, for his prowess as an extra-mural teacher. Robert Chambers' *A Biographical Dictionary of Eminent Scotsmen* (1835) describes his lectures as well attended, and 'he was generally esteemed as a good lecturer'. His success as a lecturer resulted in him teaching not merely anatomy and surgery, but going on to teach physic, chemistry and midwifery.

John Aitken (d. 1790).

South-west corner of Surgeons' Square. The building in the centre, Barclay's House (10 Surgeons' Square), was used by Barclay for anatomical teaching.

The building next to it, slightly set back, John Gordon's house (9 Surgeons' Square), was where John Gordon taught anatomy and was subsequently used by John Thomson, William Sharpey, Allen Thomson, James Young Simpson and Douglas Maclagan.

The building on the left is old Surgeons' Hall, and that on the right is the hall of the Royal Medical Society. (See map on page 78.)

As has happened not infrequently since then, the University establishment was critical of this style and sought to portray him as a provider of 'cram courses', rather than a serious scientific lecturer. Sir John Struthers (q.v.), who went on to become Professor of Anatomy in Aberdeen, wrote: 'it is difficult to look on him but as a kind of grinder [crammer] ... rather than as entitled to take rank as a scientific lecturer...' Despite that criticism, Struthers described him as the first true lecturer on anatomy in the extra-mural school. John Aitken could rightly be regarded as the founder of the extra-mural teaching of medicine in Edinburgh, a tradition that was to continue and to flourish for almost two hundred years.

Author: M. H. Kaufman

Roll number: 249

Benjamin Bell (1749–1806).

Benjamin Bell (1749–1806)

Until the latter half of the 18th century, the influence of Edinburgh surgeons was largely confined to Scotland. Some members of the Incorporation like Archibald Pitcairne (q.v.) and Alexander Monro *primus* (q.v.) had established European reputations, the former in the field of medicine and the latter in anatomy. It was Benjamin Bell, regarded by many as the 'father of the Edinburgh Surgical School', who was the first to establish an international reputation for Edinburgh surgery.

Like another notable character of the Enlightenment, Allan Ramsay, Bell was born in Dumfriesshire. After local schooling, he was apprenticed to Mr James Hill, a surgeon in Dumfries, and in 1766 entered the Edinburgh medical school. His teachers at the time included many inspiring figures. Joseph Black was Professor of Chemistry and John Hope taught botany; Monro *secundus* taught anatomy, while his father, Monro *primus*, was still lecturing in surgery. The chairs of medicine were held by William Cullen and John Gregory. In 1770 Bell was admitted to the Incorporation, which was to become the Royal College of Surgeons of Edinburgh eight years later.

Perhaps inspired by the Monros, he decided to further his studies in Paris and London. 'Medicine is taught in Edinburgh in greater perfection than in any other part of Europe,' he wrote to his father, 'but there are some particular branches which are to be had in Paris and nowhere else, particularly with regard to surgery.' He spent two years in London and Paris learning surgery. In London he studied with John Hunter (1728–93), whom he described as 'the most agreeable and at the same time the most useful acquaintance I ever met with'. His brother, William Hunter (1718–83), taught him anatomy.

This wealth of experience led to a highly successful practice when he returned to Edinburgh and at the early age of 24 he was appointed Surgeon to the Royal Infirmary. His career progression was temporarily interrupted by a fall from his horse, which forced him to take some two years off from his practice to convalesce at Liberton Farm (which still, incidentally, functions as a farm to this day) only three miles from the College. During this time he undoubtedly developed his thinking not only on surgery but on agriculture and political economy, all topics on which he was to make significant literary contributions in later life. His surgical practice and reputation continued to grow and he became the most sought-after surgeon in Scotland, causing one contemporary to write that, 'at one time nobody could die contented without having consulted Benjamin Bell'. His success as a doctor and as a teacher was enhanced by his personality. James Ward, a contemporary, described his kindly disposition and his ability to express opinions in very plain and accurate language. He possessed that all-important quality in a physician, of giving reassurance and confidence to his patients.

Bell was not only one of the foremost practical surgeons of his day, he was an original thinker and a surgical innovator. In many ways he was ahead of his time in being one of the first to emphasise the importance of reducing post-operative pain. He was an innovator too in surgical procedures, recognising that poor wound healing in amputation often resulted from insufficient skin and muscle flaps, and his technique became known as 'the triple incision of Bell'. His aphorism 'save skin' was responsible for improved wound healing in this common operation.

The use of a seton had been advocated by James Rae (q.v.). Bell, however, was the first to rationalise its use and to define the indications. These, and other innovations, were included in his magnum opus entitled *A System of Surgery*, which was published in six volumes between 1783 and 1788, and was the first comprehensive textbook of surgery in the English language. It was truly a giant work which described not only his practice of surgery but aimed 'to exhibit a view of the art of surgery as it is at present practised by the most expert surgeons in Europe'. It went through seven editions and was translated into French and German.

Another important original contribution was a paper, based on an extensive clinical experience, which showed that the causes, natural history and clinical features of gonorrhoea and syphilis were different and suggested that they were different diseases.

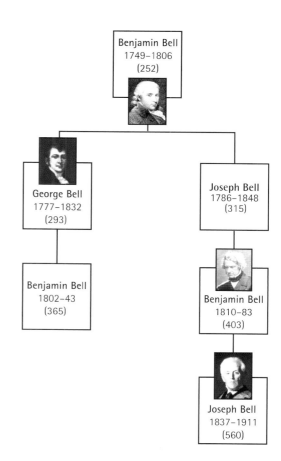

The Bell surgical dynasty
(numbers in parentheses are College roll numbers).

Benjamin Bell (1749–1806)
depicted in Kay's *Portraits*.

Besides success in surgery, Bell enjoyed success in property speculation and, by the time of his death, owned most of the suburb of Newington in Edinburgh. It was in Newington House that he was to die in 1806.

His descendants were also to achieve distinction in surgery. The Bell family tree (see above) shows this distinguished lineage. His elder son, George Bell (1777–1832), and his son in turn, Benjamin Bell (1802–43), were both Fellows of the College and surgeons in Edinburgh. His younger son, Joseph, was also a Fellow of the College and his son, Benjamin Bell, was President of the College from 1863 to 1865. His son, Joseph Bell (q.v.), great-grandson of that first Benjamin Bell, also became President of the College and famously the model for the character of Sherlock Holmes.

Roll number: 252

James Russell junior (1754–1836)

Some families have been associated with the College over several generations and notable among these are the Russells. James Russell senior, who became Deacon of the Incorporation of Surgeons in 1752, was an elder cousin of James Black, the celebrated chemist who discovered carbon dioxide and was the first to appreciate that air is a mixture of gases. As a young man Black stayed with the Russell family and it would seem that his cousin had a significant formative influence upon him. In 1764 Russell gave up surgery to become Professor of Natural Philosophy in Edinburgh University in succession to another relative, Adam Ferguson, who had resigned that Chair in order to become Professor of Moral Philosophy.

James Russell junior followed his father into a surgical career, being admitted into the Incorporation in 1777, a year before it became the Royal College of Surgeons of the City of Edinburgh. From 1780 to 1792 he served as Librarian. He became a popular teacher of surgery, teaching large classes in the extra-mural school. The surgeons had been advocating for some years that the teaching of surgery in the University was of sufficient importance to justify a chair in its own right. Earlier proposals had been resisted by Monro *secundus*, who regarded this as an infringement of his right to teach anatomy and surgery, although he was not a practising surgeon and never a Fellow of the College. Russell petitioned the Town Council to establish a chair of clinical surgery and, in 1802, he was appointed the first professor being paid by a Crown endowment of £50 per annum.

Surgeons at that time were required to retire from Royal Infirmary practice at the age of 50. Although no longer practising, he was able to continue teaching as he regularly accompanied attending surgeons on ward and home visits. His lectures and tutorials in clinical surgery were confined to teaching on the patients of practising surgeons, which, by all accounts, he accomplished with great diplomacy for the next 20 years. A contemporary description of Professor Russell is a reminder of the dress style of the day: 'The Professor was a tall, thin gentleman of the old school, who wore a red wig, was always dressed in black with a white neck cloth – a choker of the "old Beau Brummell" style. He indulged in a broad frill on his shirt breast … a morning coat … knee-breeches and silk stockings.'

Whilst not regarded as a profound thinker, he recorded several valuable clinical observations. A paper in 1803 entitled *A New and Hitherto Undescribed Variety of Hernia* is one of the earliest descriptions of direct inguinal hernia.

His final paper was dedicated to the President and Fellows of the Royal College of Surgeons 'for the Patronage afforded to the class of Clinical Surgery and for the facilities and support granted me to promote the success of the undertaking'.

He amassed a collection of paintings, including old masters, which one contemporary described as unsurpassed in Scotland.

Russell finally retired from the Chair in 1833 at the age of 79 but only on the condition that his successor should pay him £300 per year for life, as was the custom at that time. The contenders to follow him in the Chair were Robert Liston (q.v.) and James Syme (q.v.). Liston contemptuously 'and in rather coarse terms' refused to agree to pay. James Syme was therefore appointed to the Chair of Clinical Surgery.

Roll number: 260

James Russell junior (1754–1836).

James Russell junior as a boy pictured with his father,
the Professor of Natural Philosophy.

John Bennett (1740–1805)

It is fortunate that John Kay, an artist and writer, was able to record for posterity caricatures to which were later added biographical sketches of many of the characters, whether brilliant, famous or eccentric, who abounded in Edinburgh in the latter years of the 18th century. Between 1784 and 1824 he completed over 900 sketches, including those of several surgeons.

As a result of Kay's account, John Bennett has been portrayed as a practical joker during a short period at the turn of the 19th century, when such activities were both acceptable and fashionable.

John Bennett was born in Edinburgh. After studying medicine at Edinburgh University, he was appointed Surgeon to the Sutherland Fencibles, an auxiliary regiment raised for home defence, which, like many of its kind, enjoyed a short existence, being disbanded in 1783. On his return to Edinburgh he went into a partnership with James Law of Elvingston. Law was to become a Fellow of the College in 1818 (roll number: 338), and was to go on to become President of the College on two occasions, in 1800 and 1812. As a result of local pre-eminence, his portrait was painted by Raeburn.

John Bennett (1740–1805)
as portrayed in Kay's *Portraits*.

Bennett's reputation was enhanced by a public demonstration of his surgical skill. A group of merchants, after what Kay describes as a fit of hard drinking, were feigning a fight with a knife when the blade accidentally incised the throat of one Mr Dempster, jeweller in Parliament Square. The knife, at the time, was held by a Mr Hamilton, who summoned John Bennett. Bennett immediately stopped the haemorrhage and closed the wound. Hamilton, to show his gratitude, presented John Bennett with 'an elegant chariot'.

Bennett was appointed surgeon to the garrison of Edinburgh Castle in 1791 and elected President of the College in 1803. Two years later he was given an honorary commission into the Loyal Edinburgh Spearmen, a volunteer regiment in which he held the rank of Lieutenant Colonel Commandant.

He was given the freedom of the city of Londonderry in unusual circumstances, which offer an interesting insight into the times in which he lived. The freedom of that city was presented to him in a silver box by William Leckie, Senior Magistrate of Londonderry. In 1805, Leckie's son, a medical student at Edinburgh, had fought a duel at Duddingston with a fellow medical student called Romney. Four shots were exchanged and Leckie sustained a groin wound. According to Kay: 'Mr Leckie received his wound by the first fire but did not discover it. After shaking hands with his antagonist he declared that he was mortally wounded and desired Mr Romney, the seconds and the surgeon who attended [Bennett] to make their escape which they accordingly did.' While Bennett was not able to offer any help to the unfortunate Leckie, his father obviously felt that his mere presence and support at the duel deserved his gratitude.

Another insight into his life and times is in what Kay rather disapproving described as 'an unprofessional frolic'. On one occasion, Bennett had lost a bet, the wager being 'dinner and drinks'. When he lost the wager, he duly entertained the victor to dinner and drinks in what Kay describes as 'a house of good cheer' in Leith, but arranging their transport there in funeral coaches, which drove slowly through the streets of Edinburgh and Leith at a funeral pace to the embarrassment of their occupants.

Bennett died suddenly during a day's excursion to the kingdom of Fife. Having crossed on the ferry at Queensferry, he was noted to be in high spirits but was found dead later that day with a fatal shotgun wound, his gun dog beside his body. Some assumed that he had committed suicide.

Roll number: 270

John Bell (1763–1820)

The influence of the Enlightenment was felt throughout Scottish medicine during the 18th century and well into the 19th. Among doctors there was increasing knowledge of and interest in philosophy and the arts, and the Edinburgh medical school in particular began to attract students from around the world. Much of the reputation of the medical school had been built on the teaching of anatomy. John Bell and his younger brother, Charles (q.v.), were practising surgeons and at the same time articulate and inspiring teachers, whose artistic gifts allowed them to produce anatomical etchings of a very high quality. Widely regarded as the founder of applied surgical anatomy, John Bell's career as a teacher was curtailed when he fell foul of the University establishment, principally in the person of James Gregory, the Professor of Medicine. Despite this adversity, Bell was to become the most successful surgeon in Scotland during the first two decades of the 19th century.

John Bell was born in Edinburgh, the son of an Episcopalian clergyman, and older brother of Charles Bell, who was to achieve fame as an anatomist, a physiologist and a surgeon. John Bell, like his brother, was a son of the Enlightenment. From an early age he amassed a large and varied library and served as College Librarian from 1792 to 1796. His interest in literature made him a fluent writer and he was also an eloquent orator. The interest in art which he shared with his brother, Charles, resulted in superb illustrations in his textbook, *Anatomy of the Human Body*, published in 1793.

Bell's surgical training began as apprentice to Alexander Wood ('Lang Sandy') (q.v.). The two seemed to have had, on the face of it, little in common. Wood was eccentric, bohemian and convivial and Bell was bookish, disciplined and artistic. Yet Bell's respect for his teacher is demonstrated by his dedication of the first volume of his anatomy textbook to his former master. After visiting centres in Europe and Russia, he became a Fellow of the Royal College of Surgeons of Edinburgh, which allowed him to act, in rotation with others, as Surgeon to the Royal Infirmary. He made his mark as a dextrous and successful surgeon. At the same time, he came to appreciate the deficiencies of anatomy teaching in the University under the Monros. Monro *secundus*, acknowledged as a brilliant teacher, was not a practising surgeon. Furthermore, the shortage of bodies for dissection meant that as few as three dissections could take place per year. These bodies, after preservation in spirit, lost much of their value for the teaching of anatomy and the demonstrations took place some distance from the students. Bell began to teach applied anatomy, surgical anatomy relevant to the surgical procedures of the day, and produced for his students his book *Anatomy of the Bones, Muscles and Joints*, published in 1794. For the ten years from 1786 he was so successful a teacher that he established an extra-mural School of Anatomy in his house in what was later to become Surgeons' Square. Here his fame as a teacher spread.

His success provoked professional jealousies. Dr James Gregory, Professor of Medicine in the University, persuaded the authorities that only six members of the College of Surgeons should act as Surgeons to the Royal Infirmary, each for a period of two years. This effectively banished John Bell from surgical practice in the hospital and he stopped lecturing in the extra-mural school. This resulted in a vituperative, bitter war of words between the two, conducted by an exchange of letters and pamphlets, some of which were posted in public places around Edinburgh.

John Bell (1763–1820).

Frontispiece from John Bell's *Principles of Surgery*.

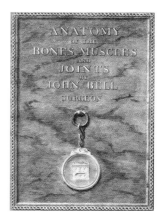

John Bell's *Anatomy of the Bones, Joints and Muscles.*

Surgical field set (c. 1800).

Bell continued in private surgical practice and, over the next 20 years, was the most successful surgeon of his day in Scotland. Among the contributions which he made to operative surgery was the technique of successfully suturing arterial lacerations. In his surgical textbook *The Principles of Surgery*, published in three volumes from 1801 to 1808, he describes, in detail, an arterial suture technique which he had practised successfully.

He possessed a holistic approach to surgery, which emphasised the importance of surgeons as physicians rather than mere operators. In an effort 'to moderate the rage for operations', he suggested that 'operations have come at last to represent the whole science, and the surgeon, far from being valued according to his sensibilities in general knowledge, is esteemed excellent only in proportion as he operates with skill in this, as in many other areas'.

His reputation resulted in invitations to many centres in Europe. While visiting Rome in 1820, he became ill and died. He was buried next to John Keats in a grave now marked by a Celtic cross, erected by the College in 1891.

Roll number: 277

James Hamilton (1767–1839)

James Hamilton succeeded his father, Alexander Hamilton (q.v.), as Professor of Midwifery in Edinburgh. Although recognised as an outstanding lecturer and author of two important textbooks, he is best remembered for his pugnacity.

James Hamilton was born in Edinburgh. His father had apparently decided when his son was very young that he should succeed him in the Chair of Midwifery. He attended medical lectures at the University of St Andrews and after graduation became a Fellow of the Royal College of Surgeons of Edinburgh in 1788 and a member of the Royal College of Physicians of Edinburgh in 1792. From an early age he had assisted his father in practice and when his father retired, succeeded him, as planned, in the Chair of Midwifery.

Contemporary accounts all attest to his adversarial temperament. His delivery was 'harsh and his intonation Scotch, pure and unsophisticated'. Two of his quarrels were to gain notoriety. In 1792 *A Guide for Gentlemen Studying Medicine at the University of Edinburgh* was published under the pseudonym 'J. Johnson'. This guide was openly critical of most of the teaching in the Faculty of Medicine with the exception of the midwifery class, which was highly praised. As rumours began to circulate that Hamilton might be the author of this inflammatory pamphlet, the Professor of Medicine, James Gregory, wrote a pamphlet denouncing the guide and suggesting that it had been written by Dr James Hamilton. Hamilton's reply was scathing in its criticism of Gregory, who retaliated by assaulting Hamilton in the street with his walking stick, an action which cost him £100 when Hamilton successfully sued him. Gregory was reported as saying that he would be willing to pay that again for the privilege of beating Hamilton a second time!

James Hamilton (the younger) (1767–1839).

Hamilton also sued Thomas Hope, the Professor of Chemistry, for slander after Hope had accused him, at the Senatus Academicus, of being an inveterate liar.

Yet much of the professional enmity which Hamilton and his father provoked resulted from their attempts to have midwifery made a compulsory subject in the undergraduate curriculum. In pursuit of this goal, Hamilton, in 1824, made a direct appeal to the Town Council, who at that time still had the ultimate authority in University matters. To the dismay and outrage of the Senate, the Town Council supported Hamilton and managed to achieve a Royal Commission to investigate the problems of medical education. In 1830 midwifery was made a compulsory subject. James Hamilton contributed much to the teaching and practice of midwifery in Edinburgh. He wrote several books, the last of which, *Practical Observations on Various Subjects Relating to Midwifery* (1836), was highly regarded and was translated into German. As early as 1808 he had written a parents' guide to childhood illness which was decades ahead of its time. He was the first British medical writer to use the term 'eclampsia'. Hamilton died at the age of 71, having resigned his Chair a few months earlier. He was succeeded in the Chair by James Young Simpson.

Roll number: 279

Frontispiece from James Hamilton's
*Practical Observations on
Various Subjects Relating to Midwifery.*

John Thomson (1765–1846)

To be described by a contemporary as the most learned physician of his time in Scotland is an impressive accolade not given lightly, but John Thomson seems to have been well worthy of that description. After successively holding chairs of surgery, military surgery and pathology, he went on to practise as a physician, and came close to being appointed to a chair of medicine. He had appreciated early on the value of political support for academic advancement.

Despite his father's wish that he should enter the Church, Thomson decided to pursue a medical career. After serving a three-year apprenticeship under Dr White of Paisley, he entered the University of Glasgow during the winter session of 1788–9 and in 1790 he transferred to Edinburgh. After several junior appointments in the Royal Infirmary in 1790 and 1791, he became a member of the Royal Medical Society, and in 1791–2 was elected one of its presidents.

He resigned from the Infirmary in July 1792, because of ill health, and proceeded to London, where for a short period he attended the Hunterian School of Medicine. Returning to Edinburgh in 1793, he became a Fellow of the College of Surgeons, which made him eligible to attend the Infirmary as a surgeon, and in 1800 he was selected by the managers to become the most junior of the six surgeons appointed to the Infirmary. This was at the suggestion of Professor James Gregory, ostensibly to improve continuity of patient care in that institution, but the decision caused concern among the members of the Royal College of Surgeons, the majority of whom found themselves excluded.

In 1804, he was elected the first Professor of Surgery of the Royal College of Surgeons of Edinburgh, in the face of considerable reservations and anxiety in the College, and much hostility in the Faculty of Medicine and the Senatus of the University. In 1806, with the support of Earl Spencer,

John Thomson (1765–1846).

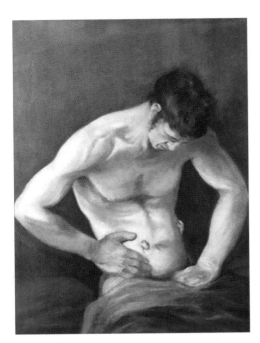

Gunshot wound of abdomen portrayed by Sir Charles Bell. This soldier was fortunate as the musket ball appears to have passed superficially under the skin. Note the greater amount of slough on the wound on the left flank indicating that this is likely to have been the exit wound.

the Home Secretary, he was appointed the first holder of the Regius Chair of Military Surgery in the University. He resigned from these two posts in 1821 and 1822, respectively. He had earlier resigned from his surgical appointment in the Infirmary because he felt that the managers had failed to support him when John Bell (q.v.) questioned his surgical competence. Bell had been for many years one of the leading operating surgeons in Edinburgh, and one of those who had been excluded from the Infirmary in 1800.

Like his contemporary Charles Bell (q.v.), Thomson visited Brussels in 1815 to see the treatment of the British and French wounded following the Battle of Waterloo, and his advice on their treatment was much valued. His lectures on military surgery in Edinburgh were attended by both medical students and experienced military medical officers. These were extremely popular, particularly after Waterloo, attracting audiences of around 300.

In 1808 he gained the MD degree from Aberdeen, and in February 1815 he was admitted a Licentiate of the Royal College of Physicians. He acted as both a consulting physician and consulting surgeon. In September 1815 he was instrumental in the establishment of the New Town Dispensary. His lectures on diseases of the eye in 1819 were said to have paved the way for the establishment of the first eye infirmary in Edinburgh in 1824. He later taught practice of physic and general pathology in the extra-mural school and, on the death of James Gregory, was a candidate for the Chair of Physic but was unsuccessful.

In 1831, following a request to Lord Melbourne, then Home Secretary, he was appointed the first holder of the Regius Chair of General Pathology in the University, but resigned from this post in 1841 due to ill health. While he, at various times, held three chairs, his two sons each held university chairs. William, his son from his first marriage, was Professor of Practice of Physic in Glasgow, and Allen (q.v.), his son from his second marriage, successively held chairs of anatomy, in Aberdeen, Institutes of Medicine (Physiology) in Edinburgh, and later anatomy in Glasgow. Not surprisingly, Dr Robert Knox (q.v.) referred to him as 'the old chair-maker'.

According to Lord Cockburn, in his *Memorials of his Time* (1856), Thomson had the reputation of being 'in his time the most learned physician in Scotland … he was for forty years the most exciting of all our practitioners and of all our teachers'.

Author: M. H. Kaufman

Roll number: 287

Sir William Newbigging (1772–1852)

In the era before antiseptic surgery and anaesthesia, many surgical operations remained hazardous well into the 19th century. Cutting for urethral and bladder stones had been practised from medieval times, and arterial ligation for aneurysm had first been carried out successfully by John Hunter in 1785. Sir William Newbigging was adept at both procedures, and regarded as the best operative surgeon in Edinburgh, until the arrival of Robert Liston (q.v.).

Born in Lanark, the son of a country solicitor, William Newbigging came to Edinburgh as apprentice to Mr Forrest Dewar (roll number: 255), a local surgeon. After examination he was admitted as a Fellow of the Royal College of Surgeons of Edinburgh in 1799. Along with George Bell (roll number: 293) he was appointed Surgeon to the Edinburgh Royal Infirmary three years later.

Newbigging established a reputation as a skilled technical surgeon particularly as a lithotomist, removing urethral and bladder stones, often large and often multiple. He was also an early and successful practitioner of arterial ligation for popliteal aneurysm, which had been performed successfully for the first time by John Hunter in London in 1785.

His surgical colleagues in the Infirmary included Alexander Gillespie (q.v.), and George Bell, with Professor James Russell (q.v.) acting as consulting surgeon, while John Wishart (q.v.) and Joseph Bell (q.v.) were assistant surgeons. During the period 1819–20, Robert Christison was appointed his house surgeon, and James Syme (q.v.) his resident clerk. Both of these were to go on to achieve fame and distinction, Syme as a surgeon, and Christison, as Professor first of Medical Jurisprudence and then of Materia Medica.

Christison was appointed to the Chair of Medical Jurisprudence in 1822, and in this capacity he was called upon to perform the post-mortem on Margery Campbell, the last victim of Burke and Hare. The Crown asked Newbigging to assist at this autopsy. They could find no evidence to support the Crown's case that she had been plied with alcohol by Burke before being smothered and suffocated to death, and both gave evidence to that effect at the trial. Burke was convicted of the crime only after Hare had turned King's evidence.

Newbigging was a member, and latterly Vice President, of the Wernerian Natural History Society, a club where men who shared an interest in natural history could meet, present papers and discuss, and exchange ideas. Other surgical members included Robert Knox (q.v.) and Sir Charles Bell (q.v.).

In 1814 Newbigging was elected President of the Royal College of Surgeons of Edinburgh and elected Fellow of the Royal Society of Edinburgh in 1824. In 1838 he was knighted by Queen Victoria. This honour was demeaned by the disparaging comments of Sir Robert Christison, his former house surgeon, that it was 'the reward for political services of a relative', and that Newbigging 'never contributed in any shape to the advancement of medicine or surgery'. Christison had by that time achieved pre-eminence. After holding the chairs of medical jurisprudence and then materia medica at Edinburgh University, he had become President of the Royal College of Physicians of Edinburgh, Physician to the Queen in Scotland, and President of the Royal Society of Edinburgh, so that his opinions carried some authority. He went on to write: 'I wish my professional brethren would set their faces against these accidental knighthoods which are no credit to medicine, and create a difference in rank among equals without adequate reason.'

Despite his damning indictment of the honours system, he was pleased to accept a baronetcy when this was offered to him in 1871.

William Newbigging's son, Patrick (q.v.), followed his father into a career in surgery, inheriting his father's practice and he too became President of the Royal College of Surgeons of Edinburgh (1861–3).

Roll number: 294

Sir William Newbigging (1772–1852).

John Cheyne (1777–1836).

John Cheyne (1777–1836)

For centuries there have been strong medical links between Scotland and Ireland. In the last quarter of the 18th century and the first quarter of the 19th, there were more Irish than Scots graduates from the medical schools of Edinburgh and Glasgow. Most returned to practise in Ireland, including such famous names as Abraham Colles, William Stokes and Sir Dominic Corrigan. No less distinguished was John Cheyne, whom many regard as the father of Irish medicine, and whose name lives on eponymously in 'Cheyne–Stokes respiration'.

Born in Leith, John Cheyne was the son of a surgeon who had succeeded his uncle in the Leith surgical practice. He, in turn, had succeeded his uncle before him. John Cheyne junior was, therefore, the fourth generation to join the practice and all were Fellows of the College. (John Cheyne senior (roll number: 248); his uncle, John Cheyne (roll number: 235); and his uncle, John Cheyne (roll number: 123), whose portrait by Medina is on display in the College.)

While still a 13-year-old schoolboy at the Royal High School in Edinburgh, he began to assist his father in dressing and bleeding patients. When he began to attend medical lectures aged only 16 he turned out to be more knowledgeable than most of his fellow students. He enrolled for formal study, graduating at the age of 18 in 1795. The day after graduation he joined the Royal Artillery as an assistant surgeon in Woolwich, seeing service in England and Ireland. His initial army career was marked by the pursuit of pleasurable activities: 'much of his time being spent in shooting, playing billiards, reading, and in the complete dissipation of time'. In 1799 he returned to Leith, where he was appointed to the charge of the Ordnance Hospital in Leith Fort and was able to act as an assistant to his father. This was to be a turning point in his career because of the opportunity it gave him to meet Dr (later Sir) Charles Bell (q.v.), who stimulated his interest in pathology and in medicine. He wrote *Essays on Diseases of Children* in 1801 and an important monograph on the pathology of the larynx and bronchi in 1809. His was reckoned to be the first description of acute hydrocephalus. Cheyne became a Fellow of the Royal College of Physicians in Edinburgh in 1810. In 1811 he moved to Dublin, where he became Physician to Meath Hospital.

He was a keen observer of clinical problems and a prolific writer, particularly about diseases of children, acute illnesses and epidemics. Able to draw on the extensive case documentations of his father and great-uncles, he made important contributions to the understanding of croup and tracheitis. His monograph on apoplexy contained what is regarded as the first illustrated case of sub-arachnoid haemorrhage. Within two years of arriving in Dublin he was appointed Professor of Medicine at the Royal College of Surgeons in Ireland.

His association with military surgery continued throughout his life and his lectures on the topic were immensely popular. In 1820 he was appointed Physician-General in Ireland, then regarded as the highest medical rank in the country but ill health forced him to retire early to England.

John Cheyne died and was buried in Sherington, Buckinghamshire. Ten years later William Stokes, in describing a pattern of respiration seen in the terminally ill, recognised its original description by Cheyne and the eponym 'Cheyne–Stokes respiration' was coined and remains in everyday use.

Roll number: 295

Royal College of Surgeons in Ireland.

Sir Charles Bell (1774–1842)

Charles Bell had a wide and impressive range of talents. His skill for drawing and painting was on a par with that of distinguished contemporary artists, and many of his oil paintings and watercolours hang in the College. Denied an appointment in the Edinburgh Royal Infirmary, he found success and fame in London both as a teacher of anatomy and a surgeon. Yet it was his seminal research on the nervous system which brought him international recognition and a knighthood. Only then did he return to Edinburgh as Professor of Surgery.

Born at Fountainbridge, Edinburgh, Charles Bell was the youngest son of the Rev. William Bell. If the young Charles was to inherit his gifts as an artist from his mother, it was surely from his father that he inherited his strength of character. His father, a Church of Scotland minister, transferred allegiance to become a rector in the Scottish Episcopal Church – a Church then suffering from the failures of the Jacobite cause in the years following Culloden. As a result, Episcopal rectories faced considerable financial hardship, made worse in his case by the death of his father when Charles was only five years old. His widowed mother, Margaret Morris, herself a gifted artist, ensured that despite the family's poverty, his artistic gifts were encouraged and developed. The Edinburgh artist David Allan (1744–96) became his mentor, and Bell would later recall these painting lessons as among the happiest memories of his life. 'Allan the painter was a man very dear to me in my early boyhood,' he wrote. 'To him I am principally indebted for my pleasure in drawing.' (An example of Allan's work illustrates the biography of William Inglis (q.v.).)

Charles enrolled as a medical undergraduate at Edinburgh University but attended anatomy classes at the extra-mural School of Anatomy run by his elder brother, John Bell (q.v.), whom he greatly admired and from whom he drew inspiration.

Both John and Charles were snubbed by the Scottish medical establishment – neither was given a post in Edinburgh Royal Infirmary. While his elder brother remained in Scotland and, in a tempestuous career, became the foremost Scottish surgeon of his day, Charles left for London, aged 30, in 1804. There he established a reputation as a teacher of anatomy and surgery and in 1814 was appointed to the staff of the Middlesex Hospital. Throughout his surgical career he continued to develop his skills as an artist in sketches, watercolours and oils. His repertoire was that of the professional painter. He also painted portraits, in many of which he sought to portray human facial emotion, based on his understanding of the anatomy of the muscles of facial expression, which he described in his *Essays on the Anatomy of Expression in Painting* (1806). His landscapes largely depicted Scotland, England and Italy.

As a surgeon he tended to the wounded in two campaigns of the Napoleonic Wars – after the retreat to Corunna, and after Waterloo. After the evacuation from Corunna, Bell attended to the wounded British soldiers in Portsmouth, where he made sketches and paintings of gunshot wounds. His drawings and watercolours of soldiers wounded at Waterloo were made in Brussels in the weeks immediately after the battle.

Many of his portraits and landscapes and all of the Corunna oils are currently on display in the Royal College of Surgeons of Edinburgh; the Waterloo watercolours are held at the Wellcome Institute for the History of Medicine in London.

Sir Charles Bell (1774–1842).

Heart of Midlothian. Sir Charles Bell.

Pastoral scene with the Malvern Hills in the background. Sir Charles Bell.

Sir Charles Bell.

Bell's other great legacy to Edinburgh was his museum collection. During his London years he taught at the Great Windmill Street School of Anatomy, which had been founded by William Hunter in 1746, and here he amassed a museum of pathology specimens. This had grown to become one of the largest collections of its time, so that by 1826 Bell decided to sell this to the Royal College of Surgeons of Edinburgh. The collection was packed under the supervision of Dr Robert Knox (q.v.) and shipped to Leith. It formed the heart of the College Museum after the Playfair building opened in 1832, and it remains on display to this day.

Bell's greatest scientific contributions were to revolutionise our understanding of the function of the nervous system. In a series of animal experiments he demonstrated that stimulation of the anterior roots of the spinal nerves resulted in muscle contraction and that similar stimulation of the posterior roots did not have this effect. This observation paved the way for our understanding of nervous pathways between the periphery and the brain. He discussed these findings with François Magendie (1783–1855), the French physiologist, in Paris in 1821. Shortly after the visit, Magendie published a classical paper demonstrating that the anterior roots served a motor function while the posterior had a sensory function, a concept encapsulated as the 'Bell–Magendie Law'. Bell's name lives on eponymously elsewhere: Bell's palsy, still common today, a lower motor neurone paralysis of the facial nerve, retains his name. Before anatomists increasingly moved away from eponyms, the nerve to serratus anterior was commonly known as the long thoracic nerve of Bell.

His contributions to science were recognised by his Fellowship of the Royal Society of London and the award of the Society's Gold Medal. He was knighted in 1831 and in 1836 returned to his native city as Professor of Surgery.

Roll number: 297

Gunshot entry and exit wounds of chest by Sir Charles Bell. Bell gave the following commentary on this painting: 'Sketch in oils. The ball entered here on the fore part near the sternum, and it came out near the 7th rib passing through the anterior part of the chest on the right side. Here there is no sloughing which indicated that the ball had entered the chest.'

A famous oil painting of opisthotonos from a soldier wounded at Corunna and evacuated to Portsmouth, where the effects of the wound infection by tetanus became dramatically apparent. Sir Charles Bell.

The years after the Napoleonic Wars saw relative stability in Europe, which allowed the development of industrialisation and urban growth on a scale never before seen.

In medicine more systematic and more detailed study of physiology and pathology led to an ever increasing understanding of the working of the body and the nature of disease. Scientific advances such as improvements in microscopy opened up the new science of cellular pathology. Among the giants of pathology were Carl Rokitanski (1804–78) in Vienna and Rudolph Virchow (1821–1902) in Berlin. The English doctors Richard Bright (1789–1858), Thomas Addison (1793–1860) and Thomas Hodgkin (1798–1866), all Edinburgh medical graduates, described important diseases for the first time. In the early part of the century physiologists such as Claude Bernard (1813–78) and François Magendie (1783–1855) began the process of experimental physiology which had become widespread throughout European medicine by the end of the century. However, from the 1850s it was advances in antiseptics and anaesthesia that were to transform surgery for ever.

Joseph Lister, Baron Lister, acclaims Louis Pasteur at Pasteur's Jubilee, Paris, 1892.

The Boston dentist William Morton (1819–68) gave his first successful public demonstration of ether anaesthesia in 1846 and the first public operation using ether outside the USA was performed by Robert Liston in London a few months later.

In Edinburgh James Young Simpson's search for anaesthetic agents resulted in his discovery of the properties of chloroform, which he reportedly first used successfully in 1847 in an operation performed by James Miller. Its use in the delivery of Queen Victoria's son, Prince Leopold, in 1853 gained the technique public acceptance.

James Young Simpson, George Keith and J. Mathews Duncan discover the anaesthetic properties of chloroform in Queen Street, Edinburgh, on 4 November 1847.

'Ether Day' in Boston, 16 October 1846. Hinckley's depiction of the first surgical operation using ether anaesthesia.

The Resurrectionists

Anatomical dissection has long been regarded as an essential part of medical studies but only became possible in Europe after a Papal decree in the late 15th century made the practice acceptable to the Church. Under the terms of the 1505 Seal of Cause, the Edinburgh surgeons were allowed to dissect one condemned man each year. By the early years of the 18th century in Edinburgh there were insufficient bodies available for anatomical teaching and demonstration by the Incorporation. In 1711 a series of complaints that graves in Greyfriars Churchyard had been robbed to provide bodies for dissection was rejected by the Incorporation as 'a scandalous report'. The fears and concerns of the citizens of Edinburgh boiled over into a public riot in 1725 which led to Alexander Monro *primus*, at that time the Professor of Anatomy, to move his collection of anatomical specimens from Surgeons' Hall, where they were relatively unprotected, to the safety of a dissecting room within the Old College of the University.

William Burke and his partner Helen McDougall.
A sketch made at the time of their trial,
24 December 1828.

Thereafter supply seems to have satisfied demand until the success of John Barclay's anatomical teaching in the extra-mural school. Barclay attracted more than 500 students at a time to his anatomical school, creating a demand which could not be met. There now seems little doubt that some of the bodies used for dissection by Monro, Barclay and Liston in the extra-mural school were obtained from graves. Grave watchers were employed to guard the graves to prevent this, but the trade was a lucrative one and the guards could be bribed. In 1828 the discovery in Dr Knox's anatomy school in 10 Surgeons' Square of the body of 'daft Jamie', a well-known local figure who was subsequently shown to have been murdered, unmasked the evil activities of Burke and Hare and caused a national outcry. Hare turned King's evidence and William Burke was hanged publicly in the High Street in 1829. Knox, a brilliant teacher of anatomy, was ruined. He later fled to London, where he died in 1862.

Despite the concerns of the public, lobbying by the surgical Colleges in Edinburgh and London resulted in the Anatomy Act 1832, which, by giving the medical profession the right to 'unclaimed bodies', satisfied the need for anatomy dissection.

The other great advance of the late 19th century was antisepsis. This had its roots in the observations of Ignaz Semmelweis (1818–65). By introducing hand-washing in chlorinated water for doctors and students, he reduced the incidence of infection following childbirth.

Louis Pasteur (1822–95) concluded that fermentation and putrefaction were due to 'small corpuscles', which he went on to identify as micro-organisms, the first step in understanding the nature of infection. Joseph Lister's meticulous, logical experimental investigation of wound sepsis and its prevention was to lead to antiseptic, then aseptic surgery. Surgery was made infinitely safer.

These two advances opened new possibilities in surgery. For the first time the successful surgery of abdominal viscera (other than simple ovarian cysts) was pioneered by Theodor Billroth (1821–94) in Vienna and developed by his pupils. Billroth in Vienna and Jules Pean in France were the early pioneers of successful gastric resection. The latter years of the 19th century saw the expansion and blossoming of the great medical colleges and teaching hospitals in the United States.

In Edinburgh the Royal College of Surgeons had outgrown the original 1697 Surgeons' Hall. A larger building was required to house a lecture hall and large anatomical and pathology collections, a library and a meeting room. William Playfair (1790–1857), the leading Scottish architect of his day, designed the new Surgeons' Hall, which opened in 1832. In 1851 a further Royal Charter from Queen Victoria severed the College's formal ties to the Town Council. In the latter years of the 19th century the College became an international one with surgeons from around the world coming to study for and sit the Fellowship examination.

The Royal College of Surgeons of Edinburgh
designed by William Playfair and opened in 1832.

Alexander Gillespie (1776–1859)

The College's collection of oil paintings, which dates from the late 17th century, includes portraits of prominent Fellows and Presidents, and the tradition of presidential portraits continues to this day. In addition to these, the College is fortunate in having photographic portraits of many Presidents, some of which date from the very earliest days of photography. The earliest of these is a calotype of Alexander Gillespie, who was President in 1810. There must be few organisations that can boast a photograph, albeit one take in much later, of the individual who was their president in that year.

Alexander Gillespie (1776–1859).

Photography began around 1840 with the daguerreotype and the calotype. William Fox Talbot had patented the latter process in England, which limited its development, but the patent did not apply in Scotland, where early photography flourished, particularly in Edinburgh. By 1850 there were no fewer than 22 photographers working in Edinburgh, the most famous of whom were David Octavius Hill and Robert Adamson, who began to produce calotypes from 1843.

There is no indication as to when this photograph of Gillespie was taken. He died at the age of 83 and his appearance in the photograph suggests that the picture was taken in the 1850s.

Alexander Gillespie was the son of a doctor who practised in Ayr and subsequently in Edinburgh. He obtained the LRCS from the Edinburgh College of Surgeons in 1794, and was President of the College in 1810 at the very early age of 34 years. In 1822 he went on to obtain the MD from St Andrews University. After service as a military surgeon in the West Indies, he became Surgeon to the Edinburgh Royal Infirmary, to Gillespie's Hospital and Donaldson's Hospital. Like many practitioners of his day, he combined surgery with general and medical practice, and was Surgeon to the Edinburgh Lunatic Asylum and the Lock Hospital (a hospital where women with syphilis or gonorrhoea could be detained for several months at a time). One of his sisters was married to James Donaldson, the founder of Donaldson's Hospital, in Edinburgh, later to become Donaldson's School for the Deaf. Like the Royal College of Surgeons, this building was designed by Playfair and was much admired by Queen Victoria, who, it is said, indicated to the local establishment that she would prefer this to Holyrood for her Edinburgh residence. When this failed to materialise, her visits to Edinburgh became much less frequent.

Alexander Gillespie became a Fellow of the Royal Society of Edinburgh and latterly, according to one contemporary, cared for 'his largely aristocratic practice with a light touch'. His son, James Donaldson Gillespie (430), became President of the College in 1869.

Roll number: 307

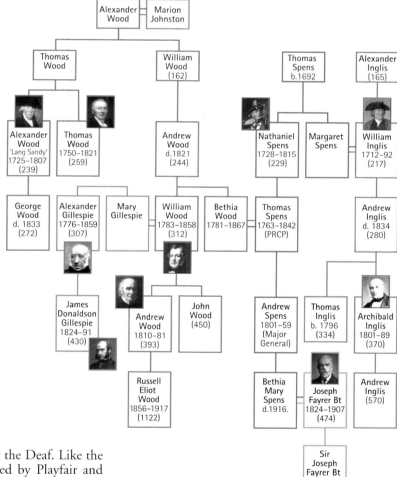

The families Wood, Spens, Inglis, Gillespie and Fayrer (numbers in parentheses are College roll numbers).

James Wardrop (1782–1869)

Educated at Edinburgh, London, Paris, Berlin and Vienna, James Wardrop took an early interest in applying the emerging principles of pathology to enhance the understanding of eye disease in the early years of the 19th century. He described keratic precipitates and coined the term 'keratitis' as well as classifying retinoblastoma as a malignant tumour. These and other original observations added to his reputation as the 'father of ophthalmic pathology'.

James Wardrop (1782–1869).

James Wardrop was born near Linlithgow, West Lothian, and educated at the Royal High School of Edinburgh, at that time housed in recently built (1777) premises in High School Yards. (That building was later to become the first surgical hospital of the Royal Infirmary and is still in use today by the University of Edinburgh.) He began medical studies at the extra-mural school under John Barclay and was apprenticed to Benjamin Bell (q.v.), James Russell (q.v.) and his own uncle, Andrew Wardrop (roll number: 263), who had been President of the College in 1788. He further studied moral philosophy under Dugald Stewart and, as a member of the Royal Medical Society, befriended David Brewster, who later became Principal of both St Andrews and Edinburgh Universities. Wardrop was fortunate to embark on a tour of major centres of learning in Europe. He went first to London, where Astley Cooper and John Abernethy taught him at Guy's and St Thomas' Hospitals. Making his way to Paris during the respite in hostilities with France afforded by the Peace of Amiens, he was arrested and interned soon after his arrival by Napoleon's troops, but made his escape bearing a false passport in the name of an American merchant. Thereafter he travelled on to Germany and Austria, learning new surgical techniques in Vienna and Berlin before returning to Edinburgh. During his time in Europe he also added to his collection of minerals.

On his return to Edinburgh he became a Fellow of the College in 1804 and was appointed to a post in the Pathological Museum, where his entries in the first catalogue can be found. He was in practice with his uncle and also at the Public Dispensary in Richmond Street, and during this time published *Essays on the Morbid Anatomy of the Human Eye* (1808), and his work on retinoblastoma (the malignant tumour of the retina occurring in childhood) entitled *Observations on the Fungus Haematodes* (1809). Finding his opportunities for developing his own clinical practice were limited, he moved to London in 1809.

In London, he established himself in practice in St James' and continued to publish case reports and a second volume of *Essays on the Morbid Anatomy of the Human Eye*. As he did not hold an appointment at a major teaching hospital, he founded the West London Surgical Hospital off Edgware Road, a voluntary hospital giving free treatment to the poor. In his private practice he attracted Scottish expatriates and members of the staff of the Prince Regent at nearby Carlton House. Through them and with his knowledge of horses dating from his childhood, he came to the attention of the Court officials, as the Prince Regent shared his interest in horse racing and hunting. In 1818 he was appointed Extraordinary Surgeon to the Prince Regent just before the death of George III, and continued in this office with the newly crowned George IV. He travelled with the King on his visit to Edinburgh in 1822, when they became more closely acquainted.

During this time he taught at the Aldersgate School of Medicine and later lectured in anatomy and surgery at the Great Windmill Street School of Anatomy. An outspoken and critical man, he antagonised senior members of the London medical establishment, who were also influential members of the King's circle. He played an active part in successfully opposing restrictive practices in medical education on the part of the Royal College of Surgeons of England. He was appointed Surgeon in Ordinary to George IV in 1828. George IV's lifestyle was anything but healthy and his illnesses became more protracted until in 1830 he died. His close medical advisers, particularly Sir William Knighton, excluded Wardrop from attending the King in his last illness and as a result he became embittered. After the King's death he published anonymous *Intercepted Letters* in *The Lancet*, which purported to be written by the late King's doctors, containing scurrilous comments on one another. Wardrop was identified as the true author and he became further alienated. His continuing support of blood-letting as a mode of treatment when it had already been discredited was detrimental to him, but he published a book on diseases of the heart nevertheless. Even his compatriot from West Lothian, Robert Liston (q.v.), who had also moved from Edinburgh to London, complained that Wardrop blocked him out of practice with the Scottish nobility. His practice progressively declined and he became ever more embittered.

In his Edinburgh days he had studied drawing and knew the artists David Wilkie and Andrew Geddes from schooldays, and he had become an art collector. At one time his collection contained works by Correggio, Rubens, Cuyp, Tiepolo, Gainsborough, Turner and Wilkie. On the formation of the National Gallery of Scotland in 1850 he donated two paintings, which remain in the collection.

He became reclusive in later years but would entertain his old friends who visited him. He died at his London home and was buried in Bathgate, near his mother's ancestral burial place, in accordance with his wishes.

His contribution to the understanding of ophthalmic pathology helped to reclassify inflammation of the eye, hitherto referred to as ophthalmia whatever the cause, and his recognition that early excision would improve the prognosis in retinoblastoma has since been justified. His observations on the management of perforating injuries of the globe in horses led to treatment by early evisceration or enucleation in humans and provided the only treatment to avoid blindness for the succeeding hundred years. Considering the primitive instruments and illumination available to him, his contributions to the advance of clinical practice were remarkable.

Author: Geoffrey Millar

Roll number: 309

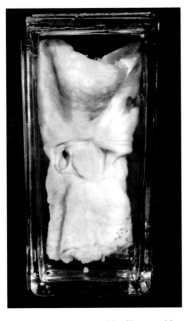

John Abercrombie (1780–1844).

John Abercrombie (1780–1844)

Few doctors can look back on a career which combines that of a successful surgeon, a successful physician and a place in history gained by first describing a common clinical condition. After admission to the College, John Abercrombie established such a thriving surgical practice in Edinburgh that he attracted many apprentices. He deployed these to provide free medical care to the poor of the city, and from his philanthropy was to emerge the Edinburgh Medical Missionary Society. Subsequently qualifying as a physician, he achieved prominence by publishing meticulous casebooks and textbooks.

Born in Aberdeen, son of the Rev. George Abercrombie, John Abercrombie went to Aberdeen Grammar School and then Marischal College, where he graduated MA at the age of 15. Thereafter he studied medicine in Edinburgh, graduating MD in 1803. After postgraduate study at St George's Hospital, London, he returned to Edinburgh and was admitted a Fellow of the College. He started in practice at 8 Nicolson Street, next to the Edinburgh Riding School, which in 1832 was to become the site of the present Royal College of Surgeons of Edinburgh. His practice flourished, and in 1805 he was appointed Surgeon to the Royal Public Dispensary in Richmond Street, a few yards from his practice. This dispensary had been founded by Dr Andrew Duncan senior to provide medical aid to the poor. The success of his practice meant that he had attracted a large number of surgical apprentices, as apprenticeship was still at that time the commonest pathway to a surgical career. This allowed Abercrombie to assign his senior apprentices to the care of the poor in different areas of the town.

His meticulous casebooks were to form the basis for two important books: the first on *Diseases of the Brain and the Spinal Cord* (1828) and the second on *Diseases of the Stomach, the Intestinal Canal, the Liver and Other Viscera of the Abdomen* (1827). Both of these books were to become standard texts. They were published in the United States, where they achieved wide acclaim, were translated into French and German; each ran to several editions. In this latter book he gave the first description of the clinical features of duodenal ulcer and most importantly of perforated duodenal ulcer. In the days before endoscopy, radiology or even abdominal surgery, it was difficult for physicians to correlate clinical features with pathology. Abercrombie's interest in the post mortem made such correlations possible. He gave the first-ever description of the clinical features of perforated duodenal ulcer confirmed by the post-mortem appearance. The specimen showing the perforated ulcer was placed in the College Museum, where it is on display to this day.

The death of James Gregory in 1821 created a vacancy for the Chair of Practice of Physic at Edinburgh University. Abercrombie's application was unsuccessful and this led him to concentrate on consultation work, which did not require a hospital appointment. To this end he became a Fellow of the Royal College of Physicians of Edinburgh in 1824. Thereafter his publications turned increasingly to philosophical and religious topics. His philanthropy continued with support for the Edinburgh Association for sending Medical Aid to Foreign Countries, which later developed into the Edinburgh Medical Missionary Society.

This specimen prepared by Abercrombie shows a perforated duodenal ulcer. It is thought to be the first occasion in which the diagnosis was made in life and confirmed at post mortem.

His consultation practice brought patients from all parts of the British Isles and from abroad. He became medical adviser to, and subsequently a close friend of, Sir Walter Scott. His abilities were recognised by his appointment as the first physician to King George IV in Scotland. The University of Oxford awarded him an honorary MD. The prestige of this award can be judged by the fact that the only other recipient in the previous 50 years was Dr Edward Jenner of vaccination fame. His alma mater honoured him by electing him Rector of Marischal College, which a few years later in 1860 was to amalgamate with King's College to form the University of Aberdeen. He was elected a member of the Royal Academy of Medicine of France and Vice President of the Royal Society of Edinburgh.

After his death, his family presented his library to the College, increasing the stock from 150 to over 1,000 books, while his extensive papers were donated to the Library of the Royal College of Physicians of Edinburgh.

Roll number: 310

John Abercrombie aged 39.

John Wishart (c. 1781–1834)

Appointed Surgeon to the Royal Infirmary of Edinburgh in 1818, John Wishart had a special interest in diseases of the eye and became one of Edinburgh's earliest ophthalmic specialists.

John Henry Wishart came from a notable academic family. His great grandfather and grandfather, who were both named William Wishart, had been Principals of Edinburgh University, and it was during his great-grandfather's term of office in 1726 that the Faculty of Medicine was established. His father, William Thomas Wishart, lived at the estate of Foxhall, Kirkliston, and John attended the High School of Edinburgh, where a fellow pupil was James Wardrop (q.v.). There he won the Murray Medal for Latin in 1795, an honour which in 1810 was also achieved by Robert Knox (q.v.).

Wishart matriculated at Edinburgh University in 1797, aged 16. He proceeded FRCSEd in 1805, and his probationary essay, dedicated to Professor Russell, was entitled *Ophthalmia*. This referred to several types of ocular inflammation including conjunctivitis, which had increased in the population as a consequence of the introduction of trachoma by soldiers returning from Egypt and Spain during the wars with Napoleon.

He had studied under the most eminent ocular surgeon of the time, Georg Josef Beer in Vienna, where he was joined by his friend James Wardrop. The two young men travelled together in Hungary, enduring severe cold in the early months of 1804, before Wishart returned to Edinburgh to practise at 5 Nicolson Square, close to where the present College building now stands. Charles Kirkpatrick Sharpe, a literary recluse and friend of Sir Walter Scott, recommended Wishart as an ophthalmic surgeon in a letter. Combining his ophthalmological interest with mainstream surgery, he translated Antonio Scarpa's treatise on aneurysm from Italian, which he had possibly learned from a private tutor, adding additional cases and notes of his own and dedicating it to Professor John Thomson (q.v.) in 1808. Later he also translated Scarpa's works on club foot and hernia, which he dedicated to James Wardrop.

A

PROBATIONARY

SURGICAL ESSAY,

ON

OPHTHALMIA,

SUBMITTED

BY AUTHORITY OF THE PRESIDENT AND HIS COUNCIL,

TO THE EXAMINATION OF THE

ROYAL COLLEGE OF SURGEONS
OF EDINBURGH,

WHEN CANDIDATE

FOR ADMISSION INTO THEIR CORPORATION,

IN CONFORMITY

TO THEIR REGULATIONS RESPECTING THE ADMISSION

OF

ORDINARY MEMBERS.

BY

JOHN HENRY WISHART,

SURGEON.

" Ingentibus vero et variis casibus oculi nostri patent. Qui cum
magnam partem ad vitae simul et usum et dulcedinem conferant
summa cura tuendi sunt." CELSUS DE MEDECINA.

SEPTEMBER 1805.

Edinburgh:

PRINTED BY ALEX SMELLIE.

1805.

Frontispiece to Wishart's
probationary essay *Ophthalmia*.

Wishart was elected President of the College in 1820. His presidency was marked by a letter from John Barclay in 1821 offering his large collection of specimens on condition that a suitable building was obtained to house them. This resulted in the construction of the present College building, completed in 1832, with the room now used as the main hall being the home for Barclay's collection. Elected a Fellow of the Royal Society of Edinburgh, he was also a member of the Royal Medical Society and the Edinburgh Medico-Chirurgical Society, and served as a surgeon to King George IV.

He had practised in the Public Dispensary in Richmond Street, but in 1822 with the young John Argyll Robertson (q.v.) founded the Edinburgh Eye Dispensary in the Lawnmarket. This was the first specialist eye hospital in Scotland, and served the sick poor as well as being a place for the teaching of medical students. Wishart moved to a large house in York Place, where his family grew up. His second son followed him into medicine, writing his MD thesis on cataract, serving in the army and dying during the Crimean War at Scutari. His youngest son left Scotland for Australia to labour in the goldfields of Victoria, where he died a bachelor.

Wishart published further papers on ophthalmia, including that occurring in neonates and that associated with gonorrhoea. He also wrote on subclavian aneurysm, ventral hernia, optic nerve tumour and retinoblastoma treated by extirpation of the globe. Notably, while President of the College in 1822, he published a *Case of Tumours in the Skull, Dura Mater, and Brain*. This is probably the first publication in English which describes Type 2 neurofibromatosis with symptoms, signs and macroscopic post-mortem appearances.

He is buried in Greyfriars Churchyard in Edinburgh, but no portrait of him is known to exist.

Author: Geoffrey Millar

Roll number: 313

John Gordon (1786–1818)

To have established by the age of 30 a national reputation as a teacher and writer often signals the start of a distinguished academic career. For John Gordon this was not to be, as he died at the tragically early age of 32.

John Gordon had been educated at the grammar school at Forres, on the Moray Firth coast in north-east Scotland. After studying at Edinburgh University, in 1801 he became the apprentice and favourite pupil of John Thomson (q.v.), who had been appointed the first appointee to the College of Surgeons' Chair of Surgery, and was in 1806 to become the first Regius Professor of Military Surgery in the University of Edinburgh. While Gordon was a student in Edinburgh, he also attended the extra-mural lectures on anatomy given by John Barclay He obtained his licentiate diploma from the College of Surgeons in the spring of 1805, and qualified with the Edinburgh MD degree later that year, at the age of 19.

While Gordon's family had intended that he should enter the medical service of the Honourable East India Company, he took the advice of his mentor, Thomson, who suggested that he should become a teacher of anatomy in Edinburgh. To ensure success in this venture he spent three years preparing meticulously for the day when he would deliver his first course of lectures before a critical student audience. In the winter of 1805, he attended James Wilson's School of Anatomy in Great Windmill Street, in London, while at the same time attending lectures on comparative anatomy given by Dr Macartney, who later moved to Dublin. It was while Gordon was at Wilson's School that he became acquainted with his demonstrator Mr (later Sir) Benjamin Brodie, and they maintained a close friendship until Gordon's death.

The second and third years of his preparation were spent in Edinburgh, where he gave a number of anatomical demonstrations on osteology to a small group of his friends. For five years from 1807, until he married in June 1812, he lived with the Thomson family. In October 1808 he became a Fellow of the College, and then formally commenced teaching, giving a combined course of lectures on anatomy and physiology. This course was only given for two years, after which time he gave two separate courses, one on anatomy and the other on physiology. The latter was generally given in the winter session, and in the evenings, but occasionally in the summer months. Daniel Ellis, Gordon's biographer, indicates that Gordon was stimulated to give these lectures on physiology after witnessing the successful series of lectures on this subject delivered by a Mr Allen in Edinburgh. This is likely to have been John Allen, who lectured in physiology at the extra-mural school from 1794.

Those students who attended Gordon's lectures were fulsome in their praise of the immaculate style of their delivery, and the superb quality of his dissections. His class size, however, probably never exceeded 100. Account has to be taken of the fact that his lectures were given in competition with those of John Barclay, who had started lecturing 11 years earlier, and was by then extremely highly regarded as a lecturer on both human and comparative anatomy. On the recommendation of Mr Playfair, in the summer of 1812, he was admitted a Fellow of the Royal Society of Edinburgh.

Gordon's classroom, at 9 Surgeons' Square, where he taught between 1808 and 1818, was located somewhat behind the Square, and faced the south side of Barclay's house and school at 10 Surgeons' Square. Its position is clearly shown in Shepherd's drawing of the south-west corner of the Square, which dates from about 1828, being slightly set back between Barclay's house to its north and the western extremity of old Surgeons' Hall, to its east.

John Gordon (1786–1818).

South-west corner of Surgeons' Square. The building in the centre, Barclay's house (10 Surgeons' Square), was used by Barclay for anatomical teaching. The building next to it slightly set back, John Gordon's house (9 Surgeons' Square), was where John Gordon taught anatomy and was subsequently used for teaching purposes by John Thomson, William Sharpey, Allen Thomson, James Young Simpson and Douglas MacLagan. The building on the left is old Surgeons' Hall and that on the right is the hall of the Royal Medical Society (see map on page 78).

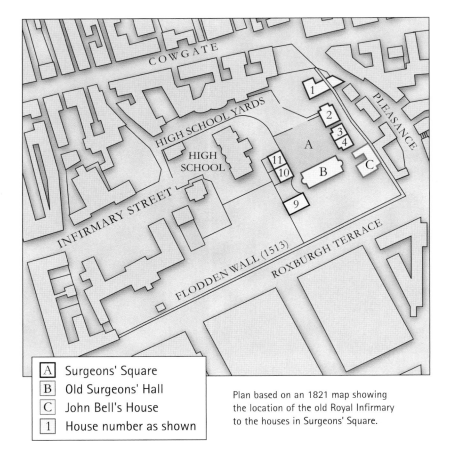

A Surgeons' Square
B Old Surgeons' Hall
C John Bell's House
1 House number as shown

Plan based on an 1821 map showing
the location of the old Royal Infirmary
to the houses in Surgeons' Square.

Gordon's dissecting room was located below his lecture theatre, and was said to have been always well stocked with cadavers, all of which were believed to have come from London. In addition to his teaching activities, he published a number of important works, on both anatomical and physiological topics. His *System of Anatomy*, published in 1815, was the first volume of a much larger work that he had hoped to publish. This contained only two of the eight parts which the whole work was designed to cover. The third part, on the 'Skeleton of the Human Body', remained in manuscript, but was never published. His *Outlines of Lectures on Human Physiology* was published only a few months before his death. This almost exclusively consisted of a series of 'headings', and presumably indicated the various topics he covered in his lectures. His last anatomical work, consisting of his *Engravings of the Skeleton*, was published shortly after his death. He also published an anonymous article in the *Edinburgh Review* in 1815, in which he was particularly critical of the work of Franz Joseph Gall and Johann Spurzheim on phrenology.

After lecturing for about six years, in 1814, Gordon felt that his income from that source was insufficient to support his family. Accordingly, he applied for and subsequently accepted an assistant surgeonship at the Royal Infirmary and, despite his young age, gained a considerable surgical practice. In June 1818, at the age of 32, he suffered a severe illness which lasted for 14 days, and from which he died. Ellis described his last few days in considerable detail.

Gordon was very highly regarded both in London and in Edinburgh, both because of the high quality of his publications and his teaching. Ellis' very sympathetic, some might say uncritical, biography of him was published shortly after his death. The members of the Royal Medical Society raised a subscription to allow the preparation of a posthumous marble bust of him by Samuel Joseph. This bust is displayed in the Library of the Royal Medical Society, and was based on a miniature portrait of him. It was said to be a very accurate likeness. Ellis used an engraving of this portrait as the frontispiece to his biography.

Author: M. H. Kaufman

Roll number: 316

Bust of John Gordon in the Royal Medical Society.

John Gairdner (1790–1876)

A milestone in the history of the College was the opening of William Playfair's magnificent Surgeons' Hall building in 1832. It was fitting that a surgeon with an obvious affection for the College and its history should have the distinction of presiding over the opening. John Gairdner, an Edinburgh surgeon who had been active in the College over his working lifetime, was President from 1830. A prolific writer, he left important legacies to College history, which have provided valuable source material for subsequent historical research.

John Gairdner (1790–1876).

John Gairdner was the son of Captain Robert Gairdner of the Bengal Artillery. Born in Ayrshire, he graduated in medicine from Edinburgh and then spent a year studying in London under Mr (later Sir) Charles Bell (q.v.). Becoming a Fellow of the College in 1813 and an examiner shortly afterwards, he was to spend most of his professional life closely associated with the College. He was President from 1830 to 1832 and as such had the honour of holding this office at an important time in its history – the opening of the new Playfair Surgeons' Hall in Nicolson Street. The College President at this time still had a seat on Edinburgh Town Council and in this capacity he promoted the Reform Bill of 1832. Another cause which he championed was that of the extra-mural medical school and it was largely as a result of his advocacy that the extra-mural school gained recognition from the University.

For many years he strived for the College Fellowship to be recognised as a medical qualification throughout the British Isles and the Medical Act of 1858 gave the Fellowship such legal status.

Of the many papers which he wrote, two in particular have proved to be valuable historic sources. Both were originally given as lectures in the College: *An Historical Sketch of the Royal College of Surgeons of Edinburgh* in 1860 and *A Sketch of the Early History of the Medical Profession in Edinburgh* in 1864.

The College list of Fellows contains valuable annotations in his clear, unmistakable hand.

His eldest son, Sir William Tennant Gairdner, went on to become Professor of the Practice of Medicine in Glasgow University.

Roll number: 325

Photographic portrait of John Gairdner
probably taken in the early 1860s.

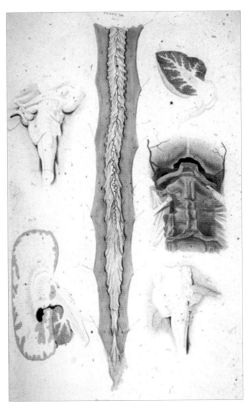

Illustrations from *System of Anatomical Plates*
by John Lizars.

John Lizars (1787–1860)

The reputation of the Edinburgh medical school in the early 19th century owed much to the talents of a series of surgeon-anatomists. John Lizars, a popular teacher in the extra-mural school, published, with his brother W. H. Lizars, a highly gifted engraver, *A System of Anatomical Plates* (1823–6), still ranked among the greatest ever produced in that era. His subsequent success as a surgeon was based on that anatomical foundation and enabled him to sustain a serious but friendly rivalry with his contemporary Robert Liston (q.v.).

John Lizars, born in Edinburgh and educated at the High School, began his medical career as an apprentice to John Bell (1763–1820) (q.v.), an Edinburgh surgeon and elder brother of Sir Charles Bell (q.v.). Having become a Licentiate of the College, he went on to graduate MD from Edinburgh University and joined the Royal Navy as a surgeon. He served in naval vessels on the Spanish and Portuguese coasts during the Peninsular War.

Returning to Edinburgh in 1815, he became a Fellow of the College and almost immediately was invited to join the partnership of his former masters John Bell and Robert Allan. John Bell had been snubbed by the Scottish surgical establishment in 1800 and, in 1790, had established an anatomical school close to Surgeons' Hall, in what was later called Surgeons' Square. His younger brother, Charles, had attended his anatomy classes and, having similarly been unsuccessful in obtaining a surgical post in Edinburgh in 1800, moved to London, where he became one of the greatest teachers of anatomy and surgery of his day, teaching at the Great Windmill Street School of Anatomy, which had been founded by William Hunter.

As a teacher of anatomy, Lizars probably surpassed even his master, John Bell. His classes grew and soon were attracting around 150 students, the success of his teaching in marked contrast to that of his contemporary in the University, Alexander Monro *tertius*, whose students deserted his lectures and of whom Charles Darwin, a long-suffering pupil, once said, 'he made his lectures on human anatomy as dull as he was himself'.

Yet in the extra-mural school, Lizars had to contend with some of the greatest anatomists of the age. It was during this time that he produced his *System of Anatomical Plates*, a superbly illustrated book of anatomical illustrations based on his own dissections. His brother William Home Lizars had established himself as Edinburgh's leading engraver, and was from 1826 to engrave the first 10 subjects of John James Audubon's *Birds of America* (1827–38). The anatomical plates which they produced were to become classics in their day.

Whilst Lizar's illustrations were immensely popular with students (who also appreciated his mnemonics to aid anatomical learning), it did not find favour with the anatomy teaching establishment of the day. In that, as in many other respects, Lizars was decades ahead of his time. Moreover, throughout his days of anatomy teaching he had continued in active surgical practice.

The Edinburgh College of Surgeons, in an attempt to make surgical teaching more specialised, decided that each teacher should only teach one subject. Lizars chose to lecture in surgery, giving over his anatomy teaching practice to his brother, Alexander, who went on to become Professor of Anatomy in Aberdeen.

In 1831, when the Chair of Surgery to the Royal College of Surgeons of Edinburgh became vacant, Lizars contested the vacancy with James Syme (q.v.). As a result of support from Robert Liston and Sir William Fergusson (q.v.), Lizars was elected. Syme took the defeat badly and the animosity between them was life-long. Lizars was openly critical of Syme, and on one occasion had to pay costs and damages for a slander about the quality of Syme's practice. Yet five years after Lizars' death, Syme put the quarrels behind him and publicly acknowledged several of Lizars' surgical innovations.

Lizars was a truly innovative surgeon. He was one of the first in Britain to perform the operation of ovariectomy (also termed ovariotomy on a regular basis). The first successful ovariectomy was performed by Ephraim McDowell in Kentucky. Like Lizars, he had been a pupil of John Bell and there is a suggestion that Bell may have suggested the possibility of the procedure to his pupils. McDowell did not publish this historic case for some seven years but rather sent an account to Bell, his former teacher. The report passed to Lizars, who went on to perform ovariectomy successfully in surgical practice, making the procedure acceptable and paving the way for abdominal surgery.

His surgical boldness is further attested to by the operation of ligation of the innominate artery for aneurysm, which he was one of the first surgeons in Britain to perform. In the pre-antiseptic, pre-anaesthetic era of surgery he successfully resected the maxilla for sarcoma.

Lizars' surgical vision is exemplified by his suggestion that enlargement of the prostate might be treated by cutting out the entire gland. For many years he operated alongside Robert Liston, often in the same theatre and before the same students. Liston's skill, speed and dexterity were such that to be compared so directly with him was the severest test to which any surgical reputation could be exposed. Unlike many others, the rivalry between Liston and Lizars was a friendly one, based on mutual respect.

In 1859, the year before his death, he published *Practical Observations on the Uses and Abuses of Tobacco*, in which he linked tobacco smoking to cancer of the mouth and tongue. With remarkable prophetic vision, he anticipated that tobacco-induced 'injury to the constitution of the young may not appear immediately, but cannot fail ultimately to become a great national calamity'.

He retired from the Chair of Surgery at the Royal College of Surgeons in Edinburgh in 1839 and the College abolished the Chair. Lizars continued with his surgical practice until his death in 1860.

Roll number: 328

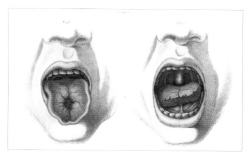

Etchings showing malignant ulceration of the tongue, which Lizars ascribed to the use of tobacco.

Frontspiece from *Practical Observations on the Use and Abuse of Tobacco* (1859).

David Maclagan (1785–1865).

David Maclagan (1785–1865)

Very few doctors have reached the highest pinnacle of success in two major branches of medicine and indeed this is nowadays well-nigh impossible. Yet David Maclagan was elected to the presidency of both the Edinburgh Royal Medical Colleges as was also his son Douglas – a truly astonishing and unique family achievement.

David Maclagan was born in Edinburgh, educated at the High School and graduated MD in 1805. Going on to study at St George's Hospital, London, he entered the army as Assistant Surgeon to the 91st Regiment of Foot, and saw active service in the Peninsular War under the Duke of Wellington. In 1810 he was posted as staff surgeon to the 9th Portuguese Brigade. He was present at the Battles of Badajoz, Salamanca and Nive and received the Peninsular Medal with six clasps. His distinguished service resulted in his promotion to Physician to the Forces. He returned to Edinburgh in 1816 and in that year was elected FRCSEd, going on to become President of the College in 1826. In 1828 he was elected a Fellow of the Royal Society of Edinburgh, and he was appointed Surgeon in Ordinary to Her Majesty in Scotland in 1838.

In addition to a large surgical practice, he continued to give a series of lectures on military surgery at 9 Surgeons' Square. In 1848 he gave up surgical practice and became a successful consulting physician, going on to become President of the Royal College of Physicians of Edinburgh in 1856. His son Andrew Douglas Maclagan (q.v.) was the only other individual to be appointed to the Royal College of Surgeons of Edinburgh and the Royal College of Physicians of Edinburgh (in 1884).

Roll number: 331

David Maclagan. A photographic portrait, for which he wears his Peninsular Medal with clasps.

Robert Liston (1794–1847)

In the pre-anaesthetic, pre-antiseptic era of surgery, the suffering of a patient undergoing a surgical operation could only be diminished by the speed and dexterity of the surgeon. Robert Liston, a son of the Scottish manse, became one of the finest operators of his generation. When his rival, James Syme (q.v.), was preferred as Professor of Clinical Surgery in Edinburgh, he left for London, where he spent the last 13 years of his life. Here, his surgical expertise ensured an equally successful career, and he was widely regarded as the best technical surgeon of his day.

Robert Liston as a young surgeon.

Robert Liston was born in Ecclesmachan in West Lothian, eight miles west of Edinburgh. His father, the Rev. Henry Liston, was a Church of Scotland minister and was the inventor of the euharmonic organ, which gave diatonic scales in perfect order. His early education was provided by his father and after graduation from the University of Edinburgh he went on to attend Dr John Barclay's lectures on anatomy and physiology in the extra-mural school in Surgeons' Square. Here, as throughout the rest of his life, Liston's uncompromising personality produced frictions and quarrels with virtually everyone with whom he came into contact. He became assistant and prosector to Dr Barclay, but the relationship was a tempestuous one, and he left to become a house surgeon in the Royal Infirmary under George Bell, the son of Benjamin Bell (q.v.). In 1816 he went to London, where he worked under Sir William Blizzard at the London Hospital and under John Abernethy at St Bartholomew's. He became a member of the Royal College of Surgeons in London that same year. On returning to Edinburgh, he began his own extra-mural anatomy class, effectively in competition with his former mentor Barclay. He recruited the young James Syme, then in his second year of medical studies, as his assistant and Syme became his partner in the anatomy class. Liston and Syme were distant cousins, and it was on Liston's advice that Syme took up medicine. Syme dedicated his dissertation for the FRCSEd to Liston, and they each assisted at the other's operations, becoming close and loyal colleagues. Their anatomy class flourished. Both were ambitious, single-minded, and in their different ways were brilliant exponents of the art and science of surgery. It was, however, only a matter of time before they quarrelled, and from 1823 the relationship deteriorated into bitter, open, personal and professional acrimony. Quarrels with professional colleagues were a hallmark of Liston's life.

Liston was admitted FRCSEd in 1818 and he established a reputation as one of the most skilled operative surgeons of his day. His speed and dexterity in operating, at a time when speed was essential, became legendary. He successfully operated on patients whom other surgeons had refused to take on, or who had been discharged from the Royal Infirmary after failed surgery. Inevitably professional jealousies arose and he was formally expelled from the Royal Infirmary for a period of five years

Robert Liston (1794–1847).

Photographic portrait of Robert Liston
taken in the 1840s.

between 1822 and 1827. The reason given by the managers was that he was guilty of 'interfering improperly in the surgical department ... and with the patients'. He was reinstated, albeit with some reluctance, 'his impudence and presumption forgotten'. Despite this expulsion his surgical reputation grew. A tall man (6 ft 2 in) with strong arms and hands, he used these physical attributes to great effect. 'I have repeatedly compressed both the femoral and humeral arteries with the fingers of one hand,' he wrote, 'whilst the other removed the limb.' Yet his technique was meticulous, whether forming flaps in amputations or dissecting the breast in mastectomy. He was beaten by Syme in the contest for the Chair of Clinical Surgery in 1833, and went to London the following year as a surgeon to University College Hospital, becoming Professor of Clinical Surgery in the University of London. Here his reputation as a bold, skilful and confident surgeon was enhanced. His limb amputations would be performed in seconds and urethral lithotomy in no more than two minutes – all without anaesthesia. He saw the value of anaesthesia before most of his colleagues and was to perform the first operation performed under ether anaesthesia in England in 1846. Liston is reported to have introduced the procedure by saying, 'We are going to try a Yankee dodge today, gentlemen, for making men insensible', a reference to Morton's successful use of an ether anaesthetic in Boston a few weeks earlier. The amputation was completed in 28 seconds, after which Liston announced, 'This Yankee dodge, gentlemen, beats mesmerism hollow.' Mesmerism was hypnosis, the use of which in surgery had been gaining in popularity until the advent of anaesthesia.

One area in which his expertise was particularly well demonstrated was in the excision of large tumours of the upper or lower jaw, which were usually considered inoperable by other surgeons. His series, published in the *Medico-Chirurgical Transactions* in 1837, describes the successful excision of giant tumours arising from the maxilla, some as big as the patient's own head.

His contributions to surgery were considerable. The two textbooks he wrote, *Elements of Surgery* (1832), and *Practical Surgery* (1837), became standard texts.

By this time Liston's reputation was at its height. In 1840 he became a member of the Council of the Royal College of Surgeons in England and three years later became one of the original 300 Fellows of that College on its becoming the Royal College of Surgeons of England. He was elected a Fellow of the Royal Society in 1841.

Those who watched him operate described his technique as appearing unhurried – the mark of the skilled surgeon whose speed was the result of an effective combination of movements performed precisely and efficiently. His death at the early age of 53 deprived Britain of a surgeon who was arguably the most courageous and technically competent of his era.

Roll number: 341

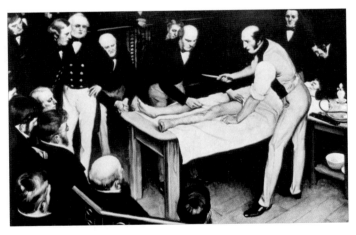

Robert Liston and the first ether operation.
The young Joseph Lister can be seen
second from the left leaning forward.

Sir George Ballingall (1776–1855)

In the early years of the 19th century, British politics were dominated by war. With British forces involved in the Napoleonic Wars and forces active in establishing an empire from Australia, through the Indian sub-continent and much of Africa to the Americas, it is little short of astonishing that Edinburgh was the only centre in Britain to offer formal instruction in military surgery. Sir George Ballingall, who was appointed to the Edinburgh Chair of Military Surgery in 1822, was instrumental in the establishment of a chair of military surgery in Dublin. He is regarded by many as the father of British military surgery.

George Ballingall was born in Forglen, near Banff, the son of the parish minister. Educated initially in the parish school of Falkland in Fife, he attended four literary sessions at the University of St Andrews, where he began an apprenticeship in medicine. Going on to study medicine in Edinburgh in 1803, he came under the influence of the anatomist John Barclay and was later to acknowledge his debt to Barclay, of whom he wrote a short biography. As a token of his debt he presented the skeleton of an elephant which he had prepared, and whose skull is still in the College Museum to this day.

After receiving his diploma from the College in 1805, he became Assistant Surgeon to the Royal Scots, the First Regiment of Foot. When the regiment was posted to Madras, he served with the expedition which captured Java from the Dutch in 1811. At this time, the Duke of Kent, who was Colonel of the regiment, recognised the potential of the young military surgeon and became his benefactor throughout most of his life. He also saw service in Europe as a military surgeon during the occupation of Paris in 1815 and on returning from the army, he became a lecturer in military surgery at Edinburgh University in 1823. At that time this was the only centre in the British Isles at which military surgery was taught. In 1825 he succeeded Professor John Thompson as Regius Professor of Military Surgery, a chair which he was to hold with distinction for 30 years. Ballingall took a more holistic view of military surgery than his predecessor. His experiences in India and France had convinced him of the need for military surgeons to be able to diagnose and treat not merely battle injuries, but the illnesses and infections to which European troops overseas were particularly liable. In particular he recognised the public-health aspects of military barracks and camps, writing about ways in which the design of camps could be changed to improve standards of hygiene.

As a result of his enthusiasm, teaching in military surgery flourished. The East India Company, at that time the biggest and most important commercial arm of Empire, required candidates for its service to attend a course in military surgery. The College altered its examination regulations so that candidates could offer military surgery as one of the two prescribed surgical courses. As a result of this, the medical departments of the army, the navy and the ordnance gave the same option to candidates for their respective branches of the service.

Ballingall played an important role in the establishment of a chair of military surgery in Dublin in 1855. He received strong support from *The Lancet* and in 1854 the War Department set aside funding for the chair.

Sir George Ballingall (1776–1855).

A scene from the Battle of Waterloo depicting
the defeat of the French cavalry
by the Highlanders and Scots Greys.

His textbook *Outlines of Military Surgery* (1838) was to become the most authoritative of its day, eventually running to five editions. In 1851 he published a monograph, *Observations on the Site and Constructions of Hospitals*, which drew on a lifetime of experience in the design of military camps.

His writing gives an insight into the limitations of abdominal surgery in the pre-anaesthetic, pre-antisepsic era. 'Wounds of the small intestines are, for the most part, fatal,' he wrote. 'No man in his senses would think of enlarging the external wound for the purpose of searching out and sewing up the wounded part of the gut … even when the wounded intestine protrudes externally.'

He was rewarded with many honours; Surgeon to the Queen in Scotland, a Fellow of the Royal Society of Edinburgh and a member of the medical societies of Paris, Vienna, St Petersburg and Berlin. He received a knighthood in 1830.

Sir George Ballingall died quite suddenly near Blairgowrie in December 1855. Before a successor was appointed, James Syme persuaded the Secretary of State for War and the University of Edinburgh that the teaching of all aspects of military surgery could be taught equally well by other departments. Syme's views carried considerable authority, and on his advice the Edinburgh Chair of Military Surgeon was abolished in 1856.

Roll number: 350

John Argyll Robertson (c. 1798–1855)

John Argyll Robertson was one of the first general surgeons to take a special interest in the surgery of the eye. One of his sons, Douglas (q.v.), was to devote his practice entirely to that specialty and make famous the family name.

John Argyll Robertson followed two older brothers, Robert and William, in studying medicine in Edinburgh, and, like William, went on to specialise in surgery. He presented his thesis for the Doctor of Medicine degree in 1819 on *Ophthalmia*. In 33 pages of Latin he describes inflammation of the anterior segment of the eye suggesting possible causes and discussing the limited available methods of treatment. One section is devoted to 'Ophthalmia Aegyptiaca', a relic of ophthalmic problems encountered during military activities against the Emperor Napoleon in Egypt and the Iberian Peninsula. The thesis is dedicated to John Henry Wishart (q.v.), a surgeon at the Edinburgh Royal Infirmary, who was President of the College in 1820. In 1822 Robertson was apprenticed as a surgeon to Wishart and in the same year they founded the Edinburgh Eye Dispensary, the first specialist ophthalmic hospital in Scotland, with premises in the Lawnmarket.

After graduation in medicine, Robertson submitted his *Probationary Essay on the Anatomy and Physiology of the Eye*, dedicated to the Rev George Home 'as a mark of affection and esteem' to become a Fellow of the College. In it he questions the view of François Magendie that tears enter the lacrimal drainage passages under gravity, and proposes capillary attraction as a mechanism. He makes the observation that the physiological blind spot corresponds to the optic disc, and refers to the concept of corresponding points in the retinae, disputing the proposition that double vision is avoided by each eye being used separately. He concludes that because persons who have had the crystalline lens extracted are able to see both near and distant objects clearly, accommodation takes place at the cornea.

In his *Remarks on Iritis*, while affirming that it is not possible (as now) to establish a cause in most cases, he listed possible aetiological factors. These included mercury (a commonly used treatment), exposure to cold, surgical or accidental injury and syphilis. He went on to describe treatment such as blood-letting, blistering, mercury, belladonna and purgatives. Yet he was also a general surgeon, publishing on cholera and a case of rupture of a carotid aneuryism. As a general and ophthalmic surgeon he was appointed to the surgical department of the Royal Infirmary in 1838, a post he held until 1842.

His *Observations on the Extraction and Displacement of the Cataract* (1836), a review of the literature on cataract treatment, describes three modes: division, or capsulotomy; extraction by an extracapsular method, and displacement, by depression or reclination of the intact lens transsclerally. Quoting the failure rates of the greatest practitioners of the time, he totals 30 per cent by extraction and 17.5 per cent by displacement, his own figure for displacement being 9.5 per cent. His own causes of failure are suppuration, atrophy of the eyeball and obliteration of the pupil, reflections of a high sepsis rate and the poor instrumentation available. He thus recommends the older method of displacement before the more modern method of lens extraction, which later became the norm with improved knowledge and techniques.

A Curator of the College Museum, he resigned on being elected President of the College in 1848. He had served less than one year when he became ill and declined to stand for re-election, being succeeded by Professor James Syme (q.v.). During his short presidential term the College supported the case of assistant surgeons in the Royal Navy who sought the rank of Ward Room Officer on grounds that 'midshipmen and cadets of inferior age and education, were unsuitable and unimproving companions', and because the surgeons were 'deprived of the necessary facilities for uninterrupted study *vis à vis* those in the Army to keep pace with the rapid march of medical sciences'. The College petitioned the House of Commons on behalf of these surgeons. Also during his presidency the premises behind the Playfair hall were purchased and converted for teaching. There was a proposal to amalgamate with the Faculty of Physicians and Surgeons of Glasgow, which failed.

Little of a personal nature is recorded of John Argyll Robertson. He was the father of three sons, who practised medicine, of whom the most famed is Douglas, who followed his father's ophthalmic footsteps. We might assume that, like him, he was a golfer because he retired to Rose Park in St Andrews, now an old people's home, where he died in January 1855, when the news of the defeat of the Russians at the siege of Sebastopol filled the newspapers.

Author: Geoffrey Millar

Roll number: 353

John Argyll Robertson (c. 1798–1855).

James Combe (1796–1883)

There are many instances in medicine where the first published account of a previously unknown condition has not resulted in eponymous fame. The clear description by a Glasgow surgeon, Sir Kennedy Dalziel, of what came to be known as Crohn's disease, preceding Crohn's description by several years, is a much-quoted example. In the same way the credit for the first description of pernicious anaemia belongs to James Scarth Combe, who became a successful Edinburgh surgeon and President of the College in 1851. It was he who clearly described the clinical features and post-mortem findings some 27 years before Addison recorded his description of the condition which bears his name.

James Scarth Combe was born in Leith, where his father was a brewer. He became a Licentiate of the College and graduated MD from Edinburgh University in 1815. Contemporary accounts describe how his viva examination in medicine was interrupted by the sound of the guns of Edinburgh Castle announcing the news of the victory at the Battle of Waterloo. After admission as Fellow of the College in 1823, he worked for a short time in India, gaining experience of cholera during a stay in Calcutta. This would have proved valuable on his return to Leith, where, during the cholera epidemic of 1832, the first therapeutic use of intravenous saline was recorded by Dr James Latta, a local general practitioner. Combe practised as a surgeon in Edinburgh, being elected to the Royal Society of Edinburgh in 1850, and became President of the College the following year.

His presentation to the Edinburgh Medico-Chirurgical Society in 1822 of a case history of anaemia was followed by a published account in the *Transactions* of the Society in 1824. In this, he describes clinical features and post-mortem findings clearly recognisable as pernicious anaemia. Some 27 years later Addison published his account of the condition. As so often happens in medicine the first description of the disease does not necessarily ensure an eponym.

Roll number: 360

James Scarth Combe (1796–1883).

James Syme (1799–1870)

At a time when Edinburgh enjoyed a golden age of surgery, James Syme was the leading surgeon of his day. As a teacher of surgery and as a surgical innovator, he was widely regarded as without peer in the country. A rival of Robert Liston (q.v.), and a contemporary of James Young Simpson he was the father-in-law and mentor of Joseph Lister (q.v.).

James Syme was the son of John Syme, an Edinburgh solicitor. After education at the Royal High School he enrolled in Edinburgh University at the age of 16, where he came under the influence initially of Thomas Hope, the Professor of Chemistry, who had discovered the element strontium. Syme was stimulated to experiment with the distillation of coal tar, which led him to discover a solvent for white rubber. This he used to treat silk and make it waterproof. His researches were published in the *Annals of Philosophy*, but it was the Glasgow chemist Charles McIntosh who was able to patent the idea and immortalise his name.

Like many contemporaries, Syme chose not to attend the University classes where the reputation of Monro *tertius* as a dull, uninspiring lecturer deterred many prospective students. Instead he enrolled in medicine at the extra-mural school, where one of his teachers was the surgeon Robert Liston, who had by that time established a reputation for speed and dexterity of surgical technique. This early friendship with Liston was to have a profound influence on Syme's future, although that friendship was to turn to rivalry and then to enmity. Syme went on to succeed Liston as a lecturer in the extra-mural school, where he established a formidable reputation as a teacher, attracting upwards of 250 students to his class. Along with William Sharpey (q.v.), he visited Paris, where he attended Jacques Lisfranc's course on operative surgery and went on ward rounds with Guillaume Dupuytren. At the age of 24 he reported the first successful amputation at the hip joint performed in Scotland. Before he was 30 his reputation as an operating surgeon was formidable and this led to jealousy and friction with Liston. Perhaps because of this, Syme was unsuccessful in his application to join the staff of the Royal Infirmary. He therefore set up his own private hospital. At Minto House, in what is now Chambers Street, Edinburgh, he established a 24-bed surgical hospital with an operating theatre and lecture theatre. (Minto House enjoyed some literary fame. Dr John Brown, Syme's assistant, wrote the short story 'Rab and his Friends' (1858), in which much of the tale is set within its walls.) Here, his surgical reputation continued to grow. He carried out operations for aneurysm, extensive resections for tumours of bone, of the maxilla, the mandible and the tongue, all without anaesthesia, all of which served to enhance his reputation as surgeon and teacher. He was probably the first surgeon to perform total excision of the tongue for cancer, and in 1829 performed the first complete excision of the maxilla in Britain. Amputation through the ankle joint, a procedure which still carries his name, was first performed in 1842.

In 1833 he was elected to the Regius Chair of Clinical Surgery in Edinburgh, defeating Liston, perhaps because the latter refused to pay the retiring professor, James Russell (q.v.), the customary allowance of £300 per year, paid for life by the successor. Syme joined an array of surgical talent in the Infirmary including Lizars (q.v.), Liston, William Fergusson (q.v.) and Sir Charles Bell (q.v.). The last three all became London surgeons distinguished in their generation. Liston had taken on the Chair of Surgery at University College, London, and on his death in 1847 Syme succeeded him. For a number of reasons, practice in London did not suit him and he returned to Edinburgh as Professor of Clinical Surgery five months later.

One of his pupils was Joseph Bell (q.v.), model for Sherlock Holmes, whose own observations on Syme will, we can be assured, be characteristically accurate. Bell wrote: 'his operating was devoid of flourish and dash. He was not very rapid and not very elegant. But on the other hand he was absolutely free from fuss and worry; all idea of self, his own dexterity and appearance was evidently banished when he took the knife into his hand. He thought of nothing but the patient and the best, not the most rapid nor the showiest, nor the easiest, but the best way of relieving him.' His operating style and his brevity were summed up by his assistant, Peddy: 'he never unnecessarily wasted a word, a drop of ink or of blood'.

James Syme (1799–1870).

James Syme and John Brown

John Brown was assistant to James Syme in Minto House. His short story 'Rab and his Friends' was based largely on that experience. The tale is written by a medical student. Rab, the central character, is a lovable dog owned by James Noble, a carter, whose wife, Eilidh, has to undergo an operation for breast cancer. Brown describes her dignified behaviour and her courage before, during and after the mastectomy in the pre-anaesthetic era. After the mastectomy, Eilidh is nursed by her devoted husband, James, but develops a major wound infection from which she dies.

Brown's descriptions of the dignity and devotion of the elderly couple, her bravery in facing the operation and the honesty of the surgeon are realistic, at times haunting and intensely moving.

Minto House Surgical Hospital in Chambers Street, established as a surgical hospital by James Syme in 1829.

The teaching methods that he established in Edinburgh were to have a profound influence for decades. His short trip to London had produced a dislike of the teaching methods he saw there, where a group of students followed their chief around the ward, relying on chance remarks when they stopped at each bed. He preferred to 'bring the cases one by one into a room where the students are comfortably seated and if the patients have not been seen by the surgeon beforehand so much the better; then ascertaining the seat and nature of their complaint. Having done this, so that everyone present knows the case under consideration, the teacher, either in the presence or absence of the patient according to circumstance, proceeds to explain the principles and the treatment with his reasons for choosing the method preferred'. This innovative style of teaching attracted students of surgery from all over the country and among these was the young Joseph Lister. Lister had planned a tour of continental surgical centres after graduation in London, but was so enthralled by Syme and his teaching that he stayed in Edinburgh and was appointed House Surgeon by Syme in 1854. Two years later he married Syme's daughter, Agnes, and continued as his father-in-law's assistant until his appointment as Professor of Surgery at the University of Glasgow in 1860. Syme remained close to Lister throughout his life and in his last clinical lecture in 1868, with characteristic vision, he predicted that the new principle of antisepsis promoted by his son-in-law would revolutionise the practice of surgery.

Syme became President of the College in 1849, became an honorary Fellow of the Royal College of Surgeons in Ireland, and received honorary degrees from the universities of Oxford, Dublin and Bonn. In later years he was able to exert considerable political influence. His letter to Lord Palmerston in 1855 proved an influential contribution to the Medical Act of 1858, which led to the setting up of the General Medical Council. His view that the Edinburgh Royal Infirmary should not be rebuilt on site but built on a larger greenfield site prevailed, ending the 'battle of the sites'.

His death in 1870 brought to an end an exciting and innovative era which saw great change in the practice and teaching of surgery and paved the way for even greater change which was to follow as surgery entered the antiseptic era. Lister's tribute to his father-in-law was fitting: 'The hostility which he excited in the few was greatly outweighed by the friendship he inspired in the many.'

Roll number: 363

James Syme. Photographic portrait.

Robert Knox (1791–1862)

Arguably the most notorious figure in the College's long history is Robert Knox, the first Conservator of the College Museum, whose career was blighted and his reputation shattered for all time by his fortuitous association with the gruesome scandal of the Burke and Hare murders. This unfortunate liaison has tended to overshadow his outstanding abilities and achievement, yet he was never formally accused, far less convicted, of any crime.

Robert Knox, the eighth child of an Edinburgh schoolmaster, was educated at the High School of Edinburgh (later the Royal High School), where, in his final year, he was Gold Medallist and Dux of the School. He entered the medical faculty of Edinburgh University in 1810 and graduated MD four years later. As an undergraduate he attended at 10 Surgeons' Square the extra-mural anatomy class of Dr John Barclay, then regarded as the foremost anatomist in the British Isles, who considered him to be his most brilliant pupil. After a period of army service as a regimental surgeon, during which he spent three years in South Africa, Knox returned to Edinburgh in 1822 and joined the staff of Dr Barclay's anatomy school as an assistant lecturer. He began to publish scientific papers on a wide variety of anatomical and pathological subjects and, in 1823, he was elected a Fellow of the Royal Society of Edinburgh.

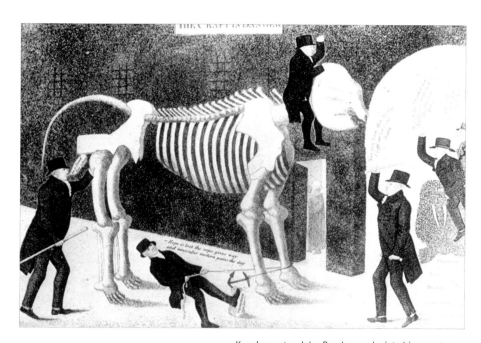

Knox's mentor, John Barclay, as depicted in a cartoon from Kay's *Portraits* entitled 'The Craft in Danger', which caricatures Barclay's application for the Chair of Comparative Anatomy in Edinburgh. Barclay is riding astride the elephant, which is being pushed forward by his solitary supporter whilst four others (including Monro, wielding the femur) obstruct his way.

In 1821, Dr Barclay had offered to the College his large personal collection of anatomical specimens on condition that it would be properly displayed in a purpose-built hall. Three years later, Knox, with Barclay's encouragement, submitted to the College a plan for a museum based on the Barclay collection and offered to supervise the establishment of such a museum within the College. This could not be done in old Surgeons' Hall and it was Dr Barclay's gift and Robert Knox's museum plan that convinced the College of its urgent need for new premises. Knox's proposals were accepted by the College Council and, early in 1825, he was formally appointed to the newly created office of Museum Conservator. Later that year Knox was admitted a Fellow of the College and granted full partnership with joint charge of his extra-mural anatomy school by Dr Barclay. On Knox's recommendation the College in 1825 purchased Sir Charles Bell's (q.v.) extensive anatomical and surgical collection; he also supervised its transfer from London to Edinburgh and made arrangements for its safe storage until such time as the College acquired new premises, in which, along with Dr Barclay's collection, it could be adequately housed.

Robert Knox, caricature.

Robert Knox lecturing. Photograph by F. C. Inglis,
posed at the front door of his studio
Rock House on Calton Hill, Edinburgh.

Dr Barclay died in 1826 leaving Knox in sole charge of his anatomy school, to which increasing numbers of students were attracted by his remarkable abilities as a teacher. The University Chair of Anatomy was at that time held by the uninspiring and unpopular Alexander Monro *tertius*. There could be no greater contrast to Monro's dull pedantry than Knox's brilliant lectures, which were always vividly illustrated by expert dissections.

A major attraction of Knox's extra-mural class was his guarantee that students attending his course would see the human body completely dissected and for the fulfilment of this promise he obviously required an ample provision of anatomical 'subjects'.

Knox's success aroused the jealousy of other anatomists and surgeons conducting extra-mural classes and their hostility was exacerbated by his intellectual arrogance and his ill-concealed contempt for their professional abilities. His major achievements as Museum Conservator were the preparation of the first comprehensive catalogue and the advice on the requirements of the museum, which he gave to William Henry Playfair, the architect of new Surgeons' Hall. Knox's teaching commitments increased rapidly and, in the academic year 1827–8, just over 500 students were enrolled in his extra-mural anatomy class. He employed a number of assistants and demonstrators, some of whom, such as William Fergusson (q.v.), ultimately gained fame in their own right as surgeons and anatomists. However, it was at this time that Knox became unwittingly involved in the macabre events which ultimately brought about his ruin.

In this biographical sketch it is not possible to give a full account of the murders committed by William Burke and William Hare in Edinburgh during 1828. They sold the bodies of their 16 victims to Knox's anatomy school, but while there is some evidence that he was aware of the provenance of these particular 'subjects', it is certain that he never met either of the two murderers. The discovery of the murders in November 1828 provoked a furious public outcry and, although Knox was never accused of any crime, the Edinburgh populace at large regarded him as being only marginally less culpable than Burke and Hare. He was publicly vilified and the Edinburgh mob attacked his house, but, although they smashed its windows, they were unable to force an entry. A special committee of inquiry formed at Knox's request exonerated him from suspicion of complicity in the Burke and Hare murders, but a general feeling of outrage persisted for many months and the committee's verdict did not prevent his numerous professional enemies from venting their spite upon him. His huge class of students did, however, remain totally loyal throughout this period and his teaching continued without interruption.

Although Knox was a Fellow, holding an official position in the College, there is no reference to the Burke and Hare scandal in any College archive and, indeed, almost at the very time when the murders came to light, the Council minutes include a warm commendation of his work as Conservator. It would seem, however, that the Senior Fellows were deeply affronted by their Museum Conservator's involvement in this shocking affair and there is no doubt that Knox was ostracised by most of his professional colleagues. There is, however, no evidence that the College ever contemplated his dismissal and he continued his work for the Museum with undiminished energy. Relations between Knox and the Council began to deteriorate some months later and this was largely due to the persistent hostility of his enemy James Syme (q.v.), who, in

September 1829, was appointed one of the Curators of the College Museum. Eventually, in July 1831, Knox submitted his resignation from the office of Conservator and this was accepted without comment. The new Surgeons' Hall was nearing completion and it must have been a bitter blow to Knox, after his devoted conservation of the Barclay and Bell collections, to be denied the opportunity of supervising their installation in a purpose-built hall, to the design of which he had made important contributions.

At first Knox's popularity as a teacher seemed unaffected by the Burke and Hare scandal. He continued also to contribute regularly to the proceedings of the Royal Society of Edinburgh and to produce a stream of papers on a wide variety of subjects. Over the next five years the size of his extra-mural class did decrease progressively and his financial circumstances became somewhat straitened. His attempt to establish an extra-mural anatomy school in Glasgow was unsuccessful as were also his applications for various academic posts in the Edinburgh University medical faculty and, in 1842, he left Edinburgh for London never to return.

The erroneous belief that he died in poverty and obscurity is widely held, but, in fact, while in London he was in frequent demand as a lecturer and continued to be a regular contributor to scientific journals. He engaged in part-time general practice and, in 1856, was appointed Pathologist to what is now the Royal Marsden Hospital – a post which he held until his death in 1862.

Knox was buried in Brookword Cemetery, near Woking, but his grave was neglected and forgotten until in 1966 it was rediscovered by Professor Eric Mekie (q.v.), his lineal successor as Conservator of the College Museum (1955–74). Professor Mekie and Sir John Bruce (q.v.) arranged for the clearance of the weeds and foliage which had overgrown the grave and for it to be marked by a granite stone inscribed simply 'Robert Knox – Anatomist, 1791–1862'.

Roll number: 373

Sir William Fergusson Bt (1808–77)

The effectiveness, safety and universal availability of modern anaesthesia makes it almost impossible to appreciate the horrors of pre-anaesthetic surgery. Nor is it easy, from the perspective of the 21st century, to comprehend fully the extraordinary fortitude of our forebears who voluntarily underwent operations without the benefit of any form of pain control. This makes it difficult for us to appreciate fully the remarkable technical skills of surgeons such as Sir William Fergusson, whose operative speed and dexterity were his only means of mitigating the suffering of his patients.

He was the last, and perhaps the greatest, of the 19th-century surgeons whose success was based solely on knowledge of anatomy and technical expertise.

William Fergusson, who established his formidable reputation before the advent of anaesthesia, was born in Prestonpans on the Firth of Forth, just east of Edinburgh. His childhood was spent in Lochmaben, Dumfriesshire, and he was educated at the High School of Edinburgh,

Dr Robert Knox, James Bridie and Dylan Thomas

The story of Dr Robert Knox, and Burke and Hare has inspired a number of literary works of which the two best known are the plays *The Anatomist* by James Bridie and *The Doctor and the Devils* by Dylan Thomas.

James Bridie (1888–1951) was the *nom de plume* of Osborne Henry Mavor. Mavor, born in Glasgow, graduated in medicine from Glasgow University in 1913. In the First World War he served in the Royal Army Medical Corps in France and Mesopotamia. After a spell in general practice in Glasgow, he became a Fellow of the Royal Faculty of Physicians and Surgeons of Glasgow and was awarded an MD. He became consulting physician to the Victoria Infirmary, Glasgow, and Professor in Medicine in the Anderson College of Glasgow. *The Anatomist* (1931) brought him literary fame. In all he wrote 42 plays and was one of the founders of the Glasgow Citizens' Theatre, where many of his plays were performed. He played a leading role in the founding of the Royal Scottish Academy of Music and Drama in 1950.

The Anatomist portrays Knox as a dandy but dedicated to the advancement of medical knowledge, even if this means complicity in murder. The play depicts him as ambitious, and almost glamorous, and questions if despicable means ever justify the most worthy of ends.

Dylan Thomas (1914–53) also drew on the Burke and Hare story in his play *The Doctor and the Devils* (1953), which appeared shortly before his death.

Like Bridie, Thomas addresses the moral issues but in addition focuses on the social and political conditions which drove desperate people to these activities.

In the play, the body-snatchers Fallon and Broom are driven to murder by the appalling poverty in which they live. Thomas describes the action amidst the squalor and depravity endured by Edinburgh's underclasses, contrasting this with the 'intimate, comfortable' rooms where doctors lived and worked.

The play concludes with Fallon being hanged while the medical men who employed him are protected in order to maintain 'the dignity of the higher professions'. Thomas characteristically comments on a society of double standards and corruption in which the poor are dispensable.

Sir William Fergusson Bt (1808–77).

after which he spent two years in a lawyer's office with the intention of making his career in the legal profession. The work did not appeal to him and in 1825 he entered the medical faculty of Edinburgh University.

Fergusson was fascinated by anatomy and became the most dedicated and assiduous member of the large extra-mural class conducted by the brilliant anatomist Dr Robert Knox (q.v.), the first Conservator of the College Museum. Knox appointed him a demonstrator in 1828 and, by spending long hours in the dissecting room, Fergusson acquired an almost encyclopaedic knowledge of anatomy along with impressive skills as a prosector. His prowess as a dissector can be seen to this day in the College Museum, where his dissections of the arteries of the foot and the cranial nerves elegantly attest to his skills. Soon he was assisting Knox with the task of lecturing to more than 500 students, a class size which made it necessary for each lecture to be given three times daily.

Knox's professional reputation and his hopes of academic preferment were ruined by his involvement in the gruesome scandal of the Burke and Hare murders. Although Knox was vilified and disgraced, his assistants escaped blame, and there is no evidence that Fergusson's career was harmed in any way by his association with Knox.

Having become a Licentiate of the College in 1828, Fergusson became a Fellow one year later, and in 1831 was appointed Surgeon to the Edinburgh Royal Dispensary, on Liston's move to London. Over the next few years, his reputation grew rapidly and in 1836 he was appointed Surgeon to the Edinburgh Royal Infirmary and elected to the Fellowship of the Royal Society of Edinburgh. From his day book, still held in the College library, it is apparent that his practice was almost equal in size to that of James Syme (q.v.), then the most famous surgeon in Scotland. Sadly, they developed a notorious ill-tempered rivalry, each complaining formally about the other to the Infirmary managers.

In 1840 Fergusson accepted an invitation to become Professor of Surgery at King's College, London, and Surgeon to King's College Hospital, where he soon became even more successful than he had been in Edinburgh. His practice increased steadily and the fame of his outstanding operative ability brought many visitors who were as impressed by his calm imperturbability in the operating theatre as by the speed and boldness of his surgery. He established a reputation which led to contemporaries regarding him as the greatest British surgeon of his era.

Fergusson's greatest surgical achievements were his operation for cancer of the maxillary antrum, his technique for the excision of tuberculous joints and his successful operative treatment of a large series of patients with hare lip and cleft palate. He was also renowned as a lithotomist, performing the procedure in 30 seconds, in an era when speed was of the essence.

He was not an eloquent lecturer, his delivery to a London audience being hampered by the broad Scots accent which he retained all his days. A more successful author, his *System of Practical Surgery*, first published in 1842, ran to five editions and was an extremely popular didactic textbook, particularly in America. His philosophy of conservative surgery, advocating caution and discipline were in contrast to the radical, even ruthless approach that had held sway until then.

Fergusson was elected to the Council of the Royal College of Surgeons of England, on which he served for 16 years and was President in 1870. In 1855 he was appointed Surgeon Extraordinary to HM Queen Victoria, and was created a baronet in 1866. He became Serjeant Surgeon to the

Queen the following year. Among other honours conferred upon him were the Fellowship of the Royal Society in 1848, the presidency of the British Medical Association in 1873 and the honorary LLD of his alma mater, the University of Edinburgh, in 1875.

He was succeeded in the Chair of Surgery at King's College Hospital by Joseph Lister (q.v.).

A tall, dignified, kindly man of genial disposition, Fergusson was famous for his hospitality and well regarded by his colleagues, his patients and his students, many of whom went on to attain surgical eminence. He had many extra-curricular accomplishments and, in particular, he was a good violinist, a skilled carpenter and an expert fly fisherman.

When involved in surgical controversy he was always conciliatory, and never more so than in his reaction to hostile criticism from James Syme, to whom he paid a generous tribute in the Hunterian Oration which he gave to the English College in 1871. Equally commendable was his defence of the scientific reputation of his mentor, Dr Robert Knox, for whose distinction as an anatomist he always expressed his utmost respect.

William Fergusson died in London and is buried at West Linton, 17 miles south-west of Edinburgh. Sir James Paget described him as 'the greatest practical surgeon of our time'. He has the distinction of being the only ordinary Fellow of the College to have become President of the Royal College of Surgeons of England and occupies an honoured place in the history of both the Edinburgh and the English Colleges.

Roll number: 387

Sir William Fergusson, portrayed in a *Vanity Fair* cartoon.

William Sharpey (1802–80)

The early years of the 19th century was a era of exciting discovery in physiology in medical centres throughout Europe. An early training in surgery, combined with periods of study at major European centres and a receptive mind, was to prove an ideal preparation for the surgeon who came to be regarded as the father of modern physiology in Britain. William Sharpey was a life-long friend of James Syme (q.v.), whose teaching had an important influence on the young Joseph Lister (q.v.). Indeed, it was Sharpey who sent Lister to join Syme in Edinburgh. One of his most distinguished pupils, Edward Schafer, acknowledged his debt to his teacher by taking on his name to become Sir Edward Sharpey-Schafer.

William Sharpey was born in Arbroath, the son of a local shipowner. He entered Edinburgh University and studied anatomy under John Barclay at the extra-mural school at 10 Surgeons' Square.

At this early stage in his life he began to visit some of the greatest continental teaching centres where the greatest advances in physiology were being made. His fluency in French and German and his links with continental colleagues allowed him to bring continental discoveries and thinking to the attention of the British scientific community. He began his remarkable pilgrimage to Europe in 1821 with a visit to Paris, where he learned clinical surgery from Guillaume Dupuytren and operative surgery under Jacques Lisfranc. It was here that he met James Syme, with whom he retained thereafter a close friendship until the latter's death in

William Sharpey (1802–80).

William Sharpey.

1870. Returning to Edinburgh to graduate MD in 1823, he settled for a short time in medical practice in Arbroath with his stepfather, Dr Arnott, but this short exposure to clinical practice appears to have convinced him that his future lay in science. In 1826 he began a prolonged tour of Europe, visiting centres in France, Switzerland, Rome, Naples, Bologna, Padua, Berlin, Heidelberg and Vienna – a trip which took almost three years. Shortly after returning, he was elected Fellow of the College in 1830 and began to give lectures on systematic anatomy in the Edinburgh extra-mural school at 9 Surgeons' Square. Sharpey became one of a small group in Edinburgh who were pioneers in the use of the achromatic lens which advanced microscopy. From this he was able to define cilia and wrote an important paper on the phenomenon of ciliary movement.

In 1834 he was elected a Fellow of the Royal Society of Edinburgh and two years later was appointed to the Chair of Anatomy and Physiology in University College, London. His referees included Dr John Abercrombie (q.v.), Sir George Ballingall (q.v.), Dr David Maclagan (q.v.) and James Syme.

His lectures at University College were popular and Lister, who attended them as a medical student, described the profound influence which they had on his career and his work. Lister was later to write 'as a student at University College, I was greatly attracted by Dr Sharpey's lectures which inspired me with a love of physiology that has never left me'.

Elected to the Fellowship of the Royal Society of London in 1839, he went on to become Secretary and played an influential role in the Society's activities. Sharpey's career flourished at a time when the important discoveries of Claude Bernard, of Hermann von Helmholtz and of Rudolph Virchow were being published and Sharpey was able to translate these and others and bring them to the attention of the British scientific community.

His legacy to British physiology was considerable. The European contacts and friendships which he made and maintained at a crucial time for scientific discovery were among his greatest assets. He was buried in the Abbey graveyard in Arbroath.

Roll number: 390

Allen Thomson (1809–84)

Doctors who have demonstrated the intellect, the organisation and the drive to be successful teachers or researchers may find these attributes equally applicable to a subsequent career as a medical politician. Allen Thomson made considerable contributions to medicine as a scientist, as a teacher and as a statesman. He had the distinction of holding successive chairs in the universities of Aberdeen, Edinburgh and Glasgow.

Allen Thomson was the son of John Thomson (q.v.). His father had successively been Professor of Military Surgery and of General Pathology in the University of Edinburgh and the first Professor of Surgery at the Royal College of Surgeons of Edinburgh. After graduating MD from Edinburgh in 1830, Allen Thomson travelled to Europe, visiting Holland and Germany, where he studied anatomical and pathological museums before returning to Edinburgh as Lecturer in Anatomy and Physiology. He became FRCSEd in 1832.

He made subsequent visits to Europe, meeting some of the foremost medical scientists of the day. In 1837 he took the unusual step of becoming Private Physician to the Duke of Bedford, before being appointed to the Chair of Anatomy in Aberdeen. From there he returned to Edinburgh in 1841 to become a teacher of anatomy in the extra-mural school and then Professor of Institutes of Medicine (Physiology) at the University of Edinburgh. From there he succeeded to the Chair of Anatomy at the University of Glasgow, which he occupied until his retirement in 1877. By the time of appointment to Glasgow, he had amassed a large collection of material for anatomical and physiological teaching which was added to the Hunterian Museum.

Allen Thomson (1809–84).

He published widely. In addition to publishing lectures on physiology, he was a collaborator in the *Encyclopaedia of Anatomy and Physiology* articles on 'Circulation' (1836), 'Generation' (1839) and 'Ovum' (1859) and contributed to the *Encyclopaedia Britannica*, 9th edn (1870–90). He was co-publisher of Quain's *Anatomy*, 8th edn (1876).

In his later years at Glasgow, he was entrusted with overseeing the new University buildings at Gilmorehill and his skills as fundraiser and administrator were largely responsible for bringing this project to a successful conclusion.

He was elected a Fellow of the Royal Society of Edinburgh in 1838 and of London in 1848, later becoming Vice President of that Society. He became President of the British Association in 1876 and was honoured with the degrees of LLD from the universities of Edinburgh and Glasgow.

Roll number: 396

Sir Douglas Maclagan (1812–1900).

Sir Douglas Maclagan – a caricature.

Sir Douglas Maclagan (1812–1900)

Following in the footsteps of a famous father can be a dangerous path. It carries the risks of accusations of nepotism and at the same time of invidious comparisons. Douglas Maclagan's father, David Maclagan (q.v.), had achieved eminence as President, successively, of both Royal Medical Colleges of Edinburgh, and was Surgeon to the Queen in Scotland and Physician to the Forces. His son emulated, perhaps even surpassed, his father, as he too achieved the presidency of both these Colleges and was the most prominent medical jurist of his day.

Andrew Douglas Maclagan was born in Ayr, and had the distinction in infancy of being christened by the minister who had christened Robert Burns. His education at the Royal High School of Edinburgh gave him a fluency in Latin which he was to put to use both professionally and socially in later life.

During his time as a medical undergraduate at Edinburgh, he was President of the Royal Medical Society, the only medical undergraduate society in the world with a Royal Charter. He graduated Licentiate (LRCSEd) from the College in 1831 and MD and FRCSEd two years later. Before the grand tour of Europe became established for young surgeons, he visited London, Berlin and Paris returning to Edinburgh, initially as assistant to his father and thereafter as an assistant surgeon to Edinburgh Royal Infirmary.

In 1845 he left surgery to become a lecturer on materia medica in the extra-mural school, and it was here during the next 18 years in this post that he laid the groundwork for his subsequent career in toxicology. He came to prominence as an expert witness on poisoning at a trial in which his opinion was at variance with that of the greatest authority of the day, Sir Robert Christison. They subsequently became friends and Christison's support undoubtedly influenced his appointment in 1862 as Professor of Medical Jurisprudence at the University, a post he held until his retiral in 1897 aged 85 years! Maclagan went on to become the leading authority on medical poisons and advised on virtually all of the medico-legal cases in Scotland where poisoning was involved. His lectures to medical and law students were renowned for their clarity of expression.

He was elected President of the College in 1859 and in 1884 was elected President of the Royal College of Physicians of Edinburgh, thus joining his father in the rare distinction of becoming President of both Edinburgh Colleges. He was knighted in 1886.

Outside medicine he was best known as a raconteur and poet, publishing a collection of poems entitled *Nugae Canorae Medicae* (1850). The most notable of these was *The Battle o' Glen Tilt*, in which he promoted the rights of ordinary people to walk the Highland hills. The Aesculapians and the Harveian Society provided an ideal outlet for his humour.

Douglas Maclagan provided a link between the 19th and 20th centuries. Born within months of Napoleon's ill-fated advance on Moscow, as a young man he visited Goethe and was a friend of Sir Walter Scott, yet he lived to see the 20th century.

Roll number: 398

Peter Handyside (1808–81)

The extra-mural School of Medicine in Edinburgh included among its lecturers some of the greatest and most distinguished teachers of anatomy and surgery. Among these was Peter Handyside, who taught both of these subjects from 1834 until a few weeks before his death.

Peter David Handyside was born and educated in Edinburgh, the son of William Handyside, Writer to the Signet, and nephew of Lord Handyside, an eminent Scottish judge. During his undergraduate career at Edinburgh, he was elected Senior President of the Royal Medical Society in 1828/9, during its 92nd Session, and continued to take an active interest in the Society's welfare for the rest of his life. Shortly after he graduated MD in 1831, he pursued his anatomical studies, initially in Paris and then in Heidelberg under Friedrich Tiedemann. His earlier apprenticeship under James Syme (q.v.) appears to have stimulated his interest in both anatomy and surgery. In 1833, he was admitted a Fellow of the College, submitting a probationary essay on osteo-aneurysm, which he dedicated to Tiedemann. He commenced the teaching of anatomy in the summer of 1834.

Initially he taught at 4 Surgeons' Square and, because of the quality of his lectures, but principally because, like John Bell (q.v.) before him, of his emphasis on the importance of anatomy in surgery, he gained a considerable class. During the summer sessions, in addition to providing anatomical classes, Handyside also gave a full course on operative surgery. Alexander Monro *tertius* was at that time Professor of Anatomy in the University, but few attended his lectures other than those who were forced to do so. At this time there were a number of distinguished lecturers in anatomy who taught in the extra-mural school (see map of Surgeons' Square on page 78). Dr Robert Knox (q.v.), who had succeeded John Barclay at 10 Surgeons' Square, had from 1833 taught a large class in old Surgeons' Hall. Dr William Sharpey (q.v.) taught at 9 Surgeons' Square, but in the summer of 1836 accepted the Chair of Physiology at University College, London. Dr Allen Thomson (q.v.), who had formerly lectured exclusively in physiology, joined Sharpey in the teaching of anatomy. Another extra-mural lecturer in anatomy at that time was Dr Alexander Jardine Lizars, who, in 1841, left Edinburgh to become Professor of Anatomy in Marischal College, Aberdeen.

In 1842 Allen Thomson was appointed to the Chair of Physiology in succession to Dr Alison, which left the School of Anatomy at 1 Surgeons' Square vacant. Handyside bought it, and lectured there for a few years on systematic surgery. It is said that in 1839 he paid Mr John Lizars (q.v.) the sum of £500 for his extensive surgical and pathological teaching collection. Handyside then set up in partnership with Henry Lonsdale and James Spence (q.v.), and, while he initially lectured exclusively on surgery, for several years they shared the teaching of anatomy. Lonsdale had formerly been in partnership with Dr Knox, and, when the latter withdrew from teaching anatomy in Argyle Square, Lonsdale succeeded him there, as well as purchasing his anatomical collection for £900 on the understanding that Knox would not undertake any further anatomical teaching in Edinburgh. Handyside's move to number one coincided with his appointment as Surgeon in the Infirmary. This tripartite alliance lasted until 1845, when Lonsdale retired.

Peter Handyside (1808–81).

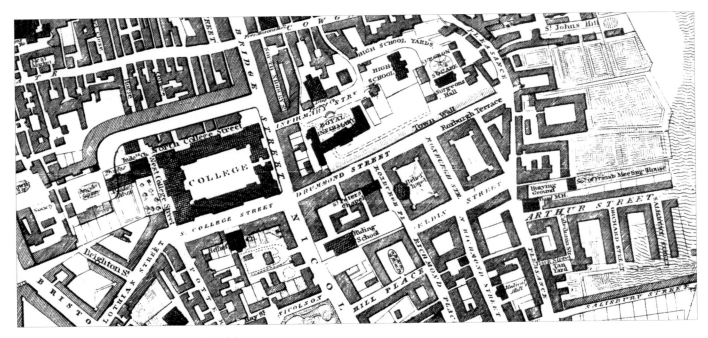

Map of Edinburgh in 1820 showing, from left to right:

Argyle Square College (extra-mural school)

The Old College of the University, labelled 'College'

The Royal Infirmary on Infirmary Street

Surgeons' Square

The Riding School to the east of Nicolson Street
is the site of Playfair's Surgeons' Hall, opened in 1817.

Handyside could number some distinguished teachers of surgery among his contemporaries in Edinburgh. These included Sir Charles Bell (q.v.), John Argyll Robertson (q.v.), who lectured at 11 Argyle Square and James Miller (q.v.), who lectured at High School Yards. When, during the 1842–3 session, James Miller was appointed to succeed Sir Charles Bell, Handyside decided to return to the teaching of anatomy. He seems to have decided that, because of Miller's relative youth, the opportunities for his own advancement in surgery in Edinburgh were likely to be limited. When Miller died in 1864, James Spence succeeded him. Handyside had been the unsuccessful candidate in his application for the Chair of Systematic Surgery in 1842, as well as for the Chair of General Pathology, vacated after the resignation of John Thomson in 1842. Dr William Henderson, then lecturing on practice of medicine, filled this post, but he was successful only by a very narrow margin over the other two candidates, Handyside and David Craigie. Handyside had also been the unsuccessful candidate for the Chair of Anatomy when John Goodsir (q.v.) was appointed. The Appointment Committee indicated that it was felt that this post ought to be filled by someone who was prepared to devote all of their time to the duties of the Chair.

The appointment of John Goodsir to succeed Monro *tertius* in 1846 coincided with Handyside's move with Dr John (later Sir John) Struthers (q.v.) as his demonstrator to the medical school at 11 Argyle Square. Handyside taught systematic anatomy there during the winter of 1846–7, but then withdrew to devote all of his time to his clinical practice. From about 1848, Struthers took over all of the anatomy teaching there, and to assist him in his teaching activities he purchased all of Handyside's anatomical and pathological preparations.

It was only when Struthers was appointed to the Chair of Anatomy in Aberdeen in 1863 that Handyside resumed the teaching of anatomy at Surgeons' Hall, and he was at that time the only extra-mural teacher of that discipline in Edinburgh. When Struthers moved to Aberdeen, he took with him both Handyside's and Knox's Museum Collections, and this required Handyside to establish yet another teaching collection for his own needs.

In his surgical practice, he was recognised as an excellent operator. He had succeeded in amputating at the hip-joint in a patient with a malignant tumour of the femur, and had also performed the operation of ovariotomy, when this was a hazardous procedure. From the first year of its existence, he was associated with the Edinburgh Medical Missionary Society, and was on its committee for over forty years. In many ways, its existence and success owed much to his enthusiasm. Despite the strong opposition of the then Dean, Professor Sir Robert Christison, both Handyside and Patrick Heron Watson (q.v.) consented to admit women to their ordinary classes of anatomy and surgery, respectively. It was only in October 1884 that the University of Edinburgh first allowed women to graduate in the Faculty of Medicine.

Author: M. H. Kaufman

Roll number: 399

Patrick Newbigging (1813–64)

Many important medical discoveries have been made by medical students. Patrick Newbigging's observations on the nature of the heart sounds and the apex beat certainly contributed significantly to the ongoing debate of the time. Unusually for a general medical practitioner, his prestige and popularity was such that he was elected President of the College of Surgeons in 1861.

Patrick Small Keir Newbigging was born in Edinburgh, the son of Sir William Newbigging (q.v.), President of the College from 1814 to 1816. Sir William was able to combine surgical practice with a large general practice, which his son would eventually inherit.

While still a medical student at Edinburgh, Patrick Newbigging joined the Royal Medical Society. In the middle of the 19th century it offered an opportunity for medical undergraduates and graduates to present research work and novel ideas, and provided a forum for debate. It was the practice to give dissertations on original observations and research. Among those who gave dissertations in this way were Richard Bright, James Syme (q.v.), Robert Liston (q.v.), William Sharpey (q.v.), Allen Thomson (q.v.) and James Young Simpson. Newbigging gave his dissertation in 1833 on the elucidation of heart sounds. He came to the significant conclusion that the apex beat was produced by ventricular systole and not diastole as William Stokes and Sir Dominic Corrigan had suggested and which was the prevalent view in the debate of the time. Newbigging went on to become President of the Royal Medical Society. His MD was written on the same topic and after graduation he became a Fellow of the College in 1834. He established himself in general practice in Edinburgh, becoming a medical officer in the New Town Dispensary. After a tour of medical centres in Europe, where he had promoted his ideas on auscultation, he translated the *Practical Treatise in Auscultation* (1847) written by J. P. Barth and Henry Roger.

On his father's death in 1852 he inherited the practice and proved to be a popular, conscientious physician. His writings cover a wide range of topics from the therapeutic action of croton oil in nervous disorders, to the non-mercurial treatment of venereal disease, and scarlet fever. In 1861 he was elected President of the College and President of the Royal Scottish Society of Arts. Ironically he was to die, aged 50, from cardiac valvular disease.

Roll number: 402

Patrick Newbigging (1813–64).

David Skae (1814–73)

Many Fellows of the College have made distinguished contributions to specialties other than surgery. David Skae was unusual if not unique in making his contribution in psychiatry. Skae was generally regarded as a founder of the Edinburgh School of Psychiatry with Dr (later Sir) Thomas Clouston as his most outstanding pupil.

David Skae (1814–73).

David Skae was born in Edinburgh, the son of an architect. With the early death of his father, the family moved to St Andrews and he began to study in the Faculty of Arts at the University of St Andrews. Thereafter he entered the Edinburgh extra-mural School of Medicine, becoming a Licentiate of the College, and a Fellow in 1836. He became a lecturer in medical jurisprudence in the Edinburgh extra-mural medical school. Here he proved to be a popular lecturer, the subject attracting more students than ever before. He went on to become a surgeon to the Lock Hospital in Edinburgh and it was during this time that his interest in psychiatry developed. In 1842 he became a lecturer on anatomy in the extra-mural school, succeeding Dr Robert Knox (q.v.). He became a close friend of Sir James Simpson.

His interest in jurisprudence led to papers on poisoning and phrenology. In 1846 he was appointed as Superintendent of the Royal Edinburgh Asylum. In this capacity he promoted the then unfashionable view that the mental hospital was a therapeutic environment rather than a custodial institution. He continued to press for improvements in the accommodation, protesting against the inhumane treatment of the mentally ill. His classification of mental illnesses by aetiology as opposed to symptoms was not accepted by British psychiatrists of the day, but it nonetheless represented an important contribution to the development of an accepted classification.

In 1867 he gave a lecture to the College on 'The Legal Relations of Insanity', in which he made a plea for psychiatry to be included as a subject in the undergraduate curriculum and for changes in the law on the criminal responsibility of the insane.

Perhaps it was as a teacher that he made his greatest mark. Widely regarded as one of the fathers of the Edinburgh School of Psychiatry, the second-oldest postgraduate school of psychiatry in the world, his assistants and pupils went on to become leading psychiatrists throughout the British Isles.

Roll number: 406

Hector Gavin (1815–55)

An early training in surgery does not at first sight appear to be ideal training for a subsequent career in public health. At least three Fellows have gone on to pursue distinguished careers in that specialty – Sir Henry Littlejohn (q.v.), his son, Harvey Littlejohn (q.v.), and Hector Gavin. A son of Edinburgh, Hector Gavin spent his working life in England, where he became a pioneer of the sanitary movement.

Hector Gavin was born and brought up in Edinburgh and apprenticed at the College at the age of 16. He proceeded to become Licentiate (LRCS) in 1835 and Fellow (FRCSEd) three years later. Moving to England, he spent the rest of his life as a pioneer of the burgeoning specialty of public health medicine. The cholera epidemic of 1848–9 brought public health to the fore and Gavin became editor of the *Journal of Public Health*. This was the era of new Public Health Acts in England and Gavin was an energetic proponent of such legislation. He made recommendations about improvements to public health in Newcastle, Dundee and London.

At the height of his career he was appointed one of three sanitary commissioners to the army in the Crimea, where their work in controlling infectious disease inspired Florence Nightingale to write to Lord Shaftesbury: 'that Commission saved the British Army'. He died, tragically, as a result of a gunshot accident in the Crimea.

Roll number: 408

James Miller (1812–64)

Arguably the single most momentous event in Scotland in the 19th century was the Disruption of 1843. Until that time, the Church of Scotland had been one of the most important national institutions in Scotland since the end of the Scottish Parliament in 1707. The Disruption saw over a third of the ministers, elders and members of the established Church leave, and the subsequent establishment of the Free Church of Scotland. Its first Moderator was Thomas Chalmers, a parish minister, academic and inspiring preacher.

James Miller was inspired by Chalmers while a student at St Andrews University. In his later years, after a distinguished surgical career, he was to write and speak in support of the Free Church and its moral values.

Like many of his medical contemporaries, James Miller was born a son of the manse, in Eassie, Forfarshire, near Glamis Castle. His initial education was at the hands of his father, whose religious influence was to profoundly influence his life. While still only 12 he began three years of study at the University of St Andrews, where he came under another powerful influence – that of Dr Thomas Chalmers, a minister and theologian, who was later to lead the dissenters from the Church of Scotland in the Disruption of 1843. That influence was to continue throughout Miller's life.

James Miller (1812–64).

James Miller, portrayed in 1845.

Miller went on to study medicine in Edinburgh, being taught by a dazzling array of teachers, including:

For anatomy – Robert Knox (q.v.) and John Lizars (q.v.)

For surgery – Richard Mackenzie (q.v.), Robert Liston (q.v.), James Syme (q.v.) and John W. Turner (q.v.)

For military surgery – George Ballingall (q.v.) and John W. Turner (q.v.)

For chemistry – Thomas Hope

For medicine – Andrew Duncan and W. P. Allison

For materia medica – James Home

For pathology – John Thomson (q.v.)

For medical jurisprudence – Dr (later Sir) Robert Christison

Having obtained the Licentiate, he became assistant to Robert Liston, who was later to become a friend and life-long admirer. When Liston went to London in 1834, he invited Miller to join him. Preferring to stay in Edinburgh, Miller inherited Liston's extensive practice and continued to attract patients from all over the world. As was still common at that time, his practice combined general with surgical practice. He obtained the Fellowship of the College in 1840.

On the death of Sir Charles Bell (q.v.) in 1842, Miller applied for the Edinburgh Chair of Surgery and was appointed in the face of formidable competition from other applicants, who included Douglas Argyll Robertson (q.v.) and John Lizars. Miller excelled as a teacher and an orator. His textbooks *Principles of Surgery* (1844) and *Practice of Surgery* (1846) ran to three editions, and were amalgamated into a fourth edition as *A System of Surgery* (1864). An American edition was also published.

Inevitably many honours came his way. He was made Surgeon in Scotland to Queen Victoria, a Fellow of the Royal Society of Edinburgh and Professor of Pictorial Anatomy to the Royal Institution, later the Royal Scottish Academy.

As a neighbour of James Young Simpson he was involved in the early experiments with chloroform, and in *Surgical Experience of Chloroform*, which he published in 1848, he describes a necrosectomy under chloroform anaesthesia which was probably the first procedure to be performed using chloroform in Edinburgh Royal Infirmary.

In his later years, his skills as an orator and a writer were increasingly devoted to promoting the Free Church of Scotland and its moral code.

Roll number: 413

Richard James Mackenzie (1821–54)

It is difficult for most surgeons to become eminent by their early thirties but Richard Mackenzie achieved that. A brilliant and innovative young Edinburgh surgeon, he was assistant to James Syme (q.v.) and seemed destined for an illustrious career in surgery. His death at the early age of 33 was seen as a great loss to British surgery, and it was Joseph Lister (q.v.) who succeeded to his lectureship in Edinburgh.

Richard Mackenzie (1821–54).

Richard James Mackenzie was born in Edinburgh, the fourth son of the Deputy Keeper of Her Majesty's Signet. His school years, at the Academy, marked him out as a distinguished scholar. At the age of 17 he became apprentice to Dr Adam Hunter, Fellow of the College (roll number: 330) and a surgeon at the Royal Infirmary. In 1840 he became resident clerk to Professor Syme in the Royal Infirmary of Edinburgh, graduated in medicine in 1842 and was elected a Fellow of the College two years later. His surgical education was rounded by a series of visits to the major continental schools of the day. After studying in Paris under Joseph Malgaigne and César Roux, he moved to Hamburg, Vienna and Berlin.

On returning to Scotland in 1844, he gave a major paper on the differences between continental and British surgical practice. He became a medical officer at the New Town Dispensary, where he established a reputation as a humanitarian. A contemporary was to write, 'The Medical Officer's duty often consists as much in deeds and words of kindness and benevolence as in the prescription of medicines.' In this position, Dr Mackenzie was regarded as friend of the poor as well as physician to the sick.

He soon distinguished himself as a lecturer. In 1849 he succeeded Dr John Argyll Robertson as a lecturer in the extra-mural school, where his eloquence marked him out as a highly successful and popular teacher, the size of his classes increasing year on year. From the time of his appointment as Surgeon to the Royal Infirmary, he wrote a remarkable series of innovative papers on surgical techniques across the whole spectrum of the surgery of his day. He described successful ligation of the subclavian artery. A modification of Syme's amputation of the ankle joint is still referred to as 'Mackenzie's operation'. Urethral stricture was largely treated by bouginage, but he described several cases of external excision. Reconstructive surgery of the upper lip, the cheek and the eyelid using multiple flaps were also described. In addition to the more customary procedures of the day he was clearly a skilful operator and an innovative surgeon.

Ward at Scutari Hospital near Istanbul, Turkey, the main British military hospital during the Crimea War.

Contemporaries regarded his surgical experience as unique for one of his age, and in his early thirties he was already regarded as a potential world leader of the profession. It was thought that he would succeed Sir George Ballingall in the Chair of Military Surgery, and to do this he needed to gain experience of military surgery. In 1854 he volunteered for active service as a surgeon in the Crimean War, travelling to join the Highland Brigade at Scutari. After acting as Field Surgeon for four months, he died of cholera.

His premature death was regarded as a particular loss to the Edinburgh School of Surgery, for which he was earmarked as a potential future leader. He was succeeded in his lectureship by Joseph Lister.

Roll number: 422

Sir John Struthers (1823–99)

Anatomy came of age as a science in the latter half of the 19th century, and enjoyed a golden age in Edinburgh during that time. Even then the concept of bodily textures and humours had not been completely dispelled. The natural history of the embryo was largely unknown, the theory of evolution had yet to be formulated and anthropology and comparative anatomy were in their infancy. Sir John Struthers lived to see all of that change and was in the vanguard of much of it.

In his younger days he had been a member of an outstanding group of young medical scientists in Edinburgh and went on as Professor of Anatomy in Aberdeen to transform the standards of anatomy teaching in that university. As Chairman of the Education Committee of the General Medical Council, he presided over some of the most important changes to date in the undergraduate medical curriculum in Britain. Yet it was with Edinburgh that he will always be most closely associated and he proved to be one of the greatest benefactors to the College.

John Struthers was born in Brucefield, Dunfermline, where his father had been a successful merchant and mill owner. Like his two brothers, he studied medicine. His elder brother, James Struthers, went on to become a consultant physician in Leith Hospital. Alexander Struthers, the youngest brother, was a fellow resident of Joseph Lister in the Royal Infirmary and appears in the famous photograph of Lister's fellow residents (see page 118). At the outbreak of the Crimea War he served in the hospital at Scutari and died of cholera at the early age of 25.

Sir John Struthers (1823–99).

John Struthers, having taken the FRCSEd, became a demonstrator in anatomy and his gifts as a teacher were immediately apparent.

As a student he had been taught by some inspiring teachers – Sir Charles Bell (q.v.), the Professor of Surgery but an anatomist at heart, Sir James Young Simpson, known as an anatomist early in his career, and the anatomists of the extra-mural school, including Robert Knox (q.v.) and Allen Thomson (q.v.).

Alexander Monro *tertius* was the University Professor of Anatomy, widely regarded as a dull, incompetent teacher, and Struthers would later talk of the valuable time that he had wasted under Monro. After teaching in the extra-mural school, he became Surgeon to the Royal Infirmary of Edinburgh, but his interest remained in anatomy and in 1863 he was appointed to the Chair of Anatomy in the University of Aberdeen. Here, he energetically set about developing the anatomy department and reforming the teaching of anatomy.

The University, formed three years earlier by the fusion of King's College and Marischal College, was receptive to Struthers' reforming zeal. Within a short time he had established a new lecture theatre, new dissecting rooms and a new museum. He set up a histology classroom, at that time a novel concept, but he had, of course, been one of the young pioneers of microscopy in Edinburgh; he taught evolutionary theory virtually from the moment it had been expounded by Darwin.

As a member of the General Medical Council, and in particular as chairman of its Education Committee, he achieved important and lasting reforms in medical education. The medical curriculum was extended to five years and the proportion of practical work in the curriculum was increased.

When he retired from the Aberdeen Chair in 1889 he returned to Edinburgh and became Chairman of the Board of Directors of Leith Hospital, with which his brother had been so closely associated. He also became a manager of the Edinburgh Royal Infirmary.

It was inevitable that he should be elected President of the College, and here his reforms continued. He improved the College Museum, and established a research laboratory for the Fellows. He was honoured by Glasgow University with an LLD and was knighted in 1898.

Roll number: 425

John Goodsir (1814–67)

One of the most influential medical textbooks ever written was Rudolf von Virchow's *Cellular Pathologie*, first published in 1858, which laid the foundations of modern histopathology. The first English edition (1860) of this monumental work was dedicated by its author to Professor John Goodsir of Edinburgh, whom he saluted as 'one of the most acute observers of cell life both physiological and pathological' – a truly impressive tribute to the scientific distinction of a great Scottish anatomist.

John Goodsir, born in Anstruther, Fife, was the son and grandson of medical practitioners bearing the same name. The family, which had been settled in Fife for several generations, was believed to be of German origin, and it was said that their name had been changed from Gutcher to Goodsir.

He was a precocious child and from the village school at Anstruther he entered St Andrews University at the age of 12; there he spent four years passing through the arts curriculum but did not take a degree.

In 1830 he was apprenticed to John Nasmyth, a well-known Edinburgh surgeon-dentist, and in the course of his indenture, he acquired a medical education, partly by attending University classes and partly from extra-mural teachers, of whom the two most notable were Robert Knox (q.v.) and James Syme (q.v.).

Having obtained the Licence of the College in 1835, Goodsir returned to Anstruther, where for the next five years he assisted his father in general medical practice, but, inspired by the teaching of Robert Knox, he was by then fired with enthusiasm for biological science. In spite of the demands of his professional duties, he intensively pursued the study of comparative anatomy and pathology and built up a large collection of anatomical and pathological specimens. In 1839 his classic paper 'On the Origin and Development of the Pulps and Sacs of the Human Teeth' was

John Goodsir (1814–67).

John Goodsir.
A photograph taken probably in the early 1860s.

published in the *Edinburgh Medical and Surgical Journal* and received international acclaim. It also established his reputation as a meticulous, original observer. In 1841 with the strong support of his former teacher James Syme, he was appointed Conservator of the College Museum in succession to William MacGillivray.

As Conservator, Goodsir also pursued anatomical and physiological researches, the results of which were communicated to the Royal Society of Edinburgh and later published in the Society's *Transactions*. They also formed the basis of a remarkable series of lectures which he gave to the College in 1842–3.

In 1844 Goodsir moved from the College to the University Department of Anatomy, and after two years as demonstrator and Museum Curator he was appointed to succeed Alexander Monro *tertius* as Professor. His intellectual dynamism, boundless energy and scientific zeal completely revitalised a department which the sloth and incompetence of Monro *tertius* had rendered virtually moribund and Edinburgh's reputation as a centre of excellence in anatomical teaching and research was triumphantly restored.

In 1845 a selection of Goodsir's papers, incorporating reports of his use of the compound microscope in the study of diseased tissues, was published as a volume entitled *Anatomical and Pathological Observations*, and it was this work which earned him the admiration and respect of Virchow.

He was an excellent teacher and the medical students who, because of the inadequacy of Monro *tertius*, had chosen to study anatomy under extra-mural teachers such as Robert Knox were attracted back to the University classes by his inspirational enthusiasm for his subject.

As a dissector of exceptional skill he produced many impressive teaching specimens for his departmental museum and dissection would seem to have been his favourite didactic activity. Comparative anatomy remained one of his greatest interests and his extra-curricular course on the invertebrates aroused widespread interest. He was consulted frequently on zoological questions relevant to animal husbandry and commercial fishing and he took part regularly in the examination of veterinary students.

On top of all this he continued to pursue researches which extended into physiology and pathology as well as anatomy, and in all of these studies microscopy played an important part. Goodsir became a Fellow of the College in 1848 and had hopes of engaging in surgical practice, but his application for appointment to the staff of the Royal Infirmary as Assistant Surgeon was rejected. This was such a bitter disappointment to him that he formally complained to the managers of the Infirmary of unfair bias on the part of the selection committee.

Thereafter he became increasingly reclusive and his health began to deteriorate, but in spite of this he took on additional teaching responsibilities, which included a course of lectures on natural history. With the slow but inexorable progression of chronic neurological illness, believed to be due to Tabes dorsalis, he delegated more and more of his lecturing to assistants but continued to devote much of his time to dissection and the preparation of museum specimens.

He was described by a contemporary as: 'Tall in stature, grave in demeanour, and almost gaunt of feature, he was the victim of poor health which displayed itself in the form of premature old age. He lived and worked by sheer force of will.'

Latterly he published very little, but his earlier papers were collected into two volumes which were published posthumously in 1868. John Goodsir remained in the Edinburgh University Chair of Anatomy until his death. Logan Turner (himself the son of a distinguished anatomist) would later write of Goodsir's 'world-wide reputation as the most philosophical anatomist of the century'. He made notable contributions to the advancement of medical science and his genius was recognised by two giants of 19th-century medicine Syme and Virchow.

Roll number: 429

William Walker (1814–85)

William Walker belonged to a notable Dumfries family whose members included a member of Parliament. His father, had made a fortune in Jamaica, probably in the sugar trade, and returned to Dumfries, where he died at the age of 60. His wife, Margaret Burnside, was the daughter of Rev. William Burnside DD, a friend of the poet Robert Burns. He was over fifty years old when his eldest son, William, was born.

When William Walker's schooling was completed, his mother took the family to Edinburgh, where they lived in Northumberland Street in the New Town. He studied medicine, obtaining the Licence of the College at the age of 22 in 1836. The notes which he made on lectures in surgery and the practice of physic in January and February of that year are in the Library of the College, providing interesting details of the teaching curriculum of the day. Doubtless he attended the clinics conducted by John Argyll Robertson at the Edinburgh Eye Dispensary, the charitable institution at 405 Lawnmarket, but he left no record of what further training he received in the subject of diseases of the eye, his chosen specialty. He became associated with the Eye Dispensary, where he practised, and, by 1842, was giving a course of 20 lectures on diseases of the eye. These lectures are recorded in manuscript, carefully corrected in red ink. He revised the text every year and the scripts of these lectures are also in the College Library.

General anaesthesia was introduced in the 1840s and in 1851 ophthalmic examinations were revolutionised by Hermann von Helmholtz's invention of the ophthalmoscope, which Walker described in a lecture at the College 10 years later: 'Helmholtz's instrument consisted of a mirror of superimposed oblong plates of glass, packed in a copper frame, which was fixed at one end of a short blackened copper tube, at an angle of $30°$ to the axis of the tube, the other end of which had a contrivance for holding a concave lens. This end the observer applied to his own eye, a lamp was so placed that its rays fell at a convenient angle upon the mirror, which threw these back upon the fundus of the eye where they underwent a second reflection and returned to the mirror.'

When John Argyll Robertson retired, Walker became the senior surgeon at the Eye Dispensary and in 1855 he was the first surgeon to be appointed to the ophthalmic surgery department of the Royal Infirmary of Edinburgh in Infirmary Street. Until that time several surgeons, including James Syme (q.v.), had undertaken ophthalmic operations as there was no specialist department of ophthalmology.

William Walker (1814–85).

William Walker – a studio photograph.

In 1862 the Eye Dispensary, of which he was a Trustee, moved from the Lawnmarket, where the building had become unsafe, to purpose-built accommodation at 54 Cockburn Street. This had been constructed through the riggs (areas of land used for cultivation) to the north of the High Street to give access from the south to the Waverley Station. In the same year, Douglas Argyll Robertson (q.v.) was appointed as a colleague at the Royal Infirmary at the age of 25, so it can be surmised that Walker was his mentor.

Having taken the Fellowship of the College in 1851, he was elected President from 1871 to 1872. During his term of office, there was a proposal that the four Scottish Universities, the two Edinburgh Colleges and the Glasgow Faculty should offer a basic medical qualification, and while this proposal was not developed, it was revived in modified form some years later as the Triple Qualification.

Walker described two cases of subluxated lenses, one in a 'tall, thin and delicate looking' man of 20, probably with Marfan's syndrome, the other 'a stout, healthy young woman' of 25, possibly a case of Weill–Marchesani syndrome. Unfortunately no more details about their habitus are given. In another paper he describes treating a case of granular conjunctivitis by inoculating the conjunctivae with gonorrhoeal discharge, following a method he had gleaned during a visit to Moorfields Hospital. The outcome was apparently successful.

In 1870 after the death of William Mackenzie, he was appointed Surgeon Oculist to Queen Victoria and when the Ophthalmological Society of the United Kingdom was founded by Sir William Bowman in 1880 he was a Vice President.

He collected many textbooks and journals, which now enrich the College Library. His career bridged the period which saw remarkable changes in surgery from therapeutic bleeding to antisepsis and then asepsis.

He died at home in 47 Northumberland Street of a complication of bronchitis, to which he was subject, and was buried alongside his parents in his birthplace of Dumfries. One of his obituaries described him as 'a gentleman who took a most sympathetic interest in the welfare of all classes of the community'. He is described further as capable of sharp repartee. 'Unobtrusive, and never courting recognition or applause, he conferred many benefits on the city and in his memoirs and consultations he was distinguished by his robust common sense. He was a cool and dextrous operator who dispensed his services with unvarying liberality, often supplementing from his purse the wants of the poor who consulted him.'

Author: Geoffrey Millar

Roll number: 432

James Spence (1812–82)

James Spence achieved distinction as Professor of Surgery in the University of Edinburgh, as President of the College and as Surgeon to the Queen in Scotland. His book, *Lectures of Surgery*, became a standard didactic text in its day. Despite these considerable achievements, Spence was regarded by contemporaries as reactionary because of his implacable opposition to the principles of antisepsis being promoted by his contemporary Joseph Lister (q.v.).

James Spence was born on South Bridge, Edinburgh, a few yards from the present site of the College. After education at the Royal High School of Edinburgh, he entered University and then the extra-mural School of Medicine. He went on to obtain the Licence of the College in 1832. His initial experience in medicine was as a doctor on an East India Company ship to Calcutta.

On return to Edinburgh he set up in practice in Rankeillor Street. At the same time he began to demonstrate anatomy in the University under Monro *tertius*. By all accounts, these were unhappy times. The teaching of anatomy in Edinburgh University under Monro *tertius* had declined both in reputation and in student numbers. Despite this, Spence made useful contributions to surgical anatomy. His paper entitled *Remarks on the Sources of Haemorrhage after Lithotomy* (1841) was based on careful dissection of that region and he was able to make detailed technical recommendations about the surgical procedure which reduced the problem of post-operative bleeding. He wrote a further paper on *The Anatomy of the 8th Pair of Nerves* (1842), a study which was probably inspired by Sir Charles Bell (q.v.), at that time Professor of Surgery in the University and the leading surgical anatomist of his day. The death of Sir Charles Bell in 1842 was almost certainly the stimulus which led him to leave the University to teach anatomy in the extra-mural school. He began to teach anatomy at 1 Surgeons' Square and moved to surgical practice in the New Town. During his time the anatomy instruction at Surgeons' Square was regarded as the best in the country and he became an authority on the anatomy of hernia and lithotomy, and of the head and neck and great vessels. He prepared anatomical specimens, and those which he prepared of the hand and foot are regarded as masterpieces of their time. A contemporary account gives an insight into his commitment and his personality: 'While others were going out to dinner or to places of amusement, Spence might be seen walking up the Bridges on his way back to the evening work in the dissecting room; and many summer evenings were thus spent in solitary devotion to anatomy and surgical pathology.'

James Spence (1812–82).

James Spence – a photographic portrait.

From teaching anatomy he moved on to give systematic lectures in surgery, initially at the extra-mural school at 4 High School Yards, where Miller and Liston had lectured, and later in Surgeons' Hall.

His biographers depict him as a careful, meticulous, but conservative surgeon. A contemporary account gives insight into his personality, which was probably obsessional and perhaps depressive: 'Before the operation Mr Spence was nervous, pre-occupied and over strung. Not brilliant, nor rapid … but careful, accurate, with every step pre-arranged and every anatomical detail expected recognised and noted. Perhaps not so calm or fertile as Syme, not so brilliant as Fergusson but Mr Spence was a successful operating surgeon.'

He was appointed to the Chair of Surgery in the University in 1864. His contemporary Joseph Lister had promoted the theory of antisepsis and introduced catgut into surgery. Spence was dismissive of both innovations. In his *Life of Lister*, Sir Rickman Godlee describes a now famous incident in which Spence obtained some of Lister's carbolised catgut from Dr Lawrie, Professor Syme's house surgeon. Spence used this to tie the right common carotid artery but the patient died three days later and Spence, in his report of the case to *The Lancet*, described sepsis in the wound for which he blamed the catgut. Dr Lawrie, with a temerity that would make later generations of house surgeons shudder, wrote to *The Lancet* suggesting that the failure was attributable to Spence's technique rather than to the catgut. Spence was understandably outraged and brought about Dr Lawrie's dismissal. Syme sprang to his young colleague's defence in the correspondence columns of *The Lancet*, and the incident, according to Godlee, stimulated Lister into continuing further development of carbolised catgut sutures for the rest of his career.

Spence's conservatism was further demonstrated in the 'battle of the sites between 1864 and 1869'. He opposed the move of the Royal Infirmary from High School Yards to the much larger site in Lauriston Place, but eventually Syme's view prevailed and the new Royal Infirmary opened in Lauriston Place in 1879. A similar debate about the future site of the Royal Infirmary was conducted over two decades in the second half of the 20th century.

Spence went on to become President of the College and was Surgeon in Ordinary in Scotland to Queen Victoria. He is remembered as much for a melancholy, even lugubrious demeanour, which earned him the nickname of 'Dismal Jimmy'. MacGillivray, in his Harveian oration of 1912, recalls an occasion when 'we met Spence with his most dismal expression, all clothed in black and crepe'. James Spence seems destined to be remembered by posterity more for his unkind nickname than for his undoubted contributions.

Roll number: 432

Thomas Keith (1827–95)

Thomas Keith (1827–95).

Several surgeons who feature in this book have achieved fame in fields not connected with surgery. Foremost among those was Thomas Keith, a pioneer of surgery of the ovary and of photography. He was a pre-eminent gynaecological surgeon of his day, whose results for the new operation of ovarian cystectomy were among the best in the world. Other pioneers in the field, Spencer Wells and Marion Sims, wrote in glowing terms of his skill and distinction as a gynaecologist. Yet his extensive obituaries in the medical journals made no mention of his distinguished achievements in another area. Thomas Keith was a pioneer of photography in Britain and his pictures demonstrate both scientific application and artistic flair.

Thomas Keith was born a son of the manse in the village of St Cyrus, five miles north of Montrose on the North Sea coast of Angus in Scotland. After schooling at Aberdeen Grammar School and Marischal College, Aberdeen, he embarked on a surgical career becoming apprentice to James Young Simpson in 1845. He had the distinction of being probably the last medical apprentice in Edinburgh, according to his brother George. Appointed House Surgeon to James Syme in the Edinburgh Royal Infirmary, he had reason to be grateful to Syme, for, early in life in Aberdeen, he had developed bladder calculi, which dogged him throughout his life. He had a urethrotomy for stones as a boy and in the 1860s Syme operated on two occasions to remove further calculi. In 1889 just six years before his death, his brother George, also a surgeon, drained a perinephric abscess, but the sinus continued to discharge for the rest of his life. In spite of continuing episodes of pain and sepsis he maintained rigorously high surgical standards for his patients.

After his apprenticeship he was appointed Surgeon to the British Ambassador at the Court of the King of Sardinia in Turin, where he stayed for two years. During this time he published a paper in a local medical journal deploring the then prevailing custom of copious blood letting for a variety of ailments. Returning to Edinburgh, he joined his brother, Dr George Skene Keith, in practice, devoting himself increasingly to gynaecological surgery. He visited Sir Spencer Wells, who had pioneered ovariotomy in London, and in 1862 performed his first ovarian cystectomy. He went on to become one of the most successful surgeons in the world at this procedure. His success was based on an obsessional attention to detail, and contemporaries described his patience, neatness and unhurried technique. Another distinguished pioneer of gynaecological surgery, the American Marion Sims, wrote that 'his success so far overtopped that of all other surgeons that it became a wonder and admiration of surgeons all over the world'. In 1877 he began to take advantage of Listerian antisepsis and was able to publish a 97 per cent recovery rate following ovarian cystectomy. He went on to pioneer hysterectomy for bleeding fibroids, where his success rate was again as good as that of any surgeon in the world.

Keith published a series of articles which formed the basis of his book *Contributions to the Surgical Treatment of Tumours in the Abdomen* (1885). His pioneering work on cautery in abdominal surgery was described in a further book, *Electricity in the Treatment of Uterine Tumours* (1889). *A Textbook of Abdominal Surgery*, published in 1894 was his magnum opus.

Dr Thomas Keith, signed etching.

Cobbled alleyway. Note the ghost-like figures on the left caused by movement during the long exposure. Calotype by Thomas Keith, c. 1853–6.

The north side of the Lawnmarket. Calotype by Thomas Keith, c. 1853–6.

North side of the Grassmarket with Edinburgh Castle in the background. Calotype by Thomas Keith, c. 1853–6.

His contemporaries describe a meticulous surgical technique and courage in pursuing a conservative course when he felt that surgery might not be the most appropriate treatment. Keith had a striking appearance – he was a tall thin figure with a high broad forehead, a shock of reddish-brown hair and a thin ascetic face. Other contemporary accounts described him as abnormally conscientious with an intense feeling of personal responsibility for patients. Marion Sims was to write 'his whole being is wrapped up in his work and after he has performed a difficult operation he eats and sleeps but little until he knows that his patient is out of danger'.

In later life he was to follow Joseph Lister (q.v.) and Matthews Duncan to London. The young Lister had succeeded him as resident to Syme and the two had remained friends throughout their lives. Keith was one of the first to promote the benefits of Listerian antisepsis.

His brother George and his colleague Matthews Duncan were, along with J. Y. Simpson, the first to discover the anaesthetic effects of chloroform. In the famous experiment at 52 Queen Street Edinburgh the three sipped liquid chloroform and inhaled the vapour becoming unconscious (see cartoon on page 69). Within two weeks chlorofom anaesthesia had begun.

Yet his surgical colleagues seemed to have been quite unaware of his distinction as a pioneer in the developing art of photography. His introduction to photography had come within a few months of Fox Talbot's patent of the calotype in 1841. Unrestricted by that patent, which did not apply in Scotland, Keith developed his own technique by meticulous experiment.

Thomas Keith had equipped himself as a photographer in 1852 but the time involved in the exposure restricted his photographic activities to midsummer and early autumn. He went on to produce romantic compositions of Edinburgh town scenes. His work was included in 1854 in Edinburgh's first photographic exhibition alongside photographs by Octavius Hill, Robert Adamson and George Washington Wilson. Keith's work was highly praised in his own lifetime. Photographic historians have recognised his superb use of light and, his flair for composition, which result in his photographs becoming bold individual statements. As with his surgery it was his meticulous attention to detail that made him a photographic pioneer in his own right. All of this was achieved in a short photographic career in Edinburgh between 1852 and 1857.

Keith established an international reputation, and travelled to Europe and the United States to operate. He was honoured with the degree of LLD by the Universities of Edinburgh and St Andrews.

Roll number: 441

Stereo prints of an outing to Craigmillar Castle by the Photographic Society of Scotland in 1856. Thomas Keith is believed to be the figure sitting front right wearing a hat.

Sir Henry Littlejohn (1826–1914)

Many Fellows of the College have pursued distinguished careers in fields other than surgery, but few have done so in public health. Hector Gavin (q.v.) achieved this, but the most famous was Henry Littlejohn, whose appointment as Medical Officer of Health for Edinburgh was the first of its kind in Scotland.

The seventh son of Thomas Littlejohn, a baker, Henry Littlejohn was born in Leith Street, Edinburgh. Schooled at Perth Academy and the Royal High School of Edinburgh, he graduated in medicine from Edinburgh University in 1847. After a short spell in general practice in Selkirk, he embarked on a career in what was then called medical jurisprudence, a combination of forensic medicine and public health. After taking the Fellowship of the College, in 1854 he became a lecturer in medical jurisprudence at the extra-mural School of Medicine at Surgeons' Hall.

In 1862 he became Medical Officer of Health for Edinburgh. He was to hold this post for almost fifty years and his tenure was a prestigious one. At this time, epidemic diseases such as cholera, typhoid, diphtheria and smallpox remained endemic in Scotland. Early in his experience he recognised the benefits of compulsory notification by general practitioners of infectious disease. The medical practitioners of the city, perhaps understandably, opposed this, but in 1879 a clause was included in the local Police Act requiring such notification, giving Edinburgh the lead to the whole of Great Britain. This was to prove one of the major advances of the 19th century in public health.

His *Report on the Sanitary Condition of the City of Edinburgh* (1865) proved a blueprint for social reform. It clearly demonstrated the effect of population density on the spread of disease and mortality. From the vast number of statistics that he had compiled and analysed, he was able to define areas of deprivation throughout the city, and demonstrated a clear correlation between deprivation, disease and mortality. His proposals to improve this included recommendations about building, sewage, water pollution and limiting overcrowding. The Town Council was responsive to his recommendations and demolished many ageing properties that had become dangers to health.

By the time of his retiral in 1908, after 46 years of service, mortality rates in Edinburgh from infectious disease had halved. Largely as a result of his efforts, cholera and typhus had disappeared and smallpox had become a rarity.

He was able to pursue a parallel, and equally distinguished, career in forensic medicine. Eloquent and erudite, he was regarded as an outstanding teacher amidst Edinburgh contemporaries, who included some of the greatest medical teachers in the world. As adviser to the Crown in criminal cases, he was an expert witness in many famous trials. In 1897, at the age of 71, he succeeded Sir Douglas Maclagan (q.v.) in the Chair of Medical Jurisprudence in the University.

He was elected President of the College in 1875 and President of the British Institute of Public Health in 1893. The University of Edinburgh conferred the honorary degree of Doctor of Laws upon him in 1907.

Roll number: 443

Sir Henry Littlejohn (1826–1914).

Henry Littlejohn as a young man.

Lord Lister (1827–1912)

It is impossible in a short biography to convey the magnitude of Joseph Lister's contribution to medicine and to humankind. He could justly be regarded as the surgeon who did more to improve surgical standards than any other. His introduction of antisepsis in surgery improved results to such an extent that surgery became measurably safer and more widely applicable. He achieved more honours than any other British surgeon – the first doctor in Britain to be made a baron; a founder member of the Order of Merit; the only Fellow by examination of this College to be made an honorary Fellow. Yet for all this pre-eminence, contemporaries described him as a gentle and kindly man, quiet, modest and unassuming, with an overt concern for the welfare of others and a disarming smile.

Joseph Lister was born in Upton House in what today is West Ham Park in London. His father, Joseph Jackson Lister, had been brought up a Quaker and was devout in that faith. He had achieved fame in his own right. Although a wine shipper by trade, he had a gift for mathematics and applied this knowledge to calculate the curvature of the lenses required for microscopes and began to grind these himself. The resultant improvements to the achromatic microscope lens resulted in him being elected a Fellow of the Royal Society.

His son, Joseph, was educated at Quaker schools, first at Hitchin and then at Grove House in Tottenham before enrolling in University College, London. He had decided early in life to become a surgeon but first graduated BA from the University of London in 1847. His interest in surgery during this time must surely have been inspired by being present at the first public demonstration of an ether anaesthetic in England by Robert Liston (q.v.) and he is shown keenly observing the operation in the famous painting (see page 84). Liston, an Edinburgh surgeon renowned for his operative speed and dexterity, had become Professor of Surgery at University College Hospital. At the time there was increasing interest in hypnosis, or mesmerism, to facilitate surgical procedures. After the operation, an amputation, Liston famously remarked to the audience: 'This Yankee dodge, gentlemen, beats mesmerism hollow.' Lister was to recall his excitement when he described the occasion to the British Association 50 years later.

For about a year while an undergraduate, Lister underwent a period of serious self-doubt about his career. He lost motivation and became depressed, but his health recovered and he resumed his studies with vigour, finding particular inspiration from the Professor of Physiology, William Sharpey (q.v.), a Scot who had left Edinburgh to become the first Professor of Physiology at University College, London. After graduating MB in 1852 and appointments as House Surgeon and House Physician, he took up dissection of animals and conducted research using the microscope, the value of which had been taught him at an early age by his father. Encouraged by Sharpey, he continued to dissect and sketch animals while developing his surgical career. He was elected Fellow of the Royal College of Surgeons of England in 1852.

Professor Sharpey suggested to him that he should tour European centres for further studies starting with Edinburgh and wrote a letter of introduction to James Syme (q.v.). Syme at this stage was widely regarded as a leading surgeon in Britain. Joseph Bell (q.v.), who had been one of his assistants, called him 'the originator of nearly every improvement in surgery in the century'. Having intended to stay in Edinburgh for a only a month, he stayed for seven years. He became a Fellow of the College in 1855. Syme was so impressed with the young Quaker that he appointed him House Surgeon in the Royal Infirmary and assistant at his private hospital in Minto House, Chambers Street. He also became a frequent visitor to Syme's house in Millbank in the Grange area – now part of the Astley Ainslie Hospital. This resulted in his meeting, and marrying, Agnes, Syme's eldest daughter. As a result he resigned his membership of the Society of Friends and became a Scottish Episcopalian, but retained many of his Quaker characteristics to the end. Throughout his life, for example, he would address his family as 'thee and thou' when writing and speaking. His Edinburgh career flourished with a popular lecture course which he established in a lecture theatre in the extra-mural school at 4 High School Yards. At the same time he continued with research on the pathology of inflammation and coagulation of blood.

In 1860 he was appointed Regius Professor of Surgery in the University of Glasgow. He was appointed Surgeon to the Glasgow Royal Infirmary, the newest of the six Scottish Royal Infirmaries, which was similar in size to St Bartholomew's, the largest hospital in London. After three years he applied for the Chair of Systematic Surgery in Edinburgh, but, surprisingly, was unsuccessful, the appointment going to James Spence (q.v.).

Joseph Lister (1827–1912).

Disappointed, he threw himself anew into research on suppuration. Sepsis, a term which he himself coined, seems to have been particularly common in Glasgow Royal Infirmary. The correlation between sepsis and dirt in hospitals had been established shortly before and the benefits resulting from doctors washing their hands had been established in the 1840s by Oliver Wendell Holmes in Boston, and by Ignaz Semmelweis in Vienna. In 1865 Thomas Anderson, the Professor of Chemistry in Glasgow, introduced Lister to Louis Pasteur's recently published work on putrefaction and drew his attention to the suggestion that the process of fermentation was caused by 'small corpuscles'. Pasteur had concluded that putrefaction could be prevented by excluding air from the tissues concerned. Lister introduced chemical antisepsis by applying carbolic acid into wounds, using it famously to speed the healing of the compound tibial fracture of James Greenleas without any infective complications. In 1867 he published the epoch-making paper *On a New Method of Treating Compound Fracture and Abscess etc. with Observations on the Conditions of Suppuration*. He went on to develop the carbolic spray which was used to disinfect the environment around the wound during operations and during dressings.

Joseph Lister while
Professor in Edinburgh.

Joseph Lister's Fellow Residents in the Royal Infirmary of Edinburgh, summer 1854.

One of the best-known portraits of Lord Lister is that taken in the summer of 1854 with his six fellow residents in the Edinburgh Royal Infirmary. Two of them besides Lister were destined to become Fellows of the College.

Alexander Struthers was the brother of John Struthers (q.v.). Within six months of the photograph, he had volunteered for service in the military hospital in Scutari on the shores of the Bosporus. Three months later he died from cholera at the age of 25.

George Hogarth Pringle (q.v.) also served in the Crimea War, acting as a surgeon on a ship conveying the sick and injured to the base hospitals at Scutari and Renkioi. Thereafter he worked as a ship's surgeon on Cunard and P&O liners, making several voyages to Australia. He settled in New South Wales, where he established an extensive practice in Parramatta. In 1870 he became a Fellow of the College. He died at sea in 1872 while travelling home from Australia.

Patrick Heron Watson (q.v.) went to the Crimea as Assistant Surgeon with the Royal Artillery. He was invalided home in 1856 and was appointed Surgeon to the Edinburgh Royal Infirmary in 1860. A pioneer in surgery of the thyroid and laryngectomy he was an accomplished abdominal surgeon. President of the College in 1877 and again in 1905 during the Quatercentennial celebrations, he was knighted in 1903 and died in 1907.

John Beddoe volunteered for medical service in the Crimea, on return from which he was appointed Physician to Bristol Royal Infirmary. His principal area of research was in anthropology and his publication entitled Races of Britain (1885) became the standard work on the subject. He retained links with Edinburgh and in particular with Sir William Turner (q.v.). His work on anthropology earned him a Fellowship of the Royal Society. He died in 1911.

David Christison was the son of Sir Robert Christison. As a result of illness contracted while serving abroad, he was for some years unable to practise as a doctor but in 1864 returned to Edinburgh and assisted his father in his practice, becoming a Fellow of the Royal College of Physicians of Edinburgh. He became a student of archaeology and was elected Secretary of the Society of Antiquaries of Scotland. He died in 1912.

John Kirk was surgeon and naturalist on David Livingstone's second journey to East Africa. In the journey from Lake Nyasa along the Zambesi river to the Victoria Falls he provided medical support to the expedition and collected local flora, which was sent back to Kew Gardens. He was appointed Medical Officer to the consulate at Zanzibar and later consul. He was influential in the building of the cathedral in Zanzibar on the site of the slave market, where it stands to this day. 'A fitting tribute', wrote Logan Turner, 'to the work of a son of the manse.' He went on to further diplomatic appointments and was elected a Fellow of the Royal Society and knighted in 1890. He died in 1922, the last survivor of the small group of residents of 1854.

Lister made a second major contribution to surgical practice – the absorbable ligature. As a result of his work on germ theory, he appreciated that the silk sutures customarily left protruding from wounds provided a track through which bacteria could produce infection around the suture. Catgut was readily available as it was used for the stringing of musical instruments, such as violins and guitars. Lister devised a catgut ligature which, when treated with carbolic, dramatically reduced the problem of deep sepsis. To overcome the problem of rapid absorption of the catgut he soaked it in chromic acid to make chromic catgut, which he introduced into surgical practice, publishing details of the technique in 1881.

In 1869 he had succeeded Syme as Professor of Clinical Surgery in Edinburgh. Here, he consolidated his work on sepsis and was forced to defend it against powerful enemies, who included James Young Simpson, the Professor of Midwifery. Increasingly, however, his technique found favour throughout Europe and the world. He became Surgeon to the Queen in Scotland and used the antiseptic technique to good effect on Queen Victoria when he drained a royal abscess at Balmoral. The successful outcome may also have been aided by the use of a rubber drainage tube, thought to be the first recorded use of this in the country.

From his home in 9 Charlotte Square, one of the most prestigious addresses in Edinburgh, he established a large and successful surgical practice. Following the death of Sir William Fergusson (q.v.), Professor of Clinical Surgery in King's College, London, in 1877, Lister was appointed to that post, taking with him as House Surgeon William (later Sir William) Watson Cheyne. Lectures and publications on improvements in antiseptic practice followed. He now enjoyed a worldwide reputation and corresponded with Pasteur, whose discovery of the germ theory of putrefaction he always freely acknowledged. Yet his return to London was not triumphant. Students demonstrated their boredom with his lectures and stayed away; the nurses opposed the introduction of his antiseptic techniques, and the establishment resented his criticism of London teaching methods. With time, all of these were won over.

He was elected to the Council of the Royal College of Surgeons of England and became its Vice President. In 1897 he was created Baron Lister of Lyme Regis and was elected President of the Royal Society, the first surgeon to hold that office. He became Serjeant Surgeon to Queen Victoria and on the coronation of King Edward VII was chosen as one of the 12 original members of the Order of Merit. Having served on the Council of the Royal College of Surgeons of Edinburgh he became its only Fellow by examination to receive the honorary Fellowship. Honours from institutions and universities around the world followed. He became a Freeman of the City of London in 1907 and of Edinburgh in 1908. Joseph Baron Lister died peacefully in 1912 at the age of 85. With no children, the Barony died with him. His contributions to surgery must rank among the greatest ever made.

Roll number: 445

Lord Lister.

Joseph Lister, W. E. Henley and RLS

W. E. Henley was born in Gloucester in 1849 and contracted tuberculosis in childhood leading to a tuberculous arthritis of the left knee joint which had necessitated amputation. When the same problem emerged in the right knee he travelled from Margate to Edinburgh to be treated by Joseph Lister in the hope that Lister would be able to save his limb. As Henley was later to acknowledge, Lister did indeed save the foot, but Henley spent some 20 months as a patient in the Edinburgh Royal Infirmary. During this time he learnt Spanish and Italian and wrote a series of poems which were to establish his reputation. It was during this prolonged stay in hospital that he befriended Robert Louis Stevenson, with whom he was to collaborate on four plays including *Deacon Brodie* (1880). Stevenson described Henley as 'boisterous and piratical' and was later to acknowledge that he had used Henley as the model for the character Long John Silver in *Treasure Island* (1883). Henley went on to a successful literary career as a critic and publisher, and, as editor of the *National Observer*, published the early works of Thomas Hardy, George Bernard Shaw, H. G. Wells, Sir James Barry and Rudyard Kipling. He also edited the centenary edition of the poems of Robert Burns.

Sir Patrick Heron Watson as a young surgeon.

Sir Patrick Heron Watson (1832–1907)

The laws of the College, as revised in 1977, make it impossible for a Fellow to hold office as President for more than one term, but despite the lack of any prior legal impediment, only one Fellow in the past 200 years has served two separate terms in the College's highest office. The fact that he was recalled to the College presidency in its Quatercentennial year is a clear indication of Patrick Heron Watson's exceptional personal qualities and professional distinction.

Patrick Heron Watson, a son of the manse, was born in Burntisland, Fife, and educated at the Edinburgh Academy and at Edinburgh University, from which he graduated MD in 1853. Having served as House Surgeon in the Edinburgh Royal Infirmary, where one of his fellow residents was the young Joseph Lister (q.v.) (see page 118), he was admitted a Fellow of the College in 1855. The Crimean War was in progress and, having joined the Army Medical Service, he was posted first to the base hospital at Scutari. The College has an interesting collection of letters that he wrote home at this time and in these he expresses vividly his disgust at the conditions in the hospital. It is also clear from his letters that he was by no means an uncritical admirer of Florence Nightingale. Eventually he was posted to the field hospital at Balaclava in the Crimea, where he gained valuable surgical experience. However, this was cut short by serious illness, on account of which he was invalided home and out of the army. For his military services in the Crimean War he was awarded the British, Turkish and Sardinian campaign medals.

He returned to Edinburgh, where, after a lengthy convalescence, he settled in general practice, but surgery remained his prime interest and he became assistant to the Professor of Surgery, James Miller (q.v.), whose daughter he married. In 1860 he was appointed Surgeon to the Royal Infirmary and was a lecturer in surgery at the School of Medicine of the Royal Colleges, in which capacity he soon laid the foundations of what was to be an impressive reputation as a teacher. His surgical practice expanded rapidly with his appointment as Surgeon to Chalmers Hospital in succession to his father-in-law, and over the next two decades his renown as a bold and dextrous operator spread far beyond Scotland. His surgical versatility was indeed extraordinary and Rutherford Morison (q.v.), who was his house surgeon in 1875, regarded him as one of the best operators he ever saw.

Heron Watson successfully removed the spleen and the kidney and resected bowel when these procedures were considered to be almost prohibitively hazardous. He was the first surgeon to carry out total laryngectomy and one of the earliest to treat hyperthyroidism by thyroidectomy. His practice of preliminary ligation of the thyroid arteries before excision of the gland was an important landmark advance in the technique of thyroid surgery.

By the late 1870s Heron Watson had become probably the most successful surgeon in Scotland, but he did not confine himself to surgery and maintained a large and lucrative general medical consulting practice. In modern terms he was as much a consultant physician as he was a consultant surgeon and, perhaps incongruously, he was the foremost authority in Scotland on venereal diseases. The only disappointment which he suffered in his career was the failure of his application in 1882 to succeed Professor James Spence (q.v.) in the University Chair of Systematic Surgery. It seems likely that the unusually wide range of his clinical activities may have been prejudicial to his candidature.

He had always been active in College affairs and in 1878 he was elected President. Edinburgh University, his alma mater, conferred on him the honorary degree of Doctor of Laws (LLD) in 1884 and from 1882 for 26 years he represented the College on the General Medical Council.

Heron Watson was an inspiring teacher at the bedside and in the lecture theatre, and as a member of the University Commission of 1889 he helped to effect important changes in the undergraduate medical curriculum. It was, however, as a vehement and persistent protagonist of medical education for women, in the face of fierce professional hostility and vilification, that he made his most important educational contribution. Indeed, there is no doubt that his powerful advocacy had a major influence on the ultimate acceptance of female medical students by his own university.

His appointment as Surgeon to HM Queen Victoria in Scotland and later as Surgeon to HM King Edward VII was followed in 1903 by the honour of knighthood, but his supreme accolade came in 1905 with his recall to the presidency of the College 27 years after his first election to that office. His re-election for a second term so that he could preside over the Quatercentennial celebrations shows that the high esteem in which he was so widely held was based on much more than his professional excellence.

Sir Patrick Heron Watson received many well-deserved honours in his lifetime; he was a wise, far-seeing man, in many ways ahead of his time, who, as surgeon, teacher and medical statesman, most worthily earned his honoured place in Scottish medical history.

Roll number: 448

Sir Patrick Heron Watson (1832–1907).

Francis Brodie Imlach (1819–91)

Along with John Smith (q.v.) and Robert Nasmyth, Francis Imlach founded the Edinburgh Dental Dispensary, the predecessor of the Edinburgh Dental Hospital and School. He was the first surgeon with an exclusively dental practice to be elected President of a surgical college.

Francis Brodie Imlach, the son of an Edinburgh solicitor, was educated at the Royal High School in Edinburgh, and became a Licentiate of the College in 1841 and a Fellow in 1856.

At that time, in the years before the first Dentists' Act 1878, training in dental surgery was much less formal. Imlach learned his dentistry in Edinburgh and Paris and he went on to establish a large dental practice.

He was an influential medical politician, credited, along with his friends John Smith and Robert Nasmyth, with the founding in 1860 of the Edinburgh Dental Dispensary in Drummond Street, close to the College. This was to evolve into the Edinburgh Dental Hospital and School.

His life-long friendship with James Young Simpson meant that he was involved in the introduction of chloroform into clinical practice from the very beginning. Within days of Simpson's initial experiment on 4 November 1847, Imlach had extracted a tooth under chloroform anaesthesia and is given the credit for being the first practitioner to do so.

He was elected President of the College in 1879, for the then customary term of two years, and had the unusual distinction of being reappointed for a third year. In 1878, following the passage of the Dentists' Act the College had created the diploma of Licence in Dental Surgery, which, with regular revision and update, was still being offered until the year 2000.

After retiral from active practice he supported and promoted what were then charitable institutions associated with medicine. He helped, in this way, Donaldson's Hospital for the Deaf, the Orphan Hospital and the Morningside Asylum. Outwith his medical practice he was President of the Royal Scottish Society of Arts and a member of the Royal Company of Archers.

Roll number: 453

Francis Brodie Imlach.
Photograph probably taken in the 1860s.

Francis Brodie Imlach (1819–91).

Sir Joseph Fayrer Bt (1824–1907)

India was regarded as the 'Jewel in the Crown' of the British Empire during the reign of Queen Victoria. Among the large number of British expatriates who sought to make their career in India were several gifted doctors and Jospeh Fayrer was one of the foremost. His systematic studies of the poisonous snakes of India and the clinical effects of their venom did much to further the understanding and treatment of snake bites.

Joseph Fayrer was born in Plymouth and spent some of his early childhood years in the Lake District, where he would later recall meeting the poets William Wordsworth and Hartley Coleridge. At the age of 18 he accompanied his father, a sea captain, on a memorable trip to Bermuda. He was inspired by the ship's surgeon and by an attachment to the naval hospital in Bermuda to become a surgeon. He entered Charing Cross Hospital to begin medical studies in 1844, where one of his fellow students was Thomas Huxley, with whom he remained friends and continued to correspond throughout his life. He was fortunate in 1847 to be able to undertake a grand tour of Europe, studying for a year in Rome, where he graduated with the degree of MD.

Almost immediately he left for India as an assistant surgeon in Bengal, beginning a connection with the Indian Medical Service which was to last for 45 years. After a spell as an assistant surgeon at Dacca, he was posted to Lucknow as Surgeon to the Residency and in addition became Honorary Assistant Resident, a post which involved political duties.

During the Indian mutiny the residency in Lucknow came under siege. Fayrer was the only surgeon available to care for the garrison and the large civilian community throughout the siege, and his house was used both as a hospital and a fortress.

In 1855 he married Bethia, the daughter of Brigadier General Andrew Spens and granddaughter of Thomas Spens, President of the Royal College of Physicians of Edinburgh. She was also a descendant of Andrew Wood (1750–1821) and cousin of Andrew Wood (1810–81) (see Wood/Spens family tree on page 71). On returning from India, it was to Edinburgh that Fayrer came in 1858 to meet his wife's family and to study for his MD degree. He studied medical jurisprudence under Sir Robert Christison, surgery under James Syme (q.v.), James Spence (q.v.), James Miller (q.v.) and Joseph Lister (q.v.). He graduated MD in 1859 and was admitted FRCSEd the same year.

On his return to India he became Professor of Surgery at the Calcutta Medical College and here he embarked on research into poisonous snakes of India. His book *The Thanatophidia of India* was published in 1872 and contains detailed colour illustrations of the snakes of India drawn by local artists. He conducted research on the effects of different snake venoms and their treatment. His recommendations that a ligature should be applied above the snake bite as rapidly as possible, and that the bite itself should be treated by immediate incision and application of potassium permanganate undoubtedly saved many lives and limbs. After his return to Britain he was to continue his research on snake venom along with Sir Thomas Lauder Brunton. He was selected to accompany two royal visitors to India, the Duke of Edinburgh in 1870 and the Prince of Wales (later King Edward VII) in 1875. He subsequently became Honorary Physician to the Prince of Wales, and formed a lasting friendship with him.

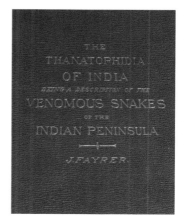

Drawings by a local artist from
Sir Joseph Fayrer's *Thanatophidia of India*.

Sir Joseph Fayrer Bt (1824–1907).

He continued his association with India through the Indian Office in London, where he worked as Surgeon General until his retiral in 1895.

He was to obtain many honours. He was elected FRCSEng in 1878, Fellow of the Royal Society of London in 1877, honorary Doctor of Laws (LLD) of Edinburgh University in 1878 and LLD St Andrews in 1890. He was knighted in 1876 and made a baronet in 1896.

His son, Joseph, succeeded him in the baronetcy and also pursued a surgical career becoming FRCSEd (roll number: 1151) and at one stage commanding the medical services in the garrison at Edinburgh Castle.

Role number: 474

Norman Bethune (1822–92)

In the Scottish Highlands one of the most famous medical families were the Beatons or Bethunes, hereditary physicians over many generations to the chiefs of two of the most powerful clans, the MacDonalds and the Macleods. Little wonder then that a Canadian branch of Bethunes was to achieve distinction in surgery over several generations. Norman Bethune, a Canadian surgeon, helped to found the Trinity College medical faculty in Toronto in 1850. His grandson, Norman Henry Bethune (q.v.), was to achieve fame as a surgeon to the army of Mao Tse-Tung and is afforded heroic status in China to this day.

Norman Bethune was born at Moose Factory, Ontario, the son of a successful businessman and politician. After studying for a Diploma in Arts at Toronto, Bethune graduated in medicine. In 1850 along with three colleagues, he established the third School of Medicine in Toronto, the Trinity College medical faculty. Here, Bethune became Professor of Anatomy, moving to the Toronto School of Medicine in 1856.

During a visit to Europe, Norman Bethune found himself involved as a surgeon at the Battle of Solferino, one of the bloodiest conflicts of the 19th century. Of the 300,000 combatants, some 40,000 were killed or injured. The sheer scale and horror of the battle injuries inspired a young businessman from Geneva, Henry Dunant, to set up the organisation that was to become the International Red Cross. In his description of the care of the injured after the battle, Dunant singled out one surgeon for particular mention in his care of the wounded – Norman Bethune. Dunant was later to receive the first Nobel Peace Prize in 1901 for establishing the International Red Cross.

On his return to Toronto in 1860, Bethune returned to teaching, going on to become Professor of the Practice of Surgery in Clinical Surgery.

Like his grandson, Norman Bethune had a creative flair and gift for drawing. His compassion for those in need was passed to his son, Malcolm, who became a Presbyterian minister, and both artistic flair and compassion were evident in his famous grandson.

Roll number: 524

Henry Dunant (1828–1910), Nobel Laureate, 1901.

John Smith (1825–1910)

John Smith was a pioneer of dental training, who planned and delivered the first lecture course in dentistry in Scotland. He was a joint founder of the Edinburgh Dental Dispensary, which later became the Edinburgh Dental Hospital and School.

John Smith was born in Edinburgh, the son of a surgeon-dentist. He attended school at the Edinburgh Institution (later to become Melville College and then Stewarts-Melville College). From schooldays, his talents for drawing, for playing the violin and for song writing were apparent. He graduated MD from the University of Edinburgh and received the LRCS diploma from the College in 1847. Shortly after graduation, he went to London and to Paris with his life-long friend Dr (later Sir) Henry Littlejohn (q.v.). During his visit to Paris, he was to witness the street fighting during the revolution which was to result in the Second Republic. He made drawings of gunshot and sabre wounds, which Professor James Spence (q.v.) was later to use in his lectures on military surgery.

On the death of his father, he decided to pursue a career in dentistry and with his friends, Robert Nasmyth and Francis Imlach (q.v.), he was to form the nucleus of what was to become the Edinburgh Dental School. In Scotland in the mid-19th century there was no formal training available in dentistry and so prospective dentists had to travel to London. Smith was to give the first formal series of dental lectures in Scotland, entitled 'Physiology and Diseases of the Teeth', which he delivered in the College starting in 1856. The following year he was appointed Dentist to the Royal Public Dispensary.

He quickly appreciated the need for a dispensary devoted exclusively to the treatment of dental problems and, along with Robert Nasmyth and Francis Imlach, he opened the Edinburgh Dental Dispensary in Drummond Street, a few yards from the College, in 1860. As a result, he was able to achieve recognition that attendance at the Dental Dispensary should be recognised by the Royal College of Surgeons of England as part of the curriculum for the Diploma in Dental Surgery. For the first time, trainee dentists in Scotland did not have to incur the expense of travelling to London to gain training experience. The Dispensary expanded, moved to Cockburn Street and finally evolved into the Edinburgh Dental Hospital and School. Widely regarded as the father of this institution, he was also a principal moving force in the founding of the Royal Edinburgh Hospital for Sick Children. It was fitting that he became the first dental surgeon to the Children's Hospital and also to the Royal Infirmary. He was made Surgeon-Dentist to Queen Victoria in 1871.

John Smith (1825–1910).

Dental chair and equipment on display in the College Museum.

Throughout his life he was active in the College as a member of Council, going on to become President in 1883, and was awarded the honorary Doctorate of Laws from Edinburgh University on the occasion of its Tercentenary the following year. His national status was recognised by his election as President of the British Dental Association. Smith was a prodigious writer on many aspects of dental practice. In 1905 he wrote a brief history of the College to commemorate the Quatercentenary.

His literary contributions outside medicine and dentistry were even greater. He was a member of the Aesculapian Club, the Medico-Chirurgical Society and the Odonto-Chirurgical Society and was, perhaps, the most gifted writer of songs in the history of these societies. His literary expertise extended to writing pantomimes, three of which were professionally produced by his friend, Robert Wyndham, a member of the family which was to found the Howard and Wyndham group of theatres. In his latter years he was able to indulge his writing, painting and music.

Roll number: 451

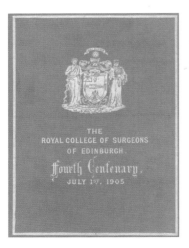

The history of the College, written by John Smith to mark the College's Quatercentenary.

Photographic portrait of John Smith.

Sir William Turner (1832–1916)

Presiding over the major reforms and modernisation of university curricula and administration in Britain at the start of the 20th century required a figure who would at the same time command respect and authority, and have the intellect to organise such a major task. Sir William Turner was widely regarded as the foremost British anatomist of the 19th century. As Principal and Vice Chancellor of Edinburgh University and Chairman of the General Medical Council, he presided over changes which were to underpin the strength of higher education, particularly medical education, in Britain.

William Turner was born in Lancaster, the son of a cabinet maker who died when he was five years old. After schooling, he was apprenticed to Dr Christopher Johnson, a highly respected local doctor, and it was this association that he was later to regard as being responsible for developing his scientific thinking. This apprenticeship included daily lectures and an evening of supervised experimentation in chemistry.

After this four-year apprenticeship he enrolled in 1850 as a medical student in St Bartholomew's Hospital, London, where he met the physiologist Dr (later Sir) James Paget, who at that time lectured on anatomy and physiology and who was to prove another major influence on his future life. His first meeting made an impression and he was later to write of Paget: 'the keen eager face, the bright penetrating eyes, his facility in speaking, his choice of language and the charm of his delivery presented the subject so as at once to attract and fix the attention of the large class of students. But in addition his pupils felt that he was interested in them as individuals. Many will recall and treasure the kindly look, the warm greeting, the affectionate shake of the hand which they received on meeting him.' Turner won several prizes in his undergraduate career and wrote scientific papers on the chemistry of the cerebro-spinal fluid and the therapeutic effects of potassium iodide, while still a student.

In 1854, John Goodsir (q.v.), the Professor of Anatomy at Edinburgh University, wrote to Paget asking him to recommend the names of young doctors who might be interested in demonstrator posts in Edinburgh. On Paget's recommendation Turner was appointed, and so began an association with Edinburgh which was to last for the rest of his life. The Edinburgh medical school at that time boasted many famous teachers. William Gregory (son of James Gregory, the Professor of Physic) held the Chair of Chemistry, and Goodsir was widely regarded as the greatest philosophical anatomist of his day. James Syme (q.v.) held the Chair of Surgery and James Young Simpson the Chair of Midwifery – the latter two famously at loggerheads. Turner was elected FRCSEd in 1861. Early in his Edinburgh days he befriended Joseph Lister (q.v.) and the friendship was to last for over sixty years. His early scientific work was on cellular pathology, then a novel concept but one which he was to develop in later life, culminating in his presidential address to the British Association in 1900.

Sir William Turner (1832–1916).

On Goodsir's death he applied for the Chair of Anatomy, supported by more than a hundred testimonials, including those from Paget, Lister, Syme and Simpson, and also from Oliver Wendell Holmes, at that time Professor of Anatomy in Harvard. During Turner's 36-year tenure of the Chair of Anatomy, he produced a series of papers on anthropology and in particular on craniology, a study of racial origins as defined by the anatomy of the skull. In this he corresponded with Charles Darwin, a former Edinburgh University student, whose theory of evolution he championed. Other exponents of the theory of evolution, like Huxley, came to rely on his expertise in craniology to support their ideas. He published over a hundred papers on comparative anatomy, over fifty on anthropology and some sixty on marine mammals. He was fascinated, as his predecessors Robert Knox (q.v.) and John Goodsir had been, by the anatomy of the whale. Other areas of interest included surface anatomy of the brain and the comparative anatomy of the placenta.

Yet it was perhaps as a medical politician and statesman that he made his most lasting contribution. As a member of the Edinburgh University Senate he was influential in fundraising for the new medical school in Teviot Place and the McEwan Hall. On the Medical Acts Commission he proved to be an influential voice in the framing of the Universities (Scotland) Act 1889, which devolved financial and administrative power to the universities and which resulted in a rationalisation of the medical degree granted by each of the universities.

The list of honours and distinctions which he achieved in his life attests to his stature. Elected to the Royal Society of Edinburgh in 1861, he became its President in 1908 in succession to Lord Kelvin. He was elected a Fellow of the Royal Society in 1877 and President of the College in 1882. He had helped found the Anatomical Society of Great Britain and Ireland and was appointed its President in 1892. In 1900 he was President of the British Association for the Advancement of Science. From 1898 to 1904 he was President of the General Medical Council. His son, Arthur Logan Turner (q.v.), a consultant otolaryngologist in Edinburgh, was to become a distinguished medical historian in his own right and, like his father, President of the College.

Roll number: 553

Sir William Turner. Etching by William Hole as one of a series to commemorate the Tercentenary of the University of Edinburgh in 1884.

Douglas Argyll Robertson (1837–1909)

The first lecturer in ophthalmology to be appointed by Edinburgh University, Douglas Argyll Robertson became an internationally known figure in his specialty. He pursued a career in ophthalmic surgery, which had hitherto been practised by general surgeons, of whom his father, John Argyll Robertson (q.v.), was one. In his twenties he instilled an extract of Calabar bean into his own eye and recorded the effects, which led to the introduction of physostigmine into ophthalmic practice, where it is widely used to this day. Shortly after this, he described the abnormal pupil reaction which won him world renown.

Douglas Moray Cooper Lamb Argyll Robertson was born in Edinburgh. After studying at Edinburgh University, at Prague and under Albrecht von Graefe in Berlin, he returned to work at the Edinburgh Eye Dispensary in Infirmary Street and the Royal Hospital for Sick Children. Robert Christison, Professor of Materia Medica, had described the systemic effects of chewing a fragment of Calabar bean, used for judicial execution in eastern Nigeria, and Dr (later Sir) Thomas R. Fraser, who isolated the active principle, drew Argyll Robertson's attention to its ability to constrict the pupil. In the company of two colleagues he instilled an extract, first in his left eye, and later at a higher concentration into both eyes, as a result of which he recommended the alkaloid physostigmine for reversing the action of atropine, used in fundoscopy since Hermann von Helmholtz's introduction of the ophthalmoscope in 1851. Physostigmine was only later used in the treatment of glaucoma.

Professor Hughes Bennett appointed him as a demonstrator in practical physiology at Edinburgh University (1865), the first such appointment in the country.

Having been admitted a member of the College, he became a Fellow in 1862 and later an examiner in ophthalmology. Having graduated MD from St Andrews University in 1857 after three days of examination, he published a paper entitled *Eye Symptoms in Spinal Disease* (1869), which described his eponymous pupil signs. Later that year he published more extensively, citing four cases, including his earlier one. He remarked that 'I could not observe any contraction of either pupil under the influence of light, but on accommodating the eyes for a near object, both pupils contracted.' The connection with neurosyphilis was not established until 1881, but in the absence of laboratory evidence the diagnosis rested on physical signs.

Among his 50 published communications he described the operation of trephining the sclera in the treatment of glaucoma and an operation for ectropion. He was deft in the operating theatre, being ambidextrous and myopic in the left eye, which enabled him to operate without spectacles. He had the habit of placing the operating knife between his lips during an operation, thus freeing his hands.

He benefited from an imposing personality and a strikingly handsome appearance. He would order the excessive smoker to throw away his pipe and give his tobacco to his bitterest enemy. He advised one parent to 'put the bread poultices in the child's stomach, never in the eye again unless ordered by a doctor'.

Douglas Argyll Robertson (1837–1909).

A photographic portrait of Douglas Argyll Robertson.

Although not a great public speaker or lecturer, he was an outstanding teacher at Surgeons' Hall, and his voluntary classes in the University were well attended as were his Sunday cliniques at the Royal Infirmary. Two volumes of notes taken at his lectures are held in the archives of the College.

His honours included Surgeon Oculist in Scotland to Queen Victoria, President of the College in 1886, President of the Ophthalmological Society of the United Kingdom and of the International Council for Ophthalmology, President of the section of ophthalmology of the British Medical Association in 1898, member of the Ophthalmological Society of Heidelberg, Corresponding Fellow of the New York Academy of Medicine, Foreign Associate of the Society of Practising Physicians of Prague and honorary member of the Neurological Society of New York. In 1896 he was awarded an honorary Doctorate of Laws from Edinburgh University.

He oversaw the transfer of the Department of Ophthalmology to the Royal Infirmary in Lauriston Place and after only a few years reported that the accommodation was inadequate.

His prowess at golf enhanced his surgical practice. He often told the tale that, early in his career, after a round of golf at St Andrews, he was approached by a spectator, who was looking for a surgeon to treat his daughter's strabismus. The father asked Robertson to perform the procedure, reasoning that the steadiness and surety of hand which he had displayed under stress on the golf course would enhance his surgical skills in the operating theatre.

He excelled at golf, competing at the Royal and Ancient Golf Club of St Andrews and the Honourable Company of Edinburgh Golfers with success, and was a skilled curler, angler and billiards player. He was also an active member of the Royal Company of Archers. He founded the Royal Colleges Golf Club, open to members of the Colleges of Physicians and Surgeons of Edinburgh, was the first captain, and presented a handsome gold medal for annual competition, winning it twice himself. He was also an art connoisseur, being an adjudicator for the Royal Scottish Academy.

Suffering from chronic respiratory disease in later life, he retired to Jersey in 1904, and it was from there that he travelled to India to visit the Thakur of Gondal, whom he had befriended while he studied to become a physician in Edinburgh. He had intended to proceed to Burma but took ill and died in Gondal. Unusually for a ruler, his host wore mourning and lit the funeral pyre when he was cremated on the banks of the river Gondli at a ceremony conducted by an Irish missionary.

Author: Geoffrey Millar

Roll number: 558

Douglas Argyll Robertson raising his top hat, pictured with Sir Thomas Clouston, lecturer on mental diseases (after whom the Thomas Cloustonclinic in Edinburgh is named). These etchings form part of a series by William Hole to commemorate the Tercentenary of the University of Edinburgh in 1884.

Joseph Bell (1837–1911)

Joseph Bell was the last in a famous Edinburgh surgical dynasty. His great-grandfather, grandfather and father before him had all been Fellows of the College and surgeons in Edinburgh. Like his father, he became President of the College; but it was his powers of observation, diagnostic acumen and the way he demonstrated these to medical students that were to bring him particular fame. One of these students, Arthur Conan Doyle, used him as the model for his famous fictional character Sherlock Holmes.

The Bells were a remarkable surgical family. Joseph was born in St Andrews Square, Edinburgh. His father, Benjamin Bell, was President of the College in 1863–4. His grandfather, also Joseph Bell, was a surgeon in Edinburgh while his great-grandfather, Benjamin Bell (q.v.), was the first of the dynasty. So for around 150 years a member of the Bell family practised surgery in Edinburgh – alternately named Benjamin and Joseph, as shown in the Bell family tree on page 57.

Joseph Bell was educated at the Edinburgh Academy, and entered Edinburgh University when he was 16, passing his final examinations before he was 21. Already described as 'keenly observant, methodical and thorough', he decided to pursue his surgical training in Edinburgh and became House Surgeon to James Syme (q.v.) and House Physician under John Gairdner (q.v.). He had impressed Syme with his graduation thesis *On Epithelial Cancer* and Syme was to become his hero and mentor. There followed two years as a demonstrator in anatomy under Professor Goodsir (q.v.) and it was here that he developed a reputation for powers of observation of meticulous detail, and outstanding ability as a teacher. He went on to lecture on systematic surgery in Surgeons' Square, attracting large classes who received his lectures with enthusiasm. But it was as a clinical teacher in the wards and clinics that Bell was in his element. His appointment as assistant to Syme in 1865 enhanced his prestige and security and allowed him to pursue two areas of interest which were to intrigue him for the rest of his life: handwriting analysis and dialectology (the science of placing a person's origin by accent and vocabulary). These were to prove valuable tools in his legendary diagnostic acumen and were to be exploited to the full by Conan Doyle, who based his fictional detective on Bell.

Arthur Conan Doyle was born in Edinburgh in 1859 at Picardy Place and enrolled in the medical school in 1876. His contemporaries at the University included J. M. Barrie and Robert Louis Stevenson, with whom he was to collaborate in later years, and his teachers in the medical school included Joseph Lister (q.v.) and James Young Simpson. Yet it was Joseph Bell who made the greatest impression on the young Conan Doyle. Bell selected him as his clerk, a patronage similar to that which Bell had received from Syme 20 years earlier. From here emerged the concept of Sherlock Holmes. Conan Doyle was later to write: 'I thought of my old teacher Joe Bell, of his eagle face, of his curious ways, and his eerie trick of spotting details. If he were a detective he would surely reduce this fascinating but disorganised business to something nearer an exact science.' Doyle sent the manuscript for *A Study in Scarlet* to Robert Louis Stevenson, by then an exile in Samoa. Stevenson, who had spent his early life in Edinbugh, wrote back to Conan Doyle in April 1893: 'I … offer my compliments on your very ingenious and very interesting adventures of Sherlock Holmes. Only one thing troubles me: can this be my old

Joseph Bell as a young surgeon.

Joseph Bell. A photograph in middle age. Upon hearing of the death of his son from appendicitis, his hair turned white over a matter of days.

Joseph Bell with his grandchildren.

Joseph Bell, Conan Doyle and Sherlock Holmes

The story of Joseph Bell, President of the College who was to inspire the young Arthur Conan Doyle to create the fictional detective Sherlock Holmes, is well known and is described briefly in Bell's biography here. The College has in its archive the letter to Bell from Conan Doyle in which he acknowledges Bell as his model. It has to be said that Joseph Bell did not at first appreciate his status as the inspiration for a fictional detective, but with the increasing success and popularity of the Sherlock Holmes novels, he came to enjoy and even revel in the unexpected status which resulted. It is said that his penchant for wearing an Inverness cape and a deer stalker hat in later years was in recognition of his famous literary creation.

friend Joe Bell?' In a now famous letter in the College archive, Conan Doyle wrote to Joseph Bell on 4 May 1892: '… it is most certainly to you that I owe Sherlock Holmes and although in the stories I have the advantage of being able to place him in all sorts of dramatic positions, I do not think that his analytical work is in the least an exaggeration of some of the effects which I have seen you produce in the out-patient ward'.

Dr Watson too was almost certainly based on Patrick Heron Watson (q.v.) – in Conan Doyle's time as a student simply Dr Watson, but later Sir Patrick Heron Watson, President of the College. Heron Watson had many of the attributes conferred on Holmes' Watson. He was a bronzed military man with a moustache, who had trained in the Crimea and was an expert in forensic medicine and on gunshot wounds. Among other contenders as the model for Watson was Sir Henry Littlejohn (q.v.).

It seems strange looking back that Bell's time-limited appointment to the Royal Infirmary ended when he was only 49 years old. He moved to what was effectively a second career at the Royal Hospital for Sick Children, located initially at Meadowside, and from 1892 in Sciennes Road. His protégé Francis Caird (q.v.), later to become Professor of Surgery, was to write of Bell's most outstanding qualities. He wrote of his punctuality, of the atmosphere of bonhomie and kindliness with which he surrounded his following of staff, students and patients. Caird regarded him as an excellent operator, dextrous, rapid and neat, but most of all he was impressed by his diagnostic acumen, his keen powers of observation, his skill in eliciting facts and his sense of humour. His association with the College was influential. He was Secretary and Treasurer for 11 years from 1876 and President from 1887 to 1889.

Bell left legacies in two other areas. His appointment as Surgeon in Charge in the Royal Infirmary in 1871 coincided with the introduction of the new system of nursing imported from St Thomas' Hospital in London. Throughout his life he maintained an interest in the continuing development of nursing care. He helped to establish the Royal Edinburgh Hospital for Incurables, later the Longmore Hospital, recognising the importance of the surgeon's duty of care to what was then an all-too-neglected group of patients.

Ironically, for one who inspired so much writing, he was not a prolific writer himself, but for 23 years was editor of the *Edinburgh Medical Journal* and his *Manual of the Operations of Surgery* (1866) enjoyed the success of seven editions during his lifetime.

In his later years he exchanged the horse and trap in which he did his rounds for one of the first motor cars in Edinburgh, enjoying long drives in the country from his beloved summer home in Mauricewood, near Penicuik.

Bell's legacy to Edinburgh surgery, to its College and to its hospitals is enormous. The emphasis on detailed observation, logical deduction and diagnosis, and on the importance of devoting time to teaching, formed the basis of the model by which the clinical teaching of the Edinburgh School of Surgery came to be judged. His early championing of Lister's carbolic spray helped to promote its widespread introduction.

Roll number: 560

Thomas Annandale (1838–1907)

To succeed Lord Lister (q.v.) as Professor of Surgery in Edinburgh would require a surgeon of exceptional talent and character. Thomas Annandale proved a worthy successor. An original thinker, he was a pioneer in the surgery of groin hernia, in the surgery of the knee and in intracranial surgery. His style in the operating theatre reflected his temperament – quiet, careful and courteous.

Born the son of a Newcastle surgeon, Thomas Annandale was one of the last to be apprenticed as a surgeon before beginning medical studies. After apprenticeship to his father, he graduated from Edinburgh University, obtaining a gold medal for his thesis on the injuries and diseases of the hip joint. This early success caught the eye of Professor James Syme (q.v.), who appointed him House Surgeon in 1860 and his private assistant the following year. Like so many aspiring surgeons of his era he demonstrated anatomy in Goodsir's (q.v.) department and at the same time began to lecture on systematic surgery in the extra-mural School of Medicine. In 1877 he was appointed to the Regius Chair of Clinical Surgery in Edinburgh in succession to Lord Lister.

By all accounts he was a natural surgeon, decisive, courageous and dextrous. On one famous occasion at a surgical congress in Philadelphia, as was the custom of the day, the visiting elite were presented with difficult cases and invited to operate. Sir William McCormack and Friedrich Esmarch declined the invitation to operate on a retropharyngeal tumour – Annandale accepted and performed the procedure successfully.

Annandale was a pioneer in the surgery of the knee joint, undoubtedly helped by the use of Listerian antisepsis. An account of his operation to remove loose bodies from the knee joint was published by his assistant Joseph Cotterill (q.v.) in 1869. This was followed by another innovative procedure: meniscectomy (the operation to remove torn medial semi-lunar cartilage from the knee joint). He was the first to perform this with a successful clinical outcome and the operation was to become a standard surgical procedure.

In May 1895 Annandale performed the first successful removal of an acoustic neuroma, a benign tumour arising from the auditory nerve within the skull. In the days before intracranial surgery was established this must have been a daunting, formidable task. In this he had the benefit of advances made by Sir Charles Bell (q.v.), who had described in detail the anatomy of the tumour from post-mortem dissections. The procedure also required a delicacy of surgical touch. His patient, pregnant at the time of the operation, did well, and delivered a healthy child six months later.

He had a further claim to fame as a pioneer of the preperitoneal approach to groin hernias. Lloyd Nyhus, in his history of the development of hernia repair, credits Annandale with the introduction of the preperitoneal approach in a paper published in the *Edinburgh Medical Journal* in 1876. He described and performed the high approach to femoral hernia before it was popularised by Georg Lotheissen, whose name is generally associated with the procedure.

Thomas Annandale. One of a series of etchings by William Hole on the occasion of the Tercentenary of the University of Edinburgh in 1884.

Thomas Annandale – a formal portrait wearing a favourite silk polka-dot cravat.

In the accompanying photograph he is wearing his favourite flowing polka-dot cravat, tied in a loose bow, emulating the style of his former mentor James Syme. While his work was characterised by an energetic bustling approach, his affability ensured widespread popularity. Logan Turner (q.v.) described him as 'a familiar figure in the streets of Edinburgh, saluted by policemen and by cabbies in the ranks, for all of whom he had a cheery greeting'.

His legacies in Edinburgh included the Annandale Gold Medal for the best undergraduate in clinical surgery, which is still awarded each year by the University of Edinburgh.

Roll number: 565

John Duncan (1839–99)

Easily recognised around Edinburgh because of a long flowing beard and his yellow dog-cart drawn by two high-stepping horses, John Duncan was a distinguished and distinctive Edinburgh surgeon. Unusually for a surgeon of his era, he was noted as a calm, precise and deliberate operator, characteristics which were allowed to flourish because of the advent of antiseptic surgery. As a colleague of Joseph Lister (q.v.), he was one of the earliest to practise and teach Listerian antisepsis.

John Duncan was born in Edinburgh the grandson of the founder of the firm Duncan Flockhart and Co., a well-known Edinburgh pharmaceutical firm from whom James Young Simpson was to buy the materials for his researches into anaesthesia. Duncan's father was a successful Edinburgh doctor who, at one time, had been Surgeon to the Royal Infirmary.

After studies at the Edinburgh High School, he graduated MA with honours from Edinburgh University, and gained his MD with distinction in 1862. For the next year he acted as House Surgeon to James Syme (q.v.) before going on to study for two years in the medical schools of Berlin, Vienna and Paris. He obtained the Fellowship of the College in 1864. On the death of his father, he inherited a large general practice but devoted himself increasingly to surgery. With his appointment as Surgeon to the Royal Infirmary he became established as a skilled surgeon, 'calm, precise and deliberate'. As a colleague of Lister in the Royal Infirmary he was an early protagonist of Listerian antisepsis and was one of the first to have a clerk in his wards to make Gram stains and to perform cultures. The outcomes of his surgical operations, at a time when abdominal surgery was in its infancy, were described as outstanding.

Duncan was among the first to practise autotransfusion of blood in 1886 by carefully collecting the blood spilled at leg amputation and transfusing it back via a femoral vein.

As a teacher too, he made an impression. Tall, bearded and distinguished, he was renowned for his patience, his consideration and his courtesy to students and younger colleagues. Besides all of this, he was a gifted sportsman, playing cricket for Scotland as a young man, an excellent shot throughout his life, a curler, a golfer and an angler.

He went on to become President of the College from 1889 to 1891.

Roll number: 587

John Duncan (1839–99).

John Rutherford Ryley (1837–84)

The speed with which the practice of Listerian antisepsis spread throughout the world owed much to the enthusiasm of those students and surgeons who had seen the benefits with their own eyes and become zealous converts to the new discipline. As an undergraduate at the University of Glasgow, John Ryley came under the influence of Joseph Lister (q.v.) and inspired by the results of Lister's innovation introduced antiseptic surgery to New Zealand.

John Rutherford Ryley was born in Ireland and studied medicine in Glasgow. He was one of the first students of Joseph Lister, who arrived as Professor of Surgery in Glasgow in 1860. Here he saw at first hand the remarkable results that Lister was able to achieve with antiseptic surgery, and was inspired. He qualified LRCSEd in 1862 and emigrated shortly thereafter to New Zealand, where he was appointed Surgeon Superintendent of the Hokitika Hospital, the principal town serving the Westland goldfields. Using Lister's antiseptic method on compound fractures in these gold mines in January 1868, Ryley published reports that year in three journals, including the *Australian Medical Journal* and *The Lancet*. The latter account was the first report from overseas published in that journal about the use of Listerian antisepsis. Ryley's more conventional method of communicating his experience with antiseptic practice is in contrast to that of Hogarth Pringle (q.v.) in Australia, who wrote up his first case report in the *Sydney Morning Herald*.

In May 1868 he returned to Scotland and was elected to the Fellowship of the College. Thereafter his life was characterised by a form of depressive illness and by a restlessness which resulted in much travelling around the world. In 1870 he was committed to the Auckland Lunatic Asylum. On discharge he moved to Fiji, where he set up in surgical practice, becoming Chief Coroner and Principal Officer of Health for Fiji the following year. From there he went to Australia, where he practised in four different towns. He then sailed for South Africa, where he was attached to a field hospital during the First Boer War. Returning to Sydney, he practised at four different locations. He died at the early age of 46 from an intentional overdose of morphine.

Roll number: 637

CARBOLIC ACID IN THE TREATMENT OF COMPOUND FRACTURES AND ABSCESSES.

By J. RUTHERFORD RYLEY, M.R.C.S.E.,
SURGEON-SUPERINTENDENT OF THE HOSPITAL, AND SURGEON TO THE GAOL AND LUNATIC ASYLUM, COUNTY OF WESTLAND, NEW ZEALAND.

THE readers of THE LANCET may be interested to know that Professor Lister's new method of treating compound fractures, &c., has already been tried on this side of the globe, and with a success which will, I think, ensure it a trial at the hands of every practitioner in these colonies who has the advancement of "conservative surgery" and the interests of his patients at heart. I studied under Professor Lister during the first two years of his teaching at the Royal Infirmary, Glasgow, and knew him to be a philosophic surgeon, and one whose researches on the nature of inflammation had already been attended with advantage to conservative surgery:

"Scire potestates herbarum usumque medendi
Maluit, et mutas agitare inglorius artes."

I, therefore, eagerly availed myself of a method of treatment which held out such prospects of success—all the more eagerly, inasmuch as the last two cases* of compound fracture treated by me in the hospital here terminated fatally.

Henry H——, aged thirty-two, miner, admitted Jan. 7th.

Ryley's 1868 paper in *The Lancet*.
(Although he styles himself MRCSE he did not receive this qualification from the College.)

John Chiene (1843–1923)

The establishment in Edinburgh of the first academic surgical research laboratory in the British Isles by Professor John Chiene is a notable landmark in the development of scientific surgery in Britain. In the words of Sir Harold Stiles (q.v.): 'Chiene set the example in the academic teaching of surgery of cultivating the subject as a science so that its art might be better taught and promoted ... I would not be occupying the Clinical Chair had it not been for the facilities which the laboratory afforded for carrying out investigations in surgical pathology.'

John Chiene, son of a chartered accountant, was born in Edinburgh and educated at the Edinburgh Academy, where he won prizes for mathematics and played both rugby football and cricket for the school. He entered the medical faculty of Edinburgh University in 1860 and interrupted his course with short periods of study in Paris, Berlin and Vienna before graduating MD with honours in 1865.

COLLEGIUM REGIUM CHIRURGORUM EDIN
MI

Meeting of Fellows, 1889

Meetings of the Fellows have always been a feature of College life. There has always been a strong tradition of portraiture and this group portrait was a departure from the traditional format.

Painted by H. A. Hay RSW, it depicts a meeting of the College in the Playfair Room. The case on the bottom left contains the papers for the meeting. These can also be seen spread across the table and floor. The painting shows a working meeting which suggests professional unity and informality. Nineteen of those in the group portrait have biographies included in this book.

To celebrate the Millennium, the College commissioned a contemporary photographic group portrait in the style of the 1889 meeting (see pages 8–9).

1. President Joseph Bell *
2. Vice President Douglas Argyll Robertson *
3. Robert J. Blair Cunynghame
4. Prof. John Struthers *
5. Henry Duncan Littlejohn *
6. David Wilson
7. John Duncan *
8. Patrick Heron Watson *
9. The Francis Brodie Imlach *
10. John Smith *
11. The James D. Gillespie
12. Prof. John Chiene *
13. Prof. Sir Douglas Maclagan *
14. Prof. Thomas Annandale *
15. Prof. Sir William Turner *
16. William Craig
17. Alexander Gordon Miller
18. James Ritchie
19. Francis Caddel
20. Prof. Sir George Husband

21. Johnson Symington
22. Charles Watson MacGillivray
23. James Dunsmure
24. George Mackay
25. Thomas D. Wilson
26. Andrew Somerville
27. John Macdonald Brown
28. W. T. Black, Surgeon Major
29. Henry Newcombe
30. Robert Mackenzie Johnston
31. David Wallace *
32. Edward M'Callum
33. Matthew James Turnbull.
34. Robert Lawson Tait *
35. Stewart Stirling
36. Harold Jalland Stiles *
37. William Booth
38. George Mackay
39. James Maxwell Ross
40. James D. Johnston

41. Peter H. Maclaren
42. Francis M. Caird *
43. Joseph Montagu Cotterill *
44. Robert Alexander Lundie
45. John Shaw M'Laren
46. Henry Alexis Thomson *
47. George Dickson
48. George Hunter
49. James William Beeman Hodsdon
50. Russel Elliott Wood
51. Charles. W. Cathcart *
52. Andrew Semple
53. Robert Henry Blaikie
54. James Hutcheson
55. Charles H. Thatcher
56. James Robertson, Solicitor
57. James Hamilton, Officer

* Biography included

After a year as House Surgeon to Professor James Syme (q.v.) in the old Royal Infirmary, Chiene became a demonstrator of anatomy under Professor John Goodsir (q.v.) and later under Professor Sir William Turner (q.v.).

In 1867 Chiene became a Fellow of the College and three years later he was appointed Lecturer in Surgery at the extra-mural medical school, where he laid the foundations of his later fame as a teacher. In 1871 he became Assistant Surgeon to the Royal Infirmary and was promoted Surgeon in Ordinary eight years later. Joseph Lister (q.v.) had returned from Glasgow to Edinburgh in 1869 as Regius Professor of Clinical Surgery in succession to James Syme and Chiene was already one of his most ardent disciples. Over the next eight years they were closely associated professionally and they developed a warm personal friendship which continued after Lister's move to London in 1878. During these years Chiene published a number of papers in which he vigorously supported and promoted Lister's scientific doctrine and he also produced in bound form his *Lectures on Surgical Anatomy* (1878), which became a popular text.

John Chiene (1843–1923).

His growing reputation as an inspiring teacher was a major factor in his appointment in 1882 to the University Chair of Systematic Surgery in succession to Professor James Spence (q.v.). As Professor, his fame as a teacher acquired an international dimension and Dr Will Mayo, after one of his visits to Europe, expressed the opinion that Chiene was the best clinical lecturer in the British Isles.

Many of John Chiene's students went on to achieve high distinction in surgery and perhaps the most notable was Sir Harold Stiles (q.v.), whose affectionate obituary memoir of him in the *British Medical Journal* is a moving tribute of a pupil to his revered teacher and exemplar.

Professor Chiene was not a rapid or spectacular operator, nor would he have ever wished to be so regarded, but his technique was meticulous and every operation was, for him, a carefully planned exercise in applied anatomy. He considered the teaching of the science and art of surgery, with the objective of making his students efficient for general practice, to be his life's chief purpose. However, his most remarkable achievement was the establishment within his academic department of a research laboratory, to which he gave substantial financial support. Bacteriological and pathological research formed the greater part of the laboratory's activity and throughout his 27-year tenure of the Chair of Surgery, John Chiene actively encouraged his assistants to pursue the scientific investigation of clinical problems.

During the Boer War (1899–1902) the British army's medical services became seriously overextended and required the support of a number of civilian-staffed field hospitals. Professor Chiene was largely responsible for the organisation of the Edinburgh field hospital and in 1900 went to South Africa as its senior surgeon. He was appointed Consulting Surgeon to the

Field Force and, in addition to being mentioned in dispatches, his distinguished military service was recognised in 1902 by his appointment as a Companion of the Order of the Bath (CB).

John Chiene was elected a Fellow of the Royal Society of Edinburgh in 1874 and was President of the College from 1897 to 1899; many other honours were bestowed upon him, including honorary doctorates from three British universities and honorary Fellowship of three foreign surgical associations. He was not a prolific writer but his book of reminiscences entitled *Looking Back*, published privately in 1907, is a valuable memoir of a bygone surgical era and contains many fascinating vignettes of the great Edinburgh medical personalities of the latter half of the 19th century.

Throughout his life, John Chiene was an enthusiastic sportsman and such was his prowess at rugby football in his younger days that when the Scottish Rugby Union was formed in 1873, he was elected its first President. He was a keen and skilful golfer and curler and he presented the handsome golfing and curling trophies for which teams from the two Edinburgh Royal Colleges compete annually.

John Chiene was held in the highest esteem and affection by his students, his colleagues and, above all, by his patients, whom he helped as much by his kindliness and compassion as by his surgical skill. In every aspect of his life he most worthily earned the nickname 'Honest John', by which he was known far and wide throughout his career.

Roll number: 638

John Chiene.

Robert Lawson Tait (1845–99)

Abdominal operations became part of regular surgical practice in the last quarter of the 19th century. The advent of antisepsis and anaesthesia allowed surgeons to operate on abdominal organs. The operations of ovariectomy and appendicectomy were among the first to be introduced and Robert Lawson Tait was a pioneer of both of these. He was the first to operate successfully for ruptured tubal pregnancy and almost certainly the first surgeon in the world to diagnose and remove successfully an acutely inflamed appendix. Because of his public criticism of Joseph Lister (q.v.) and antiseptic surgery, his championing of the anti-vivisection movement and his death at a relatively early age, he did not receive the recognition or honours in life which he undoubtedly deserved.

Robert Lawson Tait was born in Edinburgh and educated at George Heriot's School and the Edinburgh medical faculty before continuing his education in the extra-mural School of Medicine. As a student he came to work closely with James Young Simpson, the Professor of Midwifery. Simpson was to promote Tait's early career, they later were to became friends and Tait remained an admirer and disciple of Simpson throughout his life. After graduation, Tait became House Surgeon in Wakefield, Yorkshire, where he was able to put into practice the training he had received in the use of chloroform from Simpson and in surgical techniques from James Syme (q.v.). He was elected FRCSEd in 1870 and FRCSEng the following year.

Robert Lawson Tait in a characteristic pose.

Robert Lawson Tait (1845–99).

Yet in his growing surgical practice in Wakefield, he, like Simpson, rejected the principles of antisepsis, which had recently been published by Lister. Moving to Birmingham, he became Surgeon to the Birmingham and Midlands Hospital for Women and Surgeon for the diseases of women to the West Bromwich Hospital. He made his mark as a bold surgeon, an aggressive debater in the British Medical Association and a prolific writer, many of his letters being openly critical of other surgeons.

He took up the operation of ovariectomy, which had been developed by Spencer Wells in London and by Thomas Keith (q.v.) in Edinburgh. Tait's contribution was to introduce the method of simple ligation of the pedicle. He went on to make an even more original contribution in the diagnosis and management of ectopic pregnancy. By describing the diagnostic features, advocating the need for early operation and the use of appropriate ligation, he ensured the safe introduction of this procedure into surgical practice.

Despite his appointment to a hospital for women, he made important advances in abdominal gastrointestinal surgery. W. J. Mayo was to write: 'the cavities of the body were a sealed book until the father of modern abdominal surgery, Lawson Tait, carried the sense of sight into the abdomen'. Although not the first to perform cholecystostomy, he was the first surgeon to perform this successfully in Britain. His contribution to the understanding and treatment of acute appendicitis was arguably even greater. In 1880 he made the diagnosis of peritonitis due to rupture of the appendix and successfully removed a gangrenous appendix. He went on to advocate exploratory laparotomy for abdominal pain suggestive of appendicitis, a radical proposal at the time and one which made enemies for him among the advocates of a conservative approach. Tait made further enemies by his vehement criticism of Lister and Listerian antisepsis. He also espoused two unpopular causes which were to become much more popular with the passage of time. First, he became a disciple of Charles Darwin. In lengthy correspondence he showed both his appreciation of the theory of evolution and made contributions to the detail from his knowledge of human anatomy. His friendship with Darwin and the lectures which he gave on evolution to local and national audiences inevitably won him enemies. Second, he was a prominent anti-vivisectionist, which resulted in some bitter quarrels with influential doctors.

When a much-publicised lawsuit was brought against him by a general practitioner and further action threatened over his alleged seduction of a nurse, his reputation was tarnished. At the age of 48 he resigned as Surgeon to the Women's Hospital, his private practice declined, his writings diminished and he died at the age of 54.

Roll number: 659

George Hogarth Pringle (1830–72)

The spread of Listerian antisepsis progressed at a different pace in different parts of the world. In Australia, it was accepted quickly into surgical practice through a series of fortunate events. George Pringle, who had been a house surgeon along with Joseph Lister (q.v.) in Edinburgh Royal Infirmary, used the technique to dramatic effect and published the case report in the *Sydney Morning Herald*.

George Hogarth Pringle was born at Hyndlee, near Hawick. After studying at Edinburgh University, he was House Surgeon in the Royal Infirmary in 1854. His contemporaries at that time included Joseph Lister and Patrick Heron Watson (q.v.), famously depicted in the photograph of the residents taken in 1854 (see page 118). He then became a surgeon in the Crimean War, caring for the sick and wounded being transferred from the battlefield to the Scutari base hospital. Thereafter, he worked as a ship's surgeon on Cunard liners and latterly on the P&O company ships between Suez and Sydney, Australia. He settled in Parramatta, New South Wales, in 1860.

George Hogarth Pringle (1830–72).

In 1868 in a letter to the *Sydney Morning Herald*, he described the first use of Listerian antisepsis in Australia: 'I crave, in default of any local medical journal, space in your columns for a brief history of [this case], deeming it a duty to communicate as speedily as possible the results so far, of a novel mode of procedure, which promises to revolutionise our ideas of that *bête noir* of surgical practice, a compound comminuted fracture.' His patient, out shooting wallaby, had accidentally fired his shotgun through the left forearm above the wrist smashing both radius and ulna and fragmenting the soft tissues. He went on: 'I recommended immediate amputation, more especially having the dread of secondary haemorrhage and lockjaw before my eyes; but neither the patient nor his relatives would consent to this and begged for me to try and save the limb. I, therefore, duly warning them of the manifold risks, resolved to try Professor Lister's plan.' Having dressed this compound comminuted fracture with carbolic acid, he was gratified by the results. 'On the 34th day from the receipt of the injury, I found that the whole wound is completely healed up, thus converting a compound into a simple fracture. No pus whatever has appeared … firm union has taken place between the ends of the ulna and satisfactory progress made with the radius, perfect motion and sensibility retained in the hand.' He concluded, 'such are the outstanding results of this method of treatment in the first case to which I have applied it. And be it remembered this is no quack remedy, but the results of patient, scientific enquiry and thought on the part of that philosophical investigator, Joseph Lister.' Publication of a detailed case report in a national newspaper inevitably led to some criticism, but it seems likely that this was widely read by Australian doctors and led to the extensive introduction of antisepsis into Australian medical practice. Pringle's suggestion that there was no local medical journal was not entirely fair as the *Australian Medical Journal* was founded in 1856.

Pringle went on to write further case reports, mainly on antiseptic surgery but also on the radical cure of hernia. He obtained the Fellowship of the College in 1870. At the age of 41 he developed dysentery and died on board a ship taking him back to Britain.

His son, James Hogarth Pringle, returned to Scotland, and after graduating in medicine from Edinburgh University became a surgeon at Glasgow Royal Infirmary. Among the many contributions which he made to surgical practice were the 'Pringle manoeuvre' of compression of the portal triad to reduce hepatic bleeding following trauma and the use of autogenous veins as arterial grafts.

Roll number: 660

Sir John Halliday Croom (1847–1923).

Sir John Halliday Croom (1847–1923)

Many innovations in obstetrics in the 19th and 20th centuries originated in Scotland, the introduction of chloroform anaesthesia by Sir James Young Simpson and the introduction of diagnostic ultrasound into clinical practice by Professor Ian Donald being two of the most famous examples. Other obstetricians made their mark through the brilliance of their teaching, but none more so than John Halliday Croom. Croom's natural eloquence endeared him to the undergraduate and postgraduate students of the Edinburgh medical school in much the same way as Joseph Lister (q.v.) had been revered as a teacher 20–30 years previously. Contemporaries regarded him as the best teacher of his generation in the Edinburgh medical school.

John Halliday Croom was born in Sanquhar, Dumfriesshire, where his father was the United Presbyterian minister and, throughout his life, Croom was to remain deeply committed to that faith. When the family moved to Edinburgh he went to the Royal High School and studied medicine at Edinburgh University. After graduation, he travelled to London and Paris for postgraduate study and then became a general practitioner, finally establishing his practice in Charlotte Square. In later life he was to look back on his time in general practice as a particularly valuable experience.

As an undergraduate he had been inspired by James Syme (q.v.) and Sir James Young Simpson and increasingly he devoted himself to surgery and particularly to obstetrics and gynaecology. He received the FRCSEd in 1873. With the departure of Dr Thomas Keith (q.v.) to London, his practice in the latter two disciplines grew rapidly. Professor (later Sir) Alexander Simpson, who had been appointed to the Chair of Midwifery and Gynaecology in the University, appointed him as his assistant and this gave him the opportunity to begin lecturing in the extra-mural school in Minto House in Chambers Street. He instantly established himself as a brilliant lecturer and teacher, and for the next 25 years, until his appointment as Professor, his lectures on obstetrics and gynaecology were packed.

Croom's skills as a teacher were so outstanding in the Edinburgh medical school that several of his contemporaries and pupils analysed the qualities which made him so successful. His preparation was painstaking. He would write out each lecture in full on the right side of the page and on the left side would write a few key words so that his lectures always appeared spontaneous. Whenever he lectured he changed into a black swallow-tailed coat and, wearing this, the suave, courteous and sensitive physician became an animated, enthusiastic orator. His lectures were laced with humour, with trenchant aphorisms and with teaching points which would be remembered for life. A visiting American postgraduate who attended a lecture on extra-uterine pregnancy was asked about the lecture. 'I guess,' he replied, 'he makes you feel that the welfare of your mortal soul depends on your knowledge of extra-uterine pregnancy.' At the end of each lecture John Croom appeared physically drained yet mentally exhilarated.

In 1905 when Sir Alexander Simpson retired, Croom succeeded him as Professor of Midwifery in the University. The papers which he wrote throughout his life were devoted to clinical and practical topics, rather than to research. His book *Minor Gynaecological Operations and Applications for the Use of Students* (1879) ran to several editions both in Britain and America, and it gave him particular pleasure to hear that a synopsis of his systematic lectures had been translated into Chinese.

His work was recognised with many honours. He was President of the British Gynaecological Society and an honorary Fellow of the American and Belgian Societies. During his presidency of the Royal College of Surgeons of Edinburgh he was knighted. Dublin University conferred an honorary MD and Edinburgh University an honorary Doctor of Laws (LLD). He was made a Fellow of the Royal Society of Edinburgh.

Later in his career he became the first Chairman of the Central Midwives Board, the body responsible for the training, assessment and certification of midwives in Scotland, and was influential in the movement which led to the passage of the Midwives Act for Scotland.

Contemporaries write of his courtesy, his charm and his sensitivity, which perhaps originated in his deeply held religious beliefs. He retired in 1921 and for the first time in 50 years was no longer teaching. It seemed, wrote a contemporary, as though his major motivating force had expired, and he died within two years of retiral.

Roll number: 725

Sir John Halliday Croom.

Sir Montagu Cotterill (1851–1933).

Sir Joseph Montagu Cotterill (1851–1933)

Many surgeons have distinguished themselves as sportsmen, some at the highest level. Sir Montagu Cotterill was able to combine his sporting prowess with a successful career in surgery. An all-round sportsman, he was to become an early exponent of neurosurgery and President of the Royal College of Surgeons of Edinburgh.

Joseph Montagu Cotterill was educated at Grahamstown, South Africa, and later Brighton College in Sussex. His father was appointed Bishop of Edinburgh in 1871 and Montagu Cotterill had a distinguished medical undergraduate career in Edinburgh University winning prizes in surgery and pathology. He became House Surgeon to Professor Thomas Annandale (q.v.) in the final years of the old Royal Infirmary in Infirmary Street. After a period as Surgical Tutor under Annandale, he became Surgeon to the Royal Infirmary and obtained the FRCSEd in 1878. Regarded as a neat and rapid surgeon rather than an innovator, he was one of the early exponents of neurosurgery in Edinburgh, working in association with the famous medical neurologist Sir Byrom Bramwell. With the outbreak of the First World War, he was appointed Senior Surgeon to the Second Scottish Territorial General Hospital situated in Craigleith Hospital, later the Western General Hospital.

Arguably his prowess as a sportsman eclipsed his fame as a surgeon. From his earliest days he had shown a natural aptitude for ball games. In Sussex he had played cricket for the county from the age of 18 and was selected to play for the Gentlemen against the Players. He frequently batted alongside, Dr W. G. Grace, and was regarded by some contemporaries as second only to him as a batsman. During his time in Edinburgh, he was a stalwart of the Grange Cricket Club. He was captain of rugby at Edinburgh University and was skilled at golf, billiards and an excellent shot.

He was President of the College from 1907 to 1909 and was knighted in 1919.

In later years he became an enthusiastic motorcyclist and at the age of 70 was involved in an accident which resulted in a depressed skull fracture requiring elevation. With the robust constitution of a sportsman, he made a complete recovery, dying peacefully at home in his 83rd year.

Roll number: 856

Sir Thomas Chavasse (1854–1913)

There could be few better ways to start a surgical career than to learn at first hand about antiseptic surgery from Joseph Lister (q.v.), about abdominal surgery from Theodor Billroth in Vienna, and about orthopaedic surgery in Berlin from Bernard von Langenbeck, doyen of German scientific surgery. Thomas Chavasse was fortunate to learn in person, early in his career, from each of these three great masters.

Thomas Frederick Chavasse was born in Birmingham, where his father was a surgeon. As an undergraduate at Edinburgh University he was taught by Lister and learned at first hand the value of antiseptic techniques in surgery. After graduation he spent six months in Vienna attending the clinic of Theodor Billroth, who, at that time, was pioneering the surgery of the abdomen. Billroth's clinic attracted young surgeons from all over Europe and among Chavasse's contemporaries there was Dr (later Sir) George Andreas Berry (q.v.). From Vienna he moved to Berlin, where he studied under Bernard von Langenbeck, the surgeon credited with establishing scientific surgery in Germany. Whilst at that time all surgeons were general surgeons, von Langenbeck was developing particular expertise in orthopaedic procedures.

Chavasse returned to Edinburgh, becoming House Surgeon to Professor James Spence (q.v.) in the old Royal Infirmary. Spence was resolutely opposed to the practice of antiseptic surgery, which meant that Chavasse had to be diplomatic about his enthusiasm for Listerian antisepsis. He was able to do so, without offending his chief, by regularly attending Lister's Sunday afternoon clinic.

In 1877 he applied for the post of Assistant Surgeon in Birmingham. This required a Fellowship from one of the surgical Colleges. Although Chavasse had qualified for the FRCSEd he could not obtain the diploma as he had not reached the statutory age of 25. The College suspended its bylaw to enable Chavasse to receive the diploma and he was appointed to the post. He never forgot what he regarded as a great act of kindness by the College. Twenty-one years later he wrote to the then President, Sir Patrick Heron Watson (q.v.), who had been re-elected President for a second time to preside over the Quatercentenary celebrations. Chavasse wrote: 'I was looking today at my Diploma of Fellowship of your College and find it bears your honoured name as President … My indebtedness to the College is very great and I would like to celebrate my majority by a small gift to its funds.' He enclosed a cheque which the College used to buy the Chavasse cup, which remains in the College to this day.

Chavasse went on to become Honorary Surgeon to the Birmingham General Hospital, a post which he held for the next 30 years. He exerted a powerful influence in the rebuilding of the hospital and was able to encourage endowments from wealthy friends and relatives.

Chavasse became President of the Midland Medical Society, of the Birmingham branch of the British Medical Association and President of the Birmingham Medical Institute. At the meeting of the BMA in Birmingham in 1911 he was President of the section of surgery. In later life he became an active supporter of the Red Cross Society and the St John's Ambulance Brigade. He was knighted in 1905.

The Chavasse Cup.

Sir Thomas Chavasse (1854–1913).

(His nephew, Captain Noel Chavasse, VC and bar, MC, RAMC, medical officer with the 10th (Liverpool Scottish) Battalion of the King's (Liverpool) Regiment achieved immortal fame as one of the only three men to win the bar to the VC during the First World War. He was killed on active service at the Battle of Passchendaele in 1917.)

Sir Thomas Chavasse died from a pulmonary embolus following a leg fracture sustained during a riding accident.

Roll number: 863

James Rutherford Morison (1853–1939)

Many of Lister's pupils went on to achieve distinction in their own right. James Rutherford Morison learned diagnostic skills at first hand from Joseph Bell (q.v.), antiseptic technique from Joseph Lister (q.v.) and abdominal surgery from Theodor Billroth. He put that training to excellent use in his subsequent career. At least two eponyms are used in current surgical practice – Rutherford Morison's incision and Morison's pouch are still referred to as such by surgeons throughout the English-speaking world.

James Rutherford Morison was born at Hutton Henry, County Durham. His father, Dr John Morison, who had obtained the LRCPEd and MD Aberdeen, was a colliery surgeon. James studied medicine at Mason's College in Birmingham before graduating from Edinburgh University in 1874. He had been selected as a dresser to Joseph Lister and House Surgeon to Patrick Heron Watson (q.v.), early contacts which were to be hugely influential. Heron Watson was bold and skilful in the operating theatre but was opposed to Lister's 'new fangled methods' of antisepsis. Morison would later recall how he would walk the diplomatic tightrope of spending as much time as he could observing the results of antiseptic surgery in Lister's ward without appearing disloyal to his own chief.

On his father's early death he took on the financial support of his family. This meant going into general practice in Hartlepool, where he soon became Physician to the local hospital. His urge to become a surgeon was so strong that here, despite his appointment as a physician, he performed most of the surgery at the hospital and was able to pass the FRCSEd in 1879. A visit to Billroth in Vienna was also to prove hugely influential and shortly after this he was appointed Assistant Surgeon to the Royal Infirmary, Newcastle, becoming one of its first specialist surgeons.

It was first and foremost as a teacher that he acquired a reputation and he clearly inspired many undergraduate and postgraduate students who remained fiercely loyal to him throughout his life and he maintained regular correspondence with many of them. These former students would describe him as a born teacher and as an astute diagnostician, whose early skills had been honed in Edinburgh by the lectures of Joseph Bell.

In many areas of surgery he was a pioneer. He was among the first to use a sigmoidoscope; he was a pioneer of suturing of the patella for fracture and an early exponent of Annandale's operation of medial meniscectomy for torn semi-lunar cartilage of the knee joint. It was his description of the hepato-renal recess, the space between the under surface of the liver and the upper pole of the right kidney, that was to bring lasting eponymous fame. His penchant for wide exposure led to the description of the muscle-cutting incision for appendicectomy which bore his name.

James Rutherford Morison (1853–1939).

He was a diligent writer and, through his publications, his reputation spread so that his clinic became one which overseas surgeons increasingly visited. He was appointed Professor of Surgery in Newcastle in 1910, a position which he held for the next 11 years.

In 1916 his work at the Northumberland War Hospital at Gosforth inspired his introduction of BIPP (Bismuth Iodoform Paraffin Paste). Bandages soaked in BIPP were used to aid the primary healing of compound fractures and of contaminated wounds and represented a significant advance in antiseptic surgery. The technique became widely used and known throughout the world as 'Morison's method'. It is a tribute to the efficacy of this simple, effective and ingenious preparation that it was still in use in the UK at the end of the 20th century.

He retired to St Boswells, where he became an active farmer in retirement, and was buried there, within sight of his beloved Eildon Hills.

Roll number: 884

Charles Cathcart (1853–1932)

Since the office was instituted in 1826, there have been 21 Conservators of the College Museum, most of whom made their own distinctive contributions to its development, but few more significant than those of Charles Cathcart, who was Conservator from 1887 to 1900.

The sixth, seventh and eighth decades of the 19th century were for the Museum a period of stagnation, but Cathcart's energy, enthusiasm and intellectual vigour revitalised it and brought about its transformation into one of the College's most important educational assets.

Charles Walker Cathcart was educated at Loretto School, where he was captain of the school rugby XV, and at Edinburgh University, from which he graduated MA in 1873 and MB CM in 1878. As a student, he played rugby for the University and three times for Scotland against England in 1872, 1873 and 1876. He was also a notable track athlete and a skilful boxer.

Having held junior posts in the old Royal Infirmary of Edinburgh in its last years, he became a Fellow of the Royal College of Surgeons of England and of Edinburgh in 1879 and 1880, respectively.

From 1881 to 1885 he taught anatomy at the extra-mural School of Medicine at Surgeons' Hall, where, after his appointment to the 'new' Royal Infirmary as Assistant Surgeon in 1884, he also lectured in surgery. The College awarded him the Liston Victoria Jubilee Prize in 1893, and in 1900 he was appointed Surgeon-in-Ordinary to the Royal Infirmary with charge of wards.

Cathcart was an excellent teacher and together with his friend and colleague, Francis M. Caird (q.v.), he wrote the famous *Surgical Handbook*, which first appeared in 1889. The clarity of this admirable practical guide to the care of surgical patients, together with its convenient pocket size, ensured its popularity with medical students and junior doctors throughout the British Isles and over the next 18 years, 'Caird and Cathcart' passed through 13 further editions.

C. W. Cathcart (1853–1932).

The Scottish Rugby Union XV, 1873.

Cathcart had a considerable mechanical flair and designed a number of ingenious surgical appliances; the most notable was a simple microtome for immediate frozen section histopathology, an innovation which was to become routine in surgical practice. Cathcart's was one of the first instruments of its type.

During the First World War, he held the rank of Lieutenant Colonel in the Royal Army Medical Corps, but he was not posted overseas. His distinguished service as Consulting Surgeon to military hospitals in the Edinburgh area was recognised at the end of the war by his appointment as Commander of the Order of the British Empire (CBE), but no honour could, in any way, mitigate the personal tragedy of the death in action of his only son.

Charles Cathcart was Conservator of the College Museum from 1887 to 1900 and then Chairman of its Curators for the next 32 years. It would be impossible to exaggerate the importance of his contributions to the Museum.

Among his most important achievements were the establishment of a comprehensive histopathological collection, the addition of more than 1,000 specimens to the Museum and the expansion of its accommodation, which took place in stages between 1894 and 1908.

His greatest contribution was, however, the production of a completely new museum catalogue in which all specimens were reclassified on a strict pathological basis. This immeasurably increased the Museum's educational value and its potential usefulness to both research workers and to surgical historians.

The major changes to the Museum which have taken place in the last two decades of the 20th century in no way diminish the value or importance of Charles Cathcart's successful conservancy, which entitles him to an honoured place among the greatest names in the history of the College.

Roll number: 915

Francis Mitchell Caird (1853–1926)

In an era before evidence-based medicine, any innovation, particularly in surgery, tended to be viewed with suspicion and often hostility. Listerian antisepsis was no exception. Active promotion by a cohort of Joseph Lister's (q.v.) enthusiastic disciples was to a large extent responsible for its dissemination throughout the surgical world. Francis Caird, Regius Professor of Clinical Surgery in the University of Edinburgh and President of the College, had as an undergraduate served as a dresser on Lord Lister's wards. He went on to become an early and life-long advocate and teacher of Listerian antisepsis and later of asepsis.

Francis Mitchell Caird was born in Edinburgh and educated at the Royal High School of Edinburgh, where he received a medal for botany. Botany was to remain an enduring interest and on leaving school he became apprentice to a seed merchant. He went on to become an assistant in the botany department of the University and from there he became a medical undergraduate. During this time he served as a dresser and a clerk in the wards of Joseph Lister and this experience was to have a major influence on his future career and life's work. He became an early disciple of Listerian antisepsis, which he was to practise and promote throughout his working life, moving on to the techniques of aseptic surgery when these emerged as superior.

After a resident post in the Edinburgh Royal Infirmary under John Chiene (q.v.), he was elected to the Fellowship of the College in 1880. Thereafter in what was to become the first of a series of regular visits to continental centres, he went to Strasbourg, where he studied under Friedrich von Recklinghausen. After demonstrating in anatomy for three years in the extra-mural medical school, he became Surgeon to the Royal Infirmary.

On the death of Professor Annandale in 1907 he was appointed to the Regius Chair of Clinical Surgery in Edinburgh. His use of rigorous aseptic technique and earlier visits to continental surgeons such as Jan Miculicz-Radecki in Breslau and Theodor Billroth in Vienna gave him the stimulus and the confidence to allow him to pioneer successfully intestinal surgery in Scotland. He was one of the first exponents of major gastrointestinal resections in Scotland, his work extending throughout the gastrointestinal tract. His repertoire included, for example, techniques of excision of the tongue for carcinoma, closure of perforated gastric and duodenal ulcers, excision of the small bowel for tuberculous stricture and excision of the rectum for carcinoma, the latter performed under spinal anaesthesia.

His gift for drawing and painting was used to great effect in his teaching and in the *Surgical Handbook* (1889), which he wrote in collaboration with C. W. Cathcart (q.v.). This was to enjoy several editions and become a standard text.

Caird was awarded the Liston Victoria Jubilee Prize by the College in 1901 'for the greatest benefit done to practical surgery by any Fellow or Licentiate of the College' in the preceding four years. He was elected President of the College in 1912 and received the honorary degree of Doctor of Laws (LLD) from Edinburgh University in 1920. His knowledge of and enthusiasm for botany stayed with him throughout his life and he became President of the Botanical Society.

His name is perpetuated by the Francis Mitchell Caird Prize, which is awarded for the best essay on surgery or surgical pathology by a medical graduate of Edinburgh University.

Roll number: 917

Francis Mitchell Caird (1853–1926).

Sir George Andreas Berry (1853–1940).

Sir George Andreas Berry. A presidential portrait.

Sir George Andreas Berry (1853–1940)

Sir George Andreas Berry, an ophthalmologist in Edinburgh, was recognised as an international authority at an early stage in his professional career. His textbook became a standard work in many countries and he went on to become President of the College, Surgeon Oculist to the King in Scotland and Member of Parliament for the Scottish Universities.

George Andreas Berry was born in Leith, where his father, Walter Berry, was the Danish Consul. He was educated at Marlborough and after graduating MB CM from Edinburgh University in 1876, he devoted himself to the specialty of ophthalmology. He was fortunate to be able to work in Copenhagen with his distinguished uncle, Professor Hansen Grut, the first Professor of Ophthalmology in Denmark, who was later to become Bowman Lecturer of the Ophthalmic Society, and with Jannik Bjerrum, his assistant and subsequent successor. As a young doctor, Berry also studied in France, Germany, Austria and Holland and worked as Resident House Surgeon at Moorfields Eye Hospital, before becoming FRCSEd in 1881. This exposure to European ophthalmic practice allowed him to become a recognised authority in ophthalmology at a remarkably early age.

His textbook *Diseases of the Eye: A Practical Treatise for Students of Ophthalmology* (1889) enhanced his reputation in continental Europe and America. The book was dedicated to Professor Grut and the warmth of the dedication illustrates Berry's qualities of enthusiasm, dedication and loyalty. It became a standard work throughout the English-speaking world for many years.

For over twenty years he practised as Surgeon to the eye department of the Edinburgh Royal Infirmary. His later career was recognised by many honours. A founder member of the the Ophthalmological Society of the United Kingdom, he went on to become its President. Following in the footsteps of his distinguished uncle, he was elected the Bowman Lecturer, the highest accolade offered by the Society. At that time the British Medical Association was an academic as well as a political organisation and Berry became Vice President of the section of ophthalmology and President in 1905. He was elected to the Royal Society of Edinburgh, the Royal Academy of Medicine of Ireland and a member of the Court of Edinburgh University. He became President of the College from 1910 to 1912, and was Honorary Surgeon Oculist to the King in Scotland, serving both Edward VII and George V. In 1916 he received the accolade of knighthood. From 1922 he served as Member of Parliament for the Scottish Universities and on retiral from this position in 1931 was awarded the honorary degree of LLD by Edinburgh University.

He possessed many gifts, including an expertise in mathematics and fluency in several European languages. A gifted cellist, he was influential in the founding of the Reid School of Music in Edinburgh University.

Roll number: 990

Sir James Dundas-Grant (1854–1944)

A prolific writer, and an inventor of surgical instruments and procedures, James Dundas-Grant was an ear, nose and throat surgeon regarded as one of the personalities of London medical society. Outside medicine, he achieved recognition as a gifted musician and orchestral conductor.

James Dundas-Grant was the son of an Edinburgh advocate, educated at the universities of Edinburgh and Würzburg, before graduating in medicine from London in 1876 and obtaining his MD with honours three years later. That same year, he was appointed Surgeon to the Central London Throat and Ear Hospital and developed a career in otology and laryngology. He obtained the FRCSEd in 1884. In 1913, he became a consulting surgeon with appointments in several London hospitals.

He was a prolific writer, contributing to the literature on diverse aspects of ear, nose and throat practice. His knowledge of the specialty was widely regarded as encyclopaedic and he had a particular panache for devising medical instruments, several of which were widely used. An enthusiastic musician, he took particular delight in his appointment as Surgeon to the Royal Academy of Music and the Royal Society of Musicians. His leisure activities included orchestral conducting.

He became President of the section of laryngology and otology of both the British Medical Association and the Royal Society of Medicine and was President of the British Laryngological Association.

Roll number: 1061

Sir James Dundas-Grant (1854–1944).

Sir David Wallace (1862–1952)

Sir David Wallace was a pioneer of urological surgery in Edinburgh. During the Boer War he was in charge of the Edinburgh South African Hospital, an experience which impressed upon him the importance of the Red Cross movement in reducing and mitigating the horrors of war. Becoming active in the British Red Cross Society, he was instrumental in forming the Edinburgh branch and became its Chairman.

David Wallace was educated at Dollar Academy and graduated in medicine from Edinburgh University in 1884. He obtained the FRCSEd in 1887 and went on to become Assistant Surgeon in the Edinburgh Royal Infirmary, where he trained for some years under Professor John Chiene (q.v.). In 1900 he saw service in the Boer War as Surgeon in charge of the Edinburgh South African Hospital. He was mentioned in dispatches and received the South African Medal and clasp, and was appointed Commander of the Order of St Michael and St George (CMG).

This wartime experience had shown him the importance of the Red Cross Society and he was instrumental in founding the Edinburgh branch, of which he was to become Honorary Secretary and then Chairman for a total of 30 years. During the First World War he was called to the staff of the 2nd Scottish General Hospital, who were mobilised in 1914. His invaluable experience in the Red Cross, however, resulted in his being appointed Red Cross Commissioner for south-east Scotland, a post regarded by many as more demanding than an army command.

Sir David Wallace (1862–1952).

Sir David Wallace.

For his wartime service he was awarded the CBE in 1918 and was knighted (KBE) two years later.

In civilian practice he had taken an interest in urological surgery, which he developed in the Royal Infirmary. He was a lecturer in surgery at the School of Medicine of the Medical Royal College at Surgeons' Hall and then at the University, going on to become Surgeon in charge of wards in the Royal Infirmary for the customary 15-year period from 1908 to 1923. On leaving the Infirmary, he became a visiting surgeon to Liberton and Longmore Hospitals.

Wallace received many honours. He was elected to the French Association of Urology and was President of the College from 1921 to 1923. He was appointed Deputy Lieutenant of the City of Edinburgh and received from his alma mater, the honorary degree of LLD.

Roll number: 1145

Alexis Thomson (1863–1924)

Since its foundation in 1726, the Edinburgh University medical faculty has never lacked colourful personalities but none has been more extrovert or conducted themselves with greater panache than Alexis Thomson, who succeeded John Chiene (q.v.) as Professor of Systematic Surgery in 1909.

The visit of the American Society of Clinical Surgery to Edinburgh in 1910, photographed at the front entrance of the Royal Infirmary. American visitors seated in the front include Dr John B. Murphy (with the beard), Dr George Crile and Dr C. H. Mayo. The hosts in the front row include Harold Stiles, J. M. Cotterill and Alexis Thomson.

Henry Alexis Thomson was one of the seven sons of a prosperous Edinburgh businessman. He was educated at the Royal High School and at Edinburgh University, from which he graduated MB CM with honours in 1885. Before entering the University he spent two years in Germany and France, as a result of which he became fluent in both French and German. A famous Edinburgh department store, Patrick Thomson Limited, belonged to his family and, in later years as Professor of Surgery, Alexis could always raise a laugh from his students by referring with feigned contempt to 'that damned rag shop on the North Bridge' or to 'my brother, the haberdasher'. The students' amusement was made all the more piquant by their belief that Thomson had been denied a knighthood because of his connection with 'trade'.

His surgical career began with his appointment in 1887 as Clinical Tutor and private assistant to Mr John Duncan (q.v.). It was at this time that, in association with his great friend Harold Stiles (q.v.), he conducted a highly successful undergraduate course in anatomy and pathology which attracted a large number of students. He became a Fellow of the College in 1888 and in the following year the University awarded him its MD degree with the Gold Medal. In 1892 he was appointed Assistant Surgeon to the Royal Infirmary and, two years later, Surgeon to the newly opened Deaconess Hospital.

Over the next 15 years his reputation as a clinician, as an operator and as a teacher grew rapidly, and by the turn of the century he had become one of the best-known surgeons in Scotland. He travelled frequently to the great centres of academic surgery in France, Germany and Austria and established close friendships with many European surgeons.

His publications were many and varied and together with his fame as an operator attracted numerous foreign visitors to Edinburgh, all of whom were impressed by his technical skill and none more than Dr W. J. Mayo, who, in 1907, wrote: 'I had the pleasure of seeing Mr Alexis Thomson do considerable work. He is a brilliant operator and makes rapid knife dissections with exquisite delicacy ...'

When Professor Chiene retired, Alexis Thomson was his obvious successor and his appointment to the Chair of Systematic Surgery was widely acclaimed. As Professor, he was soon recognised as the most dynamic personality in the Edinburgh medical faculty and his dashing, flamboyant manner appealed greatly to the students of the pre-1914 period, for whom he was without equal as a lecturer and as a clinical teacher. His brisk repartee and caustic wit were legendary and his students reacted joyously to his verbal sallies, many of which, it must be admitted, were of a somewhat Rabelaisian flavour. He was a showman of the first order: a tall, handsome man, always immaculately dressed, who combined the grand manner with the common touch and who had been naturally endowed with an abundance of that elusive and indefinable quality which is called 'style'. All this was, however, only one side of him and behind the flourish and swagger was a razor-keen intellect linked with supreme practical ability. He was truly a master surgeon, in many respects far in advance of his times, who was held in the highest esteem by his surgical peers worldwide.

Alexis Thomson and Harold Stiles were among the first European surgeons to appreciate the rapid development of surgical science in the United States and both made several trips to American teaching centres long before this became a fashionable thing to do. They were, consequently, held in high regard by their American colleagues and when the American Society of Clinical Surgery visited the major surgical centres of Europe in 1910, they invited both Thomson and Stiles to accompany them on their tour.

In 1904, Thomson and his Royal Infirmary colleague Alexander Miles (q.v.) published their famous *Manual of Surgery*, and although the two authors could scarcely have been more different in temperament, this was an instant success. It ran to several editions and was probably the most popular English-language surgical textbook of its day.

Although aged 50 at the outbreak of the First World War, Thomson volunteered for military service and in 1915 was appointed Consulting Surgeon to the British 3rd Army in France. About 18 months later his health broke down and he had to be invalided home. His convalescence was prolonged and his old friend Harold Stiles felt that he never fully recovered either his physical energy or his intellectual vigour. In recognition of his distinguished army service, he was appointed Commander of the Order of St Michael and St George (CMG).

He retired from the Chair of Systematic Surgery in 1923 and was due to take office as President of the College later that year, but was prevented from doing so by a stroke, which left him partially paralysed. As one who had always lived life to the full, he could not reconcile himself to the prospect of prolonged invalidism and in 1924, when on holiday in southern Spain, he ended his own life in the manner of an ancient Roman.

Alexis Thomson (1863–1924).

Alexis Thomson was undoubtedly one of the most remarkable 'characters' in the long history of the Edinburgh medical school, to which he made his own distinctive contribution. He worked and played hard and is warmly remembered as the central figure of many tales and anecdotes, by no means all of them apocryphal, which have been passed down from one generation to another since his death.

The handsome dinner service presented to the College by his widow is a fitting memorial to a most distinguished Fellow, who, throughout his life, was the soul of conviviality.

Roll number: 1166

Sir Harold Stiles (1863–1946).

Sir Harold Stiles (1863–1946)

'It was a lovely evening in the first week in May 1880 when I first set foot in Edinburgh and, walking up the Calton Hill, I vowed that as I could not succeed to my father's practice, I would endeavour to make my home in Edinburgh and that I would not leave it unless I was starved out.' This was the recollection in later life of an Englishman who, far from being starved out of Edinburgh, has a strong claim to be regarded as the most distinguished surgical alumnus of the Edinburgh medical school and as one of the greatest paladins of Scottish surgery.

Harold Jalland Stiles, the son and grandson of doctors who practised in Spalding, Lincolnshire, was also born there. In 1880 he became a medical student at Edinburgh University. His elder brother, also a medical student, would in due course inherit his father's practice and Harold knew from the beginning that he would have to make his own way in medicine. Before coming to Edinburgh, he had received from his father a thorough grounding in anatomy and it is likely that his ambition to become a surgeon was stimulated by this teaching.

His undergraduate career was one of the highest academic distinction and in 1885 he graduated MB CM as Ettles Scholar with first-class honours. After serving as House Surgeon to Professor John Chiene (q.v.), he became a demonstrator in Sir William Turner's (q.v.) University Department of Anatomy before being appointed assistant in charge of pathology in the surgical laboratory established by Professor Chiene. There is no doubt that this training laid the foundations of his impressive knowledge of anatomy and pathology. He became a Fellow of the College in 1889 and during the next three years carried out impressive studies of the surgical anatomy of the breast and of the pathology of breast cancer, which brought him international recognition. It was during his time with Professor Chiene that he first made his name as a teacher, and the extramural course in anatomy and pathology which he conducted with his friend Alexis Thomson (q.v.) attracted large numbers of students.

In 1895 Stiles was appointed Assistant Surgeon to the Edinburgh Royal Infirmary and soon after this he spent six months in Berne at the Clinic of Professor Theodor Kocher, with whom he established a warm friendship. From Kocher, he acquired the practical skills on which he based his own operative technique and he translated into English his mentor's monumental textbook *Chirurgische Operationslehre* (1892). The most important result of Stiles' sojourn with Kocher was, however, his progression from Listerian antisepsis to the aseptic system of surgery and on his return from Berne he became a pioneer of asepsis in Scotland.

In 1898 Stiles was appointed Surgeon to the Edinburgh Sick Children's Hospital, which meant that he had to give up his post as Assistant Surgeon to the Royal Infirmary. Soon after this he became Surgeon to Chalmers Hospital and was thereby able to maintain his involvement in adult surgery. Within a few years his clinical brilliance, his technical innovations and his superb operative skill had earned for him an international reputation which was enhanced by his scientific publications and by the inspirational quality of his teaching. Stiles travelled widely and although a very bad sailor he made several transatlantic voyages to visit major American surgical centres. Nowhere was he more highly regarded than the United States, where he established close friendships with many distinguished American colleagues, by whom he was rated as one of the best European surgeons.

A full account of Stiles' achievements during his 20 years at the Sick Children's Hospital would fill many pages and space restrictions preclude mention of more than two of his major contributions to paediatric surgery. He showed clearly that, contrary to Robert Koch's teaching, the bovine form of the tubercle bacillus was frequently the cause of tuberculosis of the bones and joints and of the cervical lymph nodes. He was the first surgeon to treat extroversion of the bladder (ectopia vesicae) by transplantation of the ureters into the sigmoid colon and the original patient on whom, in 1911, he carried out this procedure was alive, well and content 23 years later. The operation of pyloromyotomy for congenital hypertrophic pyloric stenosis is associated with the name of Rammstedt of Münster, who first carried it out fortuitously in July 1911. Stiles did this operation as a deliberate planned procedure in February 1910, but his patient died of gastroenteritis four days post-operatively and he did not repeat it until after Rammstedt's experience and results were published in 1912.

On the outbreak of the First World War in 1914, Stiles was appointed Consultant Surgeon to the army in Scotland with charge of the large military surgical division at Bangour Hospital a few miles out of Edinburgh. Here, he was responsible for the secondary and tertiary care of battle casualties from the Western Front and other theatres of war. He became specially interested in the treatment of peripheral nerve injuries and his publications on this subject added further lustre to his reputation.

His outstanding achievements in the care and rehabilitation of the war-wounded earned for him in 1918 the honour of knighthood (KBE). In the following year, his appointment to the Edinburgh University Regius Chair of Clinical Surgery was the realisation of his most-cherished ambition. As Regius Professor, Stiles returned to the Royal Infirmary and over the next six years his fame as a teacher and as a supreme master surgeon attracted large numbers of visiting surgeons to his wards from all over the world. Among many honours and distinctions which came to him during this period were his appointment as Surgeon to HM King George V in Scotland and his presidency of the College, which he held from 1923 to 1925.

Sir Harold Stiles.

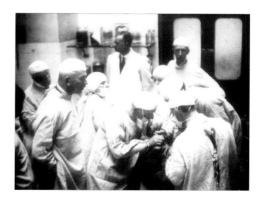

The last operation performed by Sir Harold Stiles in the Royal Infirmary of Edinburgh in 1925.

Harold Stiles during his time as surgeon to the Royal Hospital for Sick Children, Edinburgh.

In 1925 at the very peak of his prestige and influence, Stiles suddenly and inexplicably retired from the Chair of Clinical Surgery. It may be that the pace and intensity of his professional life had caused him to fear the onset of physical and mental exhaustion, but he never gave any reason for his abrupt departure. It was, however, a complete severance from all his professional activities and thereafter he devoted himself to the study of geology, botany and ornithology with photography and watercolour painting by way of relaxation.

Sir Harold Stiles set for himself the highest standards and was a perfectionist in everything he did. As 'Chief' and professor he was a hard and sometimes severe taskmaster, but his was a warm-hearted generous nature and he was held in total respect and no little affection by all who worked for him.

The originality of his ever-inquiring mind and his intellectual dynamism, no less than his teaching and his exceptional operative expertise, entitle Sir Harold Stiles, an Englishman, to an honoured place in the very first rank of Scottish surgeons and to recognition for all time as one of the College's greatest Fellows.

Roll number: 1200

Sir Robert Jones Bt (1858–1933)

Sir Robert Jones Bt (1858–1933).

Widely regarded as the father of modern British orthopaedic surgery, Robert Jones had been introduced to the specialty at an early age by his uncle, Hugh Owen Thomas, himself an early pioneer of orthopaedic surgery. Jones went on to a world reputation in orthopaedic surgery and was hugely influential in the development of orthopaedics as a specialty in its own right.

Robert Jones was born in Ryll and educated at Sydenham College and Liverpool School of Medicine. From early in his career he was introduced to the craft of orthopaedics by his uncle, Hugh Owen Thomas, who was to become known throughout the world for the leg splint which bears his name. Thomas' family had passed the skills of bonesetting to each succeeding generation, and he had duly acquired them. Thomas was the first, however, to take a medical degree. Jones learned these and other skills at the free Sunday morning clinic which his uncle ran and which he was subsequently to inherit. He became Surgeon to the Stanley Hospital and then to the Royal Southern Hospital after obtaining the Fellowship of the College in 1889. Thereafter he devoted himself principally to orthopaedics and in 1905 became one of the first specialist orthopaedic surgeons.

Liverpool at that time was the principal port of call for transatlantic passenger liners, so that American orthopaedic surgeons visiting Europe would begin or end their trip with a visit to Robert Jones. This resulted in several joint authorships with prominent American surgeons, such as R. W. Lovett of Boston (with whom he jointly wrote the book *Orthopaedic Surgery*, published in 1923), and John Ridlor in Chicago. In this way he established a reputation in the United States and indeed in continental Europe almost greater than his standing in Britain. William Mayo was to write of him: 'he is expeditious, yet neglects not the smallest detail, and his wonderful experience enables him to do wizard-like operations with a precision which is startling'. His dexterity and confidence in manipulation of fractures and in operations marked him out as a master of his craft. Sir Harry Platt, himself an eminent orthopaedic surgeon, was to describe his childhood experience as a patient of Jones as a memorable one.

Robert Jones was appointed Surgeon to the Manchester Ship Canal, then under construction. This appointment required him to organise he casualty service for the 10,000 or so workmen engaged in the project. By 1913 he was President of the section of orthopaedics at the International Medical Conference and with the outbreak of the First World War he was called up to the Royal Army Medical Corps. It was apparent that the treatment of fractures, both in the field hospitals in France and in the British hospitals, overwhelmed with evacuated soldiers, left much to be desired. Jones made representations to the War Office to set up appropriately staffed and equipped centres to treat ununited and malunited fractures, joint injuries and peripheral nerve injuries. As these military orthopaedic hospitals were established, he was promoted Major General and appointed Inspector of Military Orthopaedics with a jurisdiction over some 30,000 beds. From this developed the specialist orthopaedic hospitals which formed the basis for the specialty of orthopaedics in Britain.

Inaugural meeting of the Moynihan Chirurgical Club at the General Infirmary, Leeds, on 23 and 24 July 1909.

Berkeley Moynihan is seated centre. Robert Jones is seated on the right of the picture, with Alexis Thomson on his right. Francis Caird and Harold Stiles are also present.

After the war, he resumed his interest in the crippling diseases of childhood and their correction, which culminated in the opening of the Robert Jones and Agnes Hunt Orthopaedic Hospital at Oswestry, and led to his helping to found the Central Council for the Care of Cripples.

He was the prime mover behind the foundation of the British Orthopaedic Association, of which he was later to become President. Throughout his working life he continued to write about every facet of orthopaedics.

When contemporaries described his personal qualities, bonhomie, warmth, charm and courtesy were almost always mentioned. One contemporary, Lord Moynihan, was to write: 'in a long and very close friendship I have never heard an unjust criticism, a cruel jibe or a word of bitter cynicism on his lips. His personality radiates cheeriness, good temper and goodwill.'

He received many honours in recognition of his contributions to surgery. He was made Companion of the Bath (CB), knighted and, in 1926, created a baronet.

Roll number: 1212

Harvey Littlejohn (1862–1927).

Harvey Littlejohn (1862–1927)

To combine successfully careers as a university professor, a medical officer of health, the country's leading medical expert witness and Dean of the Faculty of Medicine required eloquence, professional expertise, scientific knowledge and organisational ability above the ordinary. Harvey Littlejohn had these in abundance and used them to great effect. Following, almost literally, in his father's footsteps as Professor of Medical Jurisprudence carried the risk of invidious comparisons, but Harvey Littlejohn came to be regarded as the best teacher in Edinburgh University and the best medical expert witness in Scotland in his own right.

Henry Harvey Littlejohn was born in Edinburgh where his father, Sir Henry Littlejohn (q.v.), was Professor of Medical Jurisprudence. At an early age he had, encouraged by his father, decided to pursue a similar career and after taking an MA degree, he qualified in medicine and went on to a BSc in Public Health. He was fortunate in being able to assist his father both in the Department of the Medical Officer of Health and by lecturing in his father's extra-mural class of medical jurisprudence at Surgeons' Hall.

In 1891 he was appointed Medical Officer of Health for the city of Sheffield, returning to Edinburgh six years later as a lecturer in medical jurisprudence in the newly styled School of Medicine of the Medical Royal Colleges at Surgeons' Hall. During this time, he established himself as a gifted and popular teacher. In the lecture theatre and in the witness box his eloquence and clarity of expression ensured success.

He was appointed to the Chair of Medical Jurisprudence in 1906, succeeding his father. This carried with it the role of Police Surgeon to the city and adviser to the Crown in criminal proceedings. As Police Surgeon he was able to enlarge the Forensic Medicine Museum which his father had started, and which, at its height, was one of the finest of its kind in Europe. In 1925 he was able to publish an *Atlas of Forensic Medicine*, illustrated with many photographs from the collection he had established in the Museum. As adviser to the Crown in criminal cases, he was frequently involved as an expert witness appearing for the Crown in some of the most important Scottish murder trials of that time.

His eloquence and his considerable administrative expertise resulted in his appointment as Dean of the medical faculty of the University of Edinburgh and he went on to become a member of the General Medical Council.

Outside medicine he was a voracious reader, and a collector of books and old prints. He had a particular penchant for books and prints on Edinburgh and was well versed in its history. He delighted in entertaining and his ready wit and gifts as a conversationalist ensured him a wide circle of friends in the Edinburgh society of the day.

Harvey Littlejohn was remembered by his peers for his vivacity and energy, as a dramatic, witty raconteur and as a popular and gifted teacher.

Roll number: 1221

David Greig (1864–1936)

The College Museum houses one of the world's greatest surgical pathology collections and its educational value, no less than its fame, owes much to the work of David Greig, its Conservator for 15 years, and undoubtedly one of the most energetic, diligent and erudite holders of that office.

David Middleton Greig, born in Dundee, was the son and grandson of general practitioners in that city and from an early age was determined to follow in the professional footsteps of his father and his paternal grandfather. He studied medicine at the universities of St Andrews and Edinburgh and graduated MB CM from the latter in 1885. After a short period in junior hospital posts in Dundee and Perth, he served for three years as an army surgeon and for a considerable part of that time was stationed in India. His father had also been an army surgeon and had seen action in the Crimean War.

On returning to his native city, David Greig joined his father in general practice but became increasingly attracted to surgery as a career and in 1890 obtained the Fellowship of the College. Soon after this he was appointed to the surgical staff of the Dundee Royal Infirmary and became a lecturer in clinical surgery and in surgical diseases of children at St Andrews University. During the next few years he gained a high reputation as an astute clinician, as a versatile and dextrous operator and as a highly effective teacher, but his enthusiasm for surgical pathology almost bordered on the obsessional and early in his career he became an avid collector of pathological specimens and particularly of those relating to diseases and abnormalities of the skeleton. He macerated, dried and mounted his specimens himself in the attic of his home in Dundee, where, in the summer months, passers-by might see 'Greig's bones' arrayed on the roof bleaching in the sun. He maintained his military connection as medical officer to the old Forfar Volunteer Artillery and in the South African War he served for two years in the Royal Army Medical Corps as a field surgeon with the rank of Major.

By 1914 Greig had become one of the senior surgeons in the Dundee Royal Infirmary and he was also surgeon to several smaller hospitals in the counties of Perth and Angus. He had a busy private practice, but the development and enlargement of his pathological collection occupied much of his time and he was also a prolific contributor to the anatomical, pathological and surgical literature. Many of his papers deal with rare and obscure diseases and developmental abnormalities, but in his writings he had the faculty of relating the rare to the commonplace and the special to the general in such a way that his observations were always educational and of relevance to surgical practice.

He became an internationally recognised authority on the pathology of bone and when, in 1920, it became known that he intended to retire from the staff of the Dundee Royal Infirmary, he was invited to become full-time Conservator of the College Museum. He held this position from 1921 until his death 15 years later. On moving to Edinburgh, he donated to the Museum his own remarkable assemblage of pathological specimens painstakingly accumulated over nearly 25 years of active surgical practice. This included more than 200 skulls, which constitute what is probably the most comprehensive collection of cranio-facial abnormalities in existence. As a result of his meticulous study of this and other material in the Museum, Greig was able to publish in 1931 the classic monograph *Some Observations on the Surgical Pathology of Bone*, which is his greatest monument.

David Greig (1864–1936).

James Jack, assistant technician
in the College Museum.

As Conservator, Greig's most notable achievement was the completion of the Herculean tasks of revising the descriptions of every specimen and artefact in the collection, of preparing a new museum catalogue based on a much-improved indexing system and of re-mounting a large proportion of the pathological specimens. Much of the latter work was done by William Waldie, the Museum technician, for whom Greig hired a special assistant, James Jack, an achondroplastic dwarf from Dundee who had been his patient. In College folklore he is reputed to have entertained the hope that in the fullness of time he might acquire the assistant technician's skeleton for the Museum. Greig was, however, long outlived by James Jack, who many years later, while still working in the College, would from time to time triumphantly declare, 'He didnae get me and he's deid!'

Roll number: 1224

Alexander Miles (1865–1953)

Alexander Miles was closely associated with the Edinburgh Medical School for 70 years and there can be few of its alumni who have given to it more devoted service than he did in several different capacities.

Born in Leith, Alexander Miles was educated at George Watson's College and at Edinburgh University, from which he graduated MB CM in 1888; three years later he obtained the degree of Doctor of Medicine (MD) with the Gold Medal for his thesis and the award of a Syme Surgical Fellowship.

After serving in the Royal Infirmary as a house surgeon and later as a clinical tutor, he obtained the Fellowship of the College in 1890 and in that year also he was Senior President of the Royal Medical Society. In 1898 he was appointed Assistant Surgeon to the Royal Infirmary and Surgeon to Leith Hospital a few months later. At this stage in his career he conducted a revision course in surgery and operative surgery in the extra-mural School of Medicine of the Edinburgh Royal Colleges, which attracted many senior medical students and which enabled him to develop the teaching skills for which he later became famous far beyond the confines of Edinburgh.

Miles was appointed full surgeon to the Royal Infirmary in 1909 and having held charge of wards for what was then the statutory period of 15 years, he retired in 1924 with the status of Consulting Surgeon. He was an impressive clinician and a rapid dextrous operator but he was held in particularly high regard for the quality of his clinical teaching and for the precision and lucidity of his writings. He made many notable contributions to surgical literature, but the most celebrated of these was the *Manual of Surgery*, which he and Alexis Thomson (q.v.) published in 1904 and which rapidly became one of the most popular didactic surgical texts in the English-speaking world. Thomson and Miles could hardly have been more different in temperament, but in their characters and abilities they complemented each other admirably and their collaboration as authors was as happy as it was successful.

When Alexis Thomson died in 1924, four editions of the *Manual* had appeared and his place as its co-author was taken by Professor D. P. D. (later Sir David) Wilkie (q.v.). The ninth edition appeared in 1939, but with Wilkie's death and the outbreak of the Second World War in that year, it seemed that this famous textbook had probably run its course.

In 1950, however, the Edinburgh surgical community was delighted to welcome a third edition of the *Operative Surgery* volume of the *Manual*, edited by Miles and Sir James Learmonth (q.v.), to which the senior editor had contributed a completely new chapter on amputations – a remarkable achievement for a man in his 85th year.

Miles' literary abilities were indeed considerable and were enhanced by what one of his obituaries called 'his almost uncanny exactness in the management of words and clauses'. He was editor of the *Edinburgh Medical Journal* from 1911 to 1935 and his 24 years in its editorial chair was a 'golden age' in that journal's long history. Another work for which he became justly famous was his *History of the Edinburgh School of Surgery before Lister* (1918), which presents much fascinating historical information in a most agreeably readable form.

In retirement Miles became increasingly involved in the affairs of his alma mater as a member of the Edinburgh University Court for 20 years. He also had the honour of being appointed one of the Curators of Patronage – that small committee with responsibility for selecting the occupants of certain University chairs – and in recognition of these and other valuable services the University, in 1925, conferred upon him its honorary Doctor of Laws (LLD).

He had an abiding interest in the Astley Ainslie Hospital for occupational therapy and rehabilitation, which was founded in 1921, and he was the first Chairman of its Board of Management. He was a founder member of the Edinburgh University Graduates' Association, which in 1948 elected him to its honorary presidency and he was also the first editor of the Association's twice yearly publication the *University of Edinburgh Journal*.

Miles' earliest service to the College was as a Fellowship examiner, but in 1920 he was appointed Secretary and Treasurer and held this office for seven years. In 1927 he was elected President in succession to Dr Arthur Logan Turner (q.v.) and in the following year he became the College representative on the General Medical Council (GMC).

He held this important position for the next 15 years, during which he made a distinguished contribution to the work of the Council as a member of several of its most important committees, such as the Executive Committee and the Penal Cases Committee, on which he served for 10 and 12 years, respectively.

The Royal College of Surgeons of Edinburgh, a history of the College from 1505 to 1905, written by Clarendon Hyde Creswell, College Officer and Sub-Librarian, was published in 1926, but Mr Creswell had died in 1918 and the task of editing and arranging his work for publication was carried out by Alexander Miles and Arthur Logan Turner. For what he did to ensure the publication of Creswell's chronicle of the College's first four centuries and for his many other great services, Alexander Miles, at the end of its fifth century, deserves the gratitude of the College and its Fellows.

Roll number: 1232

Alexander Miles (1865–1953).

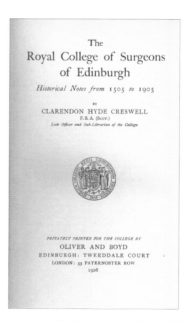

The Royal College of Surgeons of Edinburgh

Historical Notes from 1505 to 1905

BY

CLARENDON HYDE CRESWELL
F.S.A. (SCOT.)
Late Officer and Sub-Librarian of the College

PRIVATELY PRINTED FOR THE COLLEGE BY
OLIVER AND BOYD
EDINBURGH: TWEEDDALE COURT
LONDON: 33 PATERNOSTER ROW
1926

The history of the College from 1505 to 1905, written to celebrate the Quatercentenary.

Arthur Logan Turner (1865–1939).

STORY OF A GREAT HOSPITAL
THE
ROYAL INFIRMARY OF EDINBURGH
1729-1929
BY
A. LOGAN TURNER, M.D., LL.D., Hon. F.R.C.P. Edin.
FELLOW OF THE ROYAL COLLEGE OF SURGEONS OF EDINBURGH; CONSULTING SURGEON
EAR, NOSE AND THROAT DEPARTMENT, THE ROYAL INFIRMARY

EDINBURGH
OLIVER AND BOYD, TWEEDDALE COURT
LONDON: 33 PATERNOSTER ROW
1937

Arthur Logan Turner's *Story of a Great Hospital*.

Arthur Logan Turner (1865–1939)

Since 1800 the College has had 92 Presidents and it is interesting to note that there are among them eight pairs of fathers and sons* – The Maclagans (q.v.), David (PRCSEd, 1826–8) and Andrew (PRCSEd, 1859–61), are the most celebrated in that both also were elected Presidents of the Royal College of Physicians of Edinburgh but others were of scarcely lesser distinction.

An illustrious member of this remarkable group was Arthur Logan Turner, the second son of Sir William Turner (q.v.), who was born in Edinburgh, where his famous father was Professor of Anatomy. He was educated at Fettes and in 1884 entered the medical faculty of Edinburgh University, from which he graduated MB CM in 1889. After serving first as House Surgeon and then as assistant to Professor Thomas Annandale (q.v.), he obtained the Fellowship of the College in 1891 and the degree of Doctor of Medicine (MD) from the University three years later, but the effects of an accidental hand injury dissuaded him from his original intention of becoming a general surgeon. He decided instead to make his career in ear, nose and throat surgery and received his early training in this specialty from Dr Peter MacBride, Edinburgh's first specialist otolaryngologist.

Logan Turner's first appointment in his chosen specialty was to the Church of Scotland's Deaconess Hospital and in 1906 he became a surgeon for diseases of the ear, nose and throat in the Edinburgh Royal Infirmary. When he retired from this post in 1924, he had the unusual distinction of being invited to continue in his department as Honorary Surgeon Consultant. Throughout the First World War he served in the Royal Army Medical Corps as Consultant Otolaryngologist to the 2nd Scottish General Hospital with the rank of Captain, but he was not posted overseas.

Before the war he had built up a large private practice and this grew substantially in the immediate post-war period. In addition to this, he established an impressive national reputation in his specialty, which was recognised by his election to Fellowship of the Royal Society of Edinburgh (FRSE) and the award by his alma mater of its honorary Doctor of Laws (LLD). He was awarded honorary or corresponding membership of many otolaryngology societies in Europe and North America and nearer home he became President of the otology section of the Royal Society of Medicine in 1921 and of its laryngology section in 1921 and 1924. There is, however, no doubt that the honour which gave him greatest pride and pleasure was the presidency of the College, to which he was elected in 1925, as the first of two ear, nose and throat surgeons who have to date held that office. The distinction of his presidency and of his professional reputation received further recognition by his appointment in 1927 as President of the otolaryngology section of the British Medical Association and, in the same year, by his admission to the honorary Fellowship of the Royal College of Physicians of Edinburgh.

---

* William Wood PRCSEd (1828–30) and Andrew Wood PRCSEd (1855–7);
John Argyll Robertson PRCSEd (1848–9) and Douglas Argyll Robertson PRCSEd (1885–7);
Sir William Turner PRCSEd (1882–3) and Arthur Logan Turner PRCSEd (1925–7);
Sir John Struthers PRCSEd (1895–7) and John W. Struthers PRCSEd (1941–2);
Sir William Newbigging PRCSEd (1814–16) and Patrick Newbigging PRCSEd (1861–3);
Benjamin Bell PRCSEd (1863–5) and Joseph Bell PRCSEd (1887–9);
Alexander Gillespie PRCSEd (1818–20) and James Donaldson Gillespie PRCSEd (1869–71).

Logan Turner made many important clinical and scientific contributions to the advancement of his specialty, in which through his writings he became a figure of international stature. In addition to numerous papers and articles were important monographs on the nasal accessory sinuses and on intra-cranial pyogenic diseases. His reputation was further enhanced in 1924 when, together with five Edinburgh colleagues, he produced the famous *Manual of Diseases of the Nose, Throat and Ear*, which became an international best-seller and ran to four editions under his editorship.

From 1921 to 1929, he was joint editor of the *Journal of Laryngology* and during that period the journal, which had languished and faded during the First World War, was revitalised and restored to its former eminence. When Logan Turner retired from the editorial chair, the success of his stewardship was recognised by a substantial presentation contributed by a large number of the journal's subscribers. At his request this money was used to establish a prize to be awarded every five years for outstanding original work in otolaryngology.

Logan Turner was, from 1923 to 1927, a highly effective editor of the *University of Edinburgh Journal*, a periodical published by the Edinburgh University Graduates' Association, of which he was President from 1931 to 1933.

After retirement he devoted himself to history with the same dedication, energy and enthusiasm that had characterised his professional practice, and indeed his reputation as a historian is scarcely less than his fame as an otolaryngologist. Among his historical publications, the most notable are his biography of his father *The Life of Sir William Turner KCB FRS: A Chapter in Medical History* (1919), his *History of the University of Edinburgh, 1583–1933* (1933) and his great magnum opus *The Story of a Great Hospital: The Royal Infirmary of Edinburgh, 1729–1929* (1937). In addition, on behalf of the Lister Centenary Committee of the British Medical Association, he edited *Joseph Baron Lister: A Centenary Volume, 1827–1927* (1927).

The Logan Turner Room in the College.

In 1956 the original College Council chamber was converted into a handsome reception room which was designated 'the President's Room'. This conversion and refurbishment was funded from a legacy bequeathed to the College for such purposes by Arthur Logan Turner and it was decided that the room should also be known as 'the Logan Turner Room'. It is a worthy monument to a distinguished Fellow and President whose career and achievements can stand comparison with those of his famous father.

Roll number: 1243

Keith Monsarrat (1872–1968)

K. W. Monsarrat (1872–1968).

K. W. Monsarrat, a Liverpool surgeon, who was instrumental in bringing about the affiliation of Liverpool hospitals with the medical school of the University of Liverpool, went on to become Dean of its Faculty of Medicine. A life-long classical scholar, he achieved fame outside medicine as a writer, particularly of philosophy and poetry.

Keith Waldergrave Monsarrat was born in Kendal, where his father was a vicar. He was educated at King William's College on the Isle of Man, going on to Edinburgh University, where he graduated MB CM in 1894. (The University of Edinburgh conferred the degree of MB CM until 1895 when MB ChB became the primary medical degree awarded.) After taking the Fellowship of the College in 1897, he set up in surgical practice in Liverpool. He was appointed Assistant Surgeon to the Cancer Hospital and the Liverpool Children's Infirmary. In 1902 he became Honorary Surgeon to the David Lewis Northern Hospital and remained closely associated with this hospital until his retiral. His appointment followed the great expansion in surgery brought about by the introduction of antisepsis and anaesthesia. As a surgeon, he was regarded as a perfectionist for whom attention to detail was all-important and his reputation soon brought him to a prominent position in Liverpool surgery.

He was one of a small group of clinicians who wanted to establish a closer relationship between the University and the Liverpool hospitals and his efforts culminated with the establishment of the United Clinical School. His association with the University continued with his appointment as Dean of the Faculty of Medicine in 1908.

With the outbreak of the First World War, he was posted to Salonika in charge of the surgical division of the 37th General Hospital and was awarded the Serbian Order of St Sava and later the Territorial Decoration.

After the war, he returned to surgical practice and academic work. A member of the Liverpool Institution since his earliest days in that city, he became its President in 1930.

After retiring in 1932, he began to write and publish philosophy. The outbreak of the Second World War saw his recall to Liverpool, where he was given charge of organising the Emergency Medical Service. After the war, he continued to devote himself to writing. His son, Nicholas Monsarrat, was also to find fame as a best-selling author.

Roll number: 1377

K. W. Monsarrat and Nicholas Monsarrat

K. W. Monsarrat's son Nicholas was born in Liverpool in 1910. After graduating in law from Cambridge University, he decided to embark on a writing career and his first four novels were written with a social awareness which reflected his socialist leanings. Shortly after the outbreak of war he joined the Royal Naval Volunteer Reserve and saw action in the Battle of the Atlantic, an experience which was to form the basis of his novel *The Cruel Sea* (1951).

After the war he joined the diplomatic service and was posted to South Africa. His experience there provided the material for another best selling novel *The Tribe that Lost its Head* (1956). After a series of successful novels he moved to Gozo, Malta, where he wrote *The Kappillan of Malta* (1973), perhaps the most descriptive and widely read of all his works. He died in 1979 and was buried at sea from a Royal Naval destroyer.

20th Century

The development of surgical techniques has been advanced by war throughout the ages and so it was with the two world wars of the 20th century. By the time of the First World War the use of general anaesthesia and aseptic surgery allowed surgeons to become ever more invasive, and to operate successfully and safely on every body cavity. Yet in the early decades of the century, the surgical repertoire within these cavities was largely confined to excisional surgery. As the century progressed, reconstructive surgery developed, and reconstructive arterial, joint, gastro intestinal and urological surgery became commonplace. The increasing pace of technological change led to the growth of replacement surgery, and advances in immunosuppression meant that organ transplant procedures became routine by the end of the century.

Surgery became ever more specialised and sub-specialised and increasingly performed by specialist teams. The demography of the surgical workforce changed too. Surgery was no longer a male preserve, but while the number of women surgeons had increased, it was still disproportionately low by the end of the century.

Surgical practice became international and at the turn of the century was being performed in every country in the world, routinely practised in larger, more technologically complex hospitals in developing as well as developed countries.

The communications revolution had major effects on surgical practice. Details of surgical techniques were disseminated more widely and more rapidly and so became more uniform. The outcome of surgical procedures – their success rate – has been increasingly scrutinised not only by surgeons, but by an ever more educated public with ever higher expectations.

A surgical procedure in the early years of the 20th century.

Laparoscopic surgery in the latter years of the 20th century.

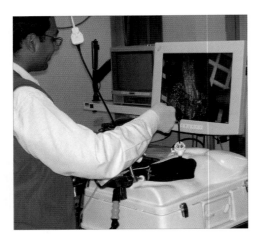

Training for laparoscopic surgery in the skills laboratory using a simulator.

The Royal College of Surgeons of Edinburgh in the 20th century became truly international. Inspections of training programmes, examinations and courses were taken to several overseas countries. At the start of the 20th century the membership had reached only 1,490 but by the end of the century that number had increased tenfold.

Three new faculties were established in the College: the Dental Faculty, the Faculty of Pre-Hospital care and the Faculty of Health Informatics.

In the latter half of the century the College expanded its campus. The former St Michael's Church in Hill Square was converted into a modern symposium hall. The College acquired the large tenement building forming the southern side of Hill Street and converted this into a postgraduate residence, and by the end of the century the College owned most of the property in Hill Square.

The original Royal Infirmary in Infirmary Street. Building began in 1738 and patients were admitted in 1741. The hospital was vacated in 1879 and was demolished in 1884.

The Royal Infirmary of Edinburgh in Lauriston Place. Building began in 1874 and the Infirmary was opened in 1879. The building was vacated in May 2003.

The Royal Infirmary of Edinburgh at Little France. Building began in 1996 and patients were admitted in 2002.

Arthur Sinclair (1868–1962)

Ophthalmology emerged as a specialty in its own right in the later years of the 19th century and the new specialty benefited from significant contributions from a series of ophthalmologists in Edinburgh. James Wardrop, John Wishart, the Argyll Robertsons, father and son, all made contributions described elsewhere in this book. Sinclair followed in this tradition and introduced quantitative perimetry into British ophthalmic practice. His technique of intra-capsular lens extraction became popular throughout the world.

Born in Kenmore, Perthshire, at the eastern end of Loch Tay, Arthur Henry Havens Sinclair was the son of the local Free Church minister. He graduated in medicine from Edinburgh in 1893 going on to obtain the degree of MD and the Fellowship of the College in 1899. Having decided on a career in ophthalmology, he studied in London and Utrecht and travelled widely, visiting clinics throughout Europe. He became Clinical Assistant to Sir George Andreas Berry (q.v.) in the Royal Infirmary of Edinburgh and, through the latter's family connection (his uncle, Professor Grut, was a distinguished ophthalmologist in Copenhagen), travelled to Scandinavia to study with Jannik Bjerrum, who was pioneering quantitative perimetry of the visual fields. The resulting researches led to Sinclair's introduction of quantitative perimetry into British surgical practice. After his appointment as Ophthalmic Surgeon in the Royal Infirmary, he developed numerous surgical techniques. The technique that is always associated with his name is intra-capsular extraction, of the lens. To overcome the disadvantages of extra-capsular extraction he developed a novel technique performed using instruments which he had designed himself. He demonstrated the safety and efficacy of this new technique, which became widely accepted into British ophthalmology.

Sinclair went on to become Surgeon Oculist to the King in Scotland from 1928, President of the Royal Ophthalmological Society and in 1933 was elected President of the Royal College of Surgeons of Edinburgh. He was a Fellow of the Royal Society of Edinburgh and a member of the Royal Company of Archers.

In his later years he was instrumental in establishing the W. H. Ross Foundation for the study of the prevention of blindness. Sinclair had originally suggested to Ross that his generous endowment should be devoted to ophthalmic research and for many years acted as director of the foundation.

In later years he enjoyed the status of doyen of lens extraction, and received visitors from all over the world, whom he entertained in his elegant Adam house in Charlotte Square, Edinburgh. In leisure moments he enjoyed escaping to his boyhood haunts in Perthshire to fish for salmon.

Roll number: 1500

Arthur H. H. Sinclair (1868–1962).

James Haig Ferguson (1862–1934)

Throughout his distinguished career in which he acquired a national reputation as one of the greatest masters of his specialty, James Haig Ferguson never lost the common touch or the ability to establish close personal rapport with his patients. In all aspects of his life and work he most thoroughly earned their complete confidence, their deep respect and their warm affection.

James Haig Ferguson was the son of the parish minister of Fossoway, near Kinross, and, through his mother, he was distantly related to Field Marshal Earl Haig, the commander-in-chief of the British army on the Western Front during the First World War. After attending the now defunct Collegiate School in Edinburgh, he entered the medical faculty of Edinburgh University, graduating MB CM in 1884. Throughout his time as a student, he was an enthusiastic member of the Royal Medical Society and in his graduation year he became one of its junior presidents.

After 18 months in resident hospital posts, he became private assistant to Dr John Halliday Croom (q.v.), who was then establishing his illustrious reputation in obstetrics and gynaecology, and it was this association which determined Haig Ferguson's future career. Dr Croom had a large general practice which he was gradually relinquishing in order to devote himself entirely to his chosen specialty and in due course his assistant fell heir to this.

In 1887 Haig Ferguson became a Member of the Royal College of Physicians of Edinburgh (MRCPEd) and two years later he was elected a Fellow (FRCPEd). In 1890 he followed this by gaining from the University the degree of Doctor of Medicine (MD) with honours.

For 20 years Haig Ferguson conducted a large general practice in which he built up an ever-increasing reputation for obstetrical expertise. During this period, he gradually made the transition from general practitioner to specialist and consultant – a change almost unthinkable nowadays but which, at that time, was not uncommon. In 1898 he was appointed Gynaecologist to Leith Hospital and Assistant Physician to the Royal Maternity Hospital one year later. He began to appreciate that gynaecology was becoming increasingly surgical in its practice and in order to establish his surgical credentials he obtained the Fellowship of the College by examination in 1902 at 40 years of age.

In 1906 Haig Ferguson was appointed Assistant Gynaecologist to the Royal Infirmary of Edinburgh and being now totally committed to a specialist career, he gave up his general practice. During the 1890s and the early years of the 20th century, he had been responsible for the teaching of obstetrics and gynaecology in the extra-mural School of Medicine of the Edinburgh Royal Colleges, but because of his greatly increased clinical responsibilities, he also gave this up. Nevertheless, he retained a keen interest in the extra-mural school and at the time of his death, he was Chairman of its Board of Governors and represented the Royal College of Surgeons of Edinburgh on the Scottish Triple Qualifications Committee of Management.

Haig Ferguson did not succeed to charge of wards in the Royal Infirmary until 1919, but within a few years of being appointed Assistant Gynaecologist he had become a very well-known figure in his specialty with a large and expanding private practice extending far outwith the confines of Edinburgh. The demands of this were never allowed to curtail

James Haig Ferguson (1862–1934).

The obstetric forceps designed by Haig Ferguson, widely used throughout the world.

his involvement in a wide variety of educational and philanthropic activities. He served on the governing bodies of the Royal Hospital for Sick Children, Donaldson's Hospital, Merchiston Castle School and the Queen's Institute of District Nursing, but his most important public service was as a member of the Central Midwives Board for Scotland and as its Chairman for 13 years up to the time of his death. He devoted much of his time to the work of the Board and guided its affairs with great wisdom. He vigorously promoted the Board's monumental survey of maternal mortality and morbidity in Scotland and was actively engaged in this work when stricken by his last illness. He also did a vast amount of work unobtrusively on behalf of the Lauriston Home for Unmarried Mothers and it would be fair to regard him as the mainspring of the activities that ensured its maintenance.

Haig Ferguson was, for 50 years, a member of the Edinburgh Obstetrical Society and the Society's *Transactions* contain many interesting papers which he presented at its meetings; his election as President of the Society for two separate terms of office gave him great pride and pleasure.

After ten years' service on the College Council, he was elected President in 1929 for what was then the statutory term of two years and in that same year he retired from his charge in the Royal Infirmary. He welcomed the establishment of the British College (later the Royal College) of Obstetricians and Gynaecologists and was proud to become one of its foundation fellows.

He was not a great public speaker and he derived little or no satisfaction from delivering formal systematic lectures, but as a clinical teacher of small groups of students at the bedside or in the out-patient clinic, he had few equals and no superiors; nor was he a prolific writer, but he made major contributions to the early editions of the famous *Combined Textbook of Obstetrics and Gynaecology* (1923). He was also co-author of the *Handbook of Obstetric Nursing* (1889), which enjoyed wide popularity.

As a gynaecological surgeon, his calm, deliberate, unspectacular technique achieved consistently good results, but it was as a supreme master of the art of obstetrics that he made his reputation. Furthermore, many years after his death, he is still universally remembered by his modified obstetric forceps, which are extensively used and which bear his name.

Haig Ferguson's multifarious commitments left him little time for recreation but he greatly enjoyed fishing and climbing. He was a member of the Monarch's Bodyguard for Scotland, the Royal Company of Archers, and on one occasion won the King's Prize for Archery.

At the time of his retirement, his academic and professional distinctions were recognised by the Royal Society of Edinburgh, which elected him to its Fellowship (FRSE) and by Edinburgh University, which conferred upon him the honorary degree of Doctor of Laws (LLD).

Haig Ferguson had a most gracious personality in which energy and determination combined with courtesy, sincerity, generosity of spirit and deep compassion to make a profound impression on all with whom he came in contact.

'His patients loved him and for them his mere presence at the bedside was a source of confidence and courage.' So wrote his colleague and obituarist, Professor R. W. Johnstone (q.v.), and an obstetrician could surely have no finer epitaph.

Roll number: 1612

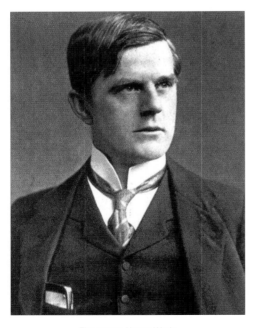

Sir Henry Wade (1876–1955).

Sir Henry Wade (1876–1955)

Sir Henry Wade was an innovative urological surgeon, a pioneer cancer research worker and a military surgeon. His contributions to the Royal College of Surgeons of Edinburgh extended over fifty years. He served as a lecturer, examiner, member of Council and as the College's representative on the General Medical Council. He was elected President in 1935.

Wade was a son of the manse, born in Falkirk. From the Royal High School of Edinburgh, he studied medicine at the University of Edinburgh, graduating with honours in 1898. He was appointed House Physician to Sir Thomas Fraser at the Royal Infirmary of Edinburgh in September 1899. The South African War broke out that year, and, inspired by the government's desperate call for surgical volunteers, Wade left for the Cape in the spring of 1900 and served as a civilian surgeon with the Royal Scots Fusiliers in the field, then for six months in a hospital in Pretoria.

On his return home two years later, Wade was invited by Francis Caird (q.v.) to be his Clinical Tutor. At the same time, he was appointed as a demonstrator in the Department of Anatomy of the University of Edinburgh. However, he soon moved to be a demonstrator in pathology and qualified FRCSEd in 1903, the year in which he was appointed Conservator of the College Museum. Pursuing research, he joined Ford Robertson, Pathologist to the Edinburgh Asylums Laboratory. The new science of bacteriology had been born and some investigators thought cancer might be a microbial disease. Wade and Ford Robertson, therefore, examined sections of human cancers using the metallic impregnation techniques employed to delineate the cells of the brain. They unwisely claimed early success. Their controversial results provoked national debate. After this experience, in which the two investigators effectively claimed to have found the cause of human cancer, Wade started a new experiment, transplanting a canine sarcoma into dogs, rabbits and foxes. In 1908, he reported his results in a beautifully illustrated paper in the *Journal of Pathology and Bacteriology*. He was awarded a gold medal for his MD thesis.

In the years ahead, he became a pioneer of prostatic surgery. Taking advantage of his experience in anatomy and pathology, Wade prepared serial whole sections through the cadaveric prostate in various stages of obstruction. He soon established an international reputation for his work, forming a close collaboration with Hugh Young of Baltimore. He was appointed Surgeon to Leith Hospital in 1909, where his surgical interests encompassed orthopaedics. By refusing to amputate the fractured leg of the young Norman Dott (q.v.), Wade determined the future career of the famous neurosurgeon. In 1912, Wade undertook the resection of a tumour of the proximal humerus from a young man whose bone defect he repaired by an allograft from the amputated femur of an elderly patient – one of the earliest examples of success with the technique of bone transplantation.

The young Henry Wade.

In September 1914, Wade was gazetted Temporary Captain in the Field Ambulance of the Scottish Mounted Brigade. Before leaving the country for Gallipoli, he had designed a mobile operating car that came into use later in the Palestinian desert as a sterilising unit. When Gallipoli was evacuated, he sailed with the Egyptian Expeditionary Force to Cairo. Weapons of war had altered little from those used in South Africa. What had changed was their mass use and the nature of the endemic diseases, such as malaria and schistosomiasis, encountered by the armies in the Nile delta and Jordan valley. Wade recorded 800 memorable photographs of the Mediterranean and Palestinian campaigns. His recollections of the 58 Edinburgh students and medical practitioners who enlisted with him in 1914 are contained in a poignant memoire entitled *The Flowers of the Field* (1920).

Henry Wade beside a mobile operating car in late 1914.

In Palestine, Wade observed that many fatalities among the wounded resulted from surgical shock caused by the long journeys to base hospitals. He encouraged the adoption of the Thomas splint and persuaded General Allenby to authorise its mass production. The use of the Thomas splint reduced the fatality rate from gunshot fracture of the femur from 40 per cent to 16 per cent. Wade became Consultant Surgeon in 1916 and commanded a surgical division. In 1919, he was twice mentioned in dispatches and was honoured with the CMG. He had already been awarded the DSO and the Order of the White Eagle of Serbia.

Returning to Edinburgh, he quickly began to develop facilities for urological surgery. He advanced the science of urinary surgery by the adoption of contrast pyelography and developed a dedicated urological diagnostic theatre in the Royal Infirmary; 21 original papers derived from this work. His contributions to urological surgery were recognised in 1932 when he gave the Ramon Guiteras lecture, and by his 1937 presidency of the section of urological surgery of the Royal Society of Medicine. He was elected President of the Royal College of Surgeons of Edinburgh in 1935, honorary Fellow of the Colleges of Surgeons of England, Ireland, America and Australasia and knighted in 1946. Soon after the Second World War broke out, Wade reluctantly accepted retirement but shortly afterwards, he was made Director of Surgical Services at the Emergency Medical Service Hospital at Bangour.

Pilmuir House.

Wade affected a simple homespun philosophy. He hid a kindly and generous disposition beneath a gruff exterior. Speaking of the Edinburgh Blood Transfusion Service, he commented that blood given 'must be the freewill offering of men who love their fellow mortals'. His wife predeceased him by nearly 30 years and towards the end of a long career, he spent much time in their country home, the beautiful 16th-century Pilmuir House, near Haddington, East Lothian. The Pilmuir estate had been owned by William Borthwick (q.v.), who had lived in Pilmuir House some 300 years before Wade. At the dinner given to mark the 50th anniversary of his first contribution to the affairs of the Royal College of Surgeons of Edinburgh, he presented to the College a copy of the famous portrait of King James IV of Scotland, who in 1506 had granted the Incorporation of Surgeons and Barbers its first Royal Charter.

Author: Dugald Gardner

Roll number: 1654

William J. Stuart (1873–1959)

W. J. Stuart (1873–1959).

'Pussy' Stuart in the Royal Infirmary of Edinburgh.

When a prominent individual from any walk of life is habitually referred to by a whimsically felicitous nickname, it usually indicates that he or she is an exceptional personality. There could be no better example of this than W. J. Stuart, who is remembered as one of the best-loved doctors ever produced by the Edinburgh medical school.

William James Stuart, a son of the manse, was born in Edinburgh and educated at the Edinburgh Academy, where he had a brilliant record both as a scholar and as an athlete. He was Gold Medallist and Dux of the school two years in succession and captained the Academy school teams at rugby, football and cricket. After leaving school, he played rugby for the Edinburgh Academicals over an eight-year period, during which they won the Scottish rugby club championship four times, and in 1901 he was first reserve for one of the greatest-ever Scottish International XVs. An aggressive, rampaging and superbly fit forward, he was rated the hardest tackler in Scottish rugby and many of his contemporaries felt that he was very unlucky not to have been awarded at least one international cap.

After school he entered Edinburgh University, from which he graduated MA in 1894 and MB ChB with honours in 1899. He then held resident posts in the Royal Infirmary and the Royal Hospital for Sick Children. In his first postgraduate year, he had the honour of being elected Senior President of the Royal Medical Society. Stuart then became an assistant in the University Department of Surgery under Professor John Chiene (q.v.) and, in 1903, he obtained the Fellowship of the College. In 1906 he was appointed Assistant Surgeon at the Church of Scotland Deaconess Hospital and three years later he achieved equivalent status at the Royal Infirmary as assistant to Sir Montagu Cotterill (q.v.), for whom he had the utmost respect and admiration, both as a surgeon and as a sportsman.

When war broke out in 1914, Stuart, who held a Territorial commission in the Royal Army Medical Corps, was mobilised for duty as an army surgeon and from 1916 to 1918 he served in this capacity with the British forces in Salonika and Macedonia. After the war, he returned to hospital and private practice in Edinburgh and in 1923 was appointed Surgeon in charge of wards in the Royal Infirmary – a position which he held until his retirement 15 years later. Throughout this period he had been increasingly involved in College affairs and in 1938 he was elected President – an office which had been held by his uncle, John Duncan, from 1889 to 1891. When the Second World War broke out in 1939, he was called from retirement so that a younger surgeon could be released for military service and he resumed charge of wards in the Royal Infirmary for a further three years.

During his early schooldays at the Edinburgh Academy, he had acquired the nickname 'Pussy' and this stuck to him for the rest of his life. It was a nickname affectionately bestowed and happily borne, but, to many, it seemed inappropriate for a tall, dignified, stately man of imposing presence and even less appropriate when his formidable prowess on the rugby field was recalled.

It was his conduct of his hospital practice that made his nickname seem entirely fitting, for there never was a kindlier, gentler or more compassionate doctor. No one could have been more completely dedicated to the relief of suffering. This intense feeling for his patients, combined with his courtesy, his integrity and his warm benevolence, earned for him the profound respect and affection of all who came in contact with him.

Stuart was an impressive diagnostician, a safe, if unspectacular, operator and an excellent lecturer but, throughout his 15 years as a chief in the Royal Infirmary, it was clinical teaching at the bedside that gave him the greatest satisfaction. He gloried in physical fitness and proceeded everywhere on foot or on his famous Sunbeam bicycle. He despised the motor car, the increasing use of which he predicted would lead to evolutionary atrophy of the hind limbs in *homo sapiens* and pitied all who seemed dependent on it. A dignified figure on his bicycle, he was a familiar sight on the streets of Edinburgh and the story of his daily passage across the busy road junction at the West End of Princes Street has become part of the city's folklore. He had operated successfully on the wife of the policeman who controlled the traffic at the West End and this worthy man's way of showing his gratitude was to halt the flow of vehicles coming from all directions and to stand rigidly at the salute as the surgeon pedalled unimpeded across the junction.

Stuart was a man of deep religious convictions who lived his life in accordance with strict Christian principles, but there was nothing austere or puritanical about him and he greatly enjoyed convivial gatherings, particularly if they included a generous leavening of young people. Throughout his life he was renowned as an after-dinner speaker and some of his most sparkling, post-prandial speeches were delivered when he was past his 80th year. His former house surgeons, several of whom achieved high professional distinction, would foregather at intervals for dinner in honour of their former 'Chief' and, on one of these occasions to his great delight, they presented to him a silver salver engraved with the figure of a cat riding a bicycle. It is sad that he died soon after a dinner given by his ex-residents in honour of his 85th birthday, but his career had been one of happiness and fulfilment and his end was as serene and dignified as his life had been.

Napoleon spoke of Baron Larrey, the chief surgeon of his *Grande Armée*, as 'the most virtuous man I have ever known' and all who worked with Stuart or who came under his care could and did say the same of him.

Roll number: 1675

H. M. Traquair (1875–1954)

Over the past 150 years ophthalmic surgeons have constituted a relatively small percentage of the College's total fellowship and, although in recent times their numbers have grown significantly, they remain a minor group in comparison with Fellows in the other surgical specialties. Given this numerical imbalance, it is remarkable that of the 64 Fellows who since 1855 have held the College's highest office, no fewer than seven were ophthalmic surgeons. Their election to the presidency is a striking testimony to their outstanding personal qualities as well as to their professional distinction and this is well exemplified by H. M. Traquair.

Harry Moss Traquair, born in Edinburgh, was the son of Ramsay Traquair MD, FRS, a distinguished anatomist, zoologist and palaeontologist who was keeper of the Natural History Collections in the Royal Scottish Museum. His mother, Phoebe Traquair, was a highly talented artist and craftswoman, celebrated in her own lifetime as a book illustrator, bookbinder, embroiderer, enamellist and particularly as a mural painter. Her artistic reputation, which had faded to some degree in the middle decades of the 20th century, has, in recent years, had a triumphant renaissance.

The Royal Medical Society

In 1734 six Edinburgh medical students acquired a cadaver which they dissected completely and when they finished this task they spent a convivial evening in a tavern.

After discussion of what they had learned from their anatomical labours they decided that they should meet regularly and that, at their meetings, each in turn should read a dissertation on a medical subject. This objective was not fully achieved until three years later when the original six students and four of their classmates formally constituted themselves as the 'Medical Society of Edinburgh'. This was the origin of the Royal Medical Society, which, having had a continuous existence since 1737, is probably the oldest undergraduate society in the world. It is certainly the only one to possess a Royal Charter which was granted by King George III in 1778.

The Society thrived from the beginning and within a few years had a large membership which included young doctors as well as medical students. It acquired its own Hall in Surgeons' Square close to old Surgeons' Hall, the home of the College from 1697 to 1828. For the next four years the College had no meeting place of its own but was granted, by the Society, rent-free accommodation in its Hall whilst Playfair's 'new Surgeons' Hall' was under construction. When in the 1960s the Society found itself temporarily homeless, the College generously reciprocated the hospitality it had received from the Society in 1828 and provided it, without rental, rooms in which it could continue its meetings. The Society now has commodious premises within the Edinburgh University Student Centre but as the autonomous owner of these premises it is entirely independent from the University.

The Royal Medical Society continues to flourish in the 21st century and the reading of a dissertation by a member is still an important feature of most of its meetings, which, along with its multifarious educational and social activities, are its considerable contribution to the quality of undergraduate medical training in the Edinburgh medical school.

Some of the most distinguished Fellows of the College whose lives and achievements are outlined in this book were active members of the Society in their student days and were profoundly influenced by it.

Harry Moss Traquair (1875–1954).

Harry Traquair was educated at the Edinburgh Academy and at Edinburgh University, from which, in spite of contracting tuberculosis, he graduated MB CM with first-class honours in 1901. One year later he took the Diploma in Public Health (DPH) and this was followed by a period of postgraduate study at the University of Halle in Germany. He obtained the degree of Doctor of Medicine (MD) from Edinburgh University in 1903 and in the following year he became a Fellow of the College. For health reasons he then went to South Africa and spent some three and a half years as a general practitioner in the Orange Free State.

Having decided to devote himself to ophthalmology, he returned to Edinburgh and was in due course appointed Assistant Ophthalmic Surgeon to the Royal Infirmary, to Leith Hospital and to the Edinburgh Eye Dispensary. At the same time he established himself in private practice and through his clinical and scientific publications acquired over the next few years a national reputation in his specialty. His foremost clinical and research interests lay in neuro-ophthalmology and for his work in this field he received a number of important awards, including the Middlemore Prize (1920), the Nettleship Medal (1922) and the Doyne Memorial Medal (1923).

In 1927 Traquair was appointed Ophthalmic Surgeon in charge of wards in the Royal Infirmary and also Lecturer in Diseases of the Eye in Edinburgh University. He was a member of the University's Senatus Academicus from 1932 to 1941 and served on the University Court from 1941 to 1949. His famous monograph, *An Introduction to Clinical Perimetry*, first published in 1927, ran to six editions and embodies the results of painstaking observations and investigations extending over many years. It became a world classic in a branch of ophthalmology with which the name of Traquair will always be associated.

He had for long been involved in College affairs and in 1939 was elected President; he held office over the first two years of the Second World War and it would be impossible to exaggerate the value to the College of his guidance and leadership at that difficult time. In 1940 he was due to retire from the staff of the Royal Infirmary but because of the absence on military service of younger colleagues, he was asked to continue in charge of wards and did so until 1943.

In 1943 and 1944 Traquair was President of the Ophthalmological Society of the United Kingdom and a member of the Council of the Faculty of Ophthalmologists. In 1948 he published another book, *Clinical Ophthalmology for Practitioners and Students*, which was well received and provided a popular, simple guide to its subject for the readership at which it was aimed.

Harry Traquair died after a long and distressing illness, which he bore with great fortitude. His contributions to neuro-ophthalmology were of the utmost importance and he could have no better epitaph than the words of Professor Norman Dott (q.v.): 'A man gifted with a powerful intellect, he had wide interests in biology and philosophy. These he focussed on his chosen work as a clinical oculist and as an ophthalmological research scientist ... a man exemplifying scientific integrity and comradeship, he was recognised and respected as an acknowledged authority on neurological aspects of ophthalmology or visual aspects of neurology throughout the world.'

Roll number: 1696

Duncan Fitzwilliams (1878–1954)

The Worshipful Society of Apothecaries, founded in 1617, occupies an honoured place among the historic Livery Companies of the City of London, and to be elected Master of this venerable and illustrious body is a notable distinction for any doctor. It is one which has been achieved by three Fellows of the College and the first of these was D. C. L. Fitzwilliams, who became a Liveryman of the Society in 1929 and served as Master in 1949–50.

Duncan Campbell Lloyd Fitzwilliams, known to friends, colleagues and students throughout his professional life simply as 'Fitz' was born in Newcastle Emlyn, Cardiganshire, Wales, and received his medical education at Edinburgh University. As an undergraduate he participated enthusiastically in several sports but concentrated mainly on boxing and rowing, at both of which he represented the University. His height of 6 ft 4 in and his rugged physique made him a formidable opponent in the ring and he not only won the amateur heavyweight championship of Scotland, but successfully defended his title one year later.

When the Boer War broke out, he volunteered for duty as a surgical dresser in the field hospital which, in support of the overextended resources of the Royal Army Medical Corps, was organised and led in South Africa by Professor John Chiene (q.v.). For this service, Fitzwilliams was awarded the Queen's South Africa medal with four clasps and having returned to Edinburgh for completion of his medical studies, he graduated MB ChB in 1902.

As a student, Fitzwilliams won several academic prizes and had the honour of being elected Senior President of the Royal Medical Society.

After holding junior hospital posts in Edinburgh and London, he obtained the Fellowship of the College in 1904 and the English Fellowship two years later. He became a demonstrator of anatomy at King's College and was appointed Clinical Assistant to the surgical out-patient departments at the West London Hospital and at the Hospital for Sick Children, Great Ormond Street.

He was awarded the MD with Gold Medal and the ChM with high commendation by Edinburgh University. In 1909 his 45 years of devoted service to St Mary's Hospital, Paddington, and its famous medical school started with his appointment as Surgeon to its out-patient department. There soon followed appointments to what would now be designated consultant posts in other hospitals, including Paddington Green Children's Hospital and the Mount Vernon Hospital and Radium Institute for Cancer.

At the beginning of the First World War he served with the 1st City of London Field Ambulance RAMC and later with the rank of Lieutenant Colonel. He was consulting surgeon, first in Malta and then in Rumania.

Towards the end of the war, he was seconded as consulting surgeon to the expeditionary force sent to fight the Bolsheviks in north Russia and in that campaign he had some remarkable experiences.

He was twice mentioned in dispatches and in 1919 was appointed Commander of the Order of St Michael and St George (CMG) in recognition of his distinguished military service. In addition, the French government made him a Chevalier of the Légion d'Honneur and he received a number of decorations from Rumania and from Russia.

D. C. L. Fitzwilliams (1878–1954).

The Worshipful Society of Apothecaries.

After demobilisation he returned to civil practice in London and in 1924 he was appointed Surgeon in charge of wards at St Mary's Hospital. In this capacity, he devoted himself mainly to the surgery of malignant disease and became a leading exponent of the use of radium combined with surgery in the treatment of several forms of cancer.

He was particularly interested in breast cancer, but his views on its treatment, which he promoted vigorously in lectures and in his publications, were, at that time, regarded as being almost heretical because of the challenge which they presented to the, then current, concepts of the mode of spread of cancer. Fitzwilliams, having cast doubt upon the scientific rationale of the Halstead radical mastectomy, began to practise local excision of small breast carcinomata and his vehement advocacy of this form of treatment aroused fierce controversy.

In spite of much highly unfavourable criticism, he adhered firmly to his beliefs, which he defended stoutly and which have ultimately been vindicated by modern advances in oncology. His ideas on breast cancer and its treatment are now recognised to have been ahead of their time. Indeed, it is interesting to compare the disparagement they received with the furore aroused by Robert McWhirter's (q.v.) early publications on the same subject.

'Fitz' was a rapid, dextrous operator with a technical delicacy remarkable in such a large, powerful man, which he probably derived from his extensive paediatric experience. He was an excellent teacher whether in the lecture hall or at the bedside and this, combined with his clinical wisdom and his warm, extrovert personality, made him popular with the St Mary's students and with young people generally.

He served terms as President of the clinical section of the Royal Society of Medicine, of the West London Medico-Chirurgical Society and of the Harveian Society of London. His election to this latter office was an appropriate recognition of his enthusiasm for the study of the history of medicine and of the erudition of his historical publications.

A keen Freemason, he attained high rank in Grand Lodge and for many years was Consultant Surgeon to the Royal Masonic Hospital. During the months of the London 'Blitz' in the winter of 1940–1, he resided at that hospital treating the air-raid casualties which were admitted every night.

Fitz's rural upbringing had imbued him with a love of country pursuits and field sports which persisted throughout his life and, until well past late middle age, he remained a skilled angler, an excellent shot and a low-handicap golfer.

He was renowned for his hospitality and for his unobtrusive, self-effacing generosity to all sorts of worthy charitable causes. Well described by one of his obituarists as a 'commanding presence, a good companion, a loyal colleague and a faithful friend', his career and its achievements brought honour to the College and to Edinburgh University, his alma mater.

Roll number: 1716

Benjamin Philip Watson (1880–1976)

Several surgeons have held university chairs in two different countries and one Douglas Roy (q.v.) in three. In the English-speaking world Professor B. P. Watson achieved the distinction of having directed academic clinical departments of obstetrics and gynaecology in three countries.

Benjamin Philip Watson was born in Anstruther, Fife, and educated in the town of his birth at Waid Academy. At an early age he decided that he wished to become a doctor and from school he went to St Andrews University for pre-clinical studies. He then moved to Edinburgh University, where he had a brilliant undergraduate career and from which in 1902 he graduated MB ChB with first-class honours and the award of the Ettles and Buchanan Scholarships.

Three years later the University conferred upon him its Doctorate of Medicine (MD) with a gold medal for his thesis and in the same year he became a Fellow of the College. In that year also he became a university tutor in Diseases of Women and held this post until 1912. For the last two years of this appointment he was a lecturer at the extra-mural School of Medicine of the Edinburgh Royal Colleges.

In 1912 Watson accepted an invitation to become Professor of Obstetrics and Gynaecology in the University of Toronto and Director of these departments in the Toronto General Hospital – the first time they had been united under one chief. In these capacities he rapidly established his reputation as an outstanding clinician, teacher and promoter of research. His academic activities were interrupted by the First World War, during which he held the rank of Captain in the Royal Canadian Army Medical Corps and served in England, Salonika and Macedonia.

Following Sir John Halliday Croom's (q.v.) retirement from the Edinburgh Chair of Midwifery in 1921, the University decided to amalgamate its Departments of Midwifery and Diseases of Women. Watson was invited to become Professor of the combined disciplines and in 1922 he returned to his alma mater. His tenure of the Edinburgh Chair was brief but within four years he radically reorganised the teaching of obstetrics and gynaecology in a manner which had important beneficial academic repercussions not only for the Edinburgh medical school but for several others in the British Isles. He considered that a thorough knowledge of pathology was the essential basis of sound gynaecological practice and the book *Gynaecological Pathology and Diagnosis* (1923), which in collaboration with Dr A. Freeland Barbour he wrote while Professor in Edinburgh, is one of the earliest English-language didactic texts devoted exclusively to this subject.

In 1926 Watson crossed the Atlantic again in response to an invitation to become Professor of Obstetrics and Gynaecology at Columbia University and Director of the Sloan Hospital for Women in New York City. He held these appointments for the next 20 years, during which he became a leading figure of the highest international stature in his field of medicine. Under his guidance the Columbia University Department of Obstetrics and Gynaecology became a world-renowned centre of excellence from which flowed an ever-increasing volume of impressive clinical and laboratory research, most of which had important practical applications. There could be no more significant testimony to the inspirational quality of his leadership than the fact that nine of his pupils and assistants went on to occupy university chairs in Great Britain, in Canada and the United States.

B. P. Watson (1880–1976).

Professor Watson was a Fellow of the American College of Surgeons, a foundation Fellow of the Royal College of Obstetricians and Gynaecologists and in 1936 had the honour of becoming President of the American Gynacological Society. There could be no more emphatic manifestation of the high regard in which he was held by the entire medical profession in the eastern United States than his election in 1948 to the presidency of the New York Academy of Medicine for a term which included its centennial celebrations.

After demitting office as President of the Academy, he returned to Scotland in 1951 to receive from Edinburgh University its highest honour, the honorary Doctor of Laws (LLD). He never forgot the land of his birth and nothing gave him greater pride than his election to the presidency of the St Andrew's Society of New York State.

Throughout his time in New York he did his utmost to increase his fellow citizens' awareness of Scotland and the Scottish contribution to American medicine, and his constant aim was to strengthen the ties of friendship between Great Britain and the United States.

Following retirement, Professor Watson continued to live in America and in 1975, as doyen of the College, he was delighted to receive its formal congratulations on his 70 years as a Fellow. He died the following year at his home in Danbury, Connecticut, aged 96.

Roll number: 1793

Robert W. Johnstone (1879–1969)

The Scottish educational system was traditionally based on exposure to a breadth of subjects across the curriculum, rather than the in-depth study of a few. Supporters of this approach will cite examples of the scientist or the doctor who is at the same time a connoisseur of arts, well versed in the classics, and fluent with language. Professor R. W. Johnstone will be remembered as much as a master of the written and spoken word as a respected professor of obstetrics and gynaecology. The quality of his writing is evident in his *Textbook of Midwifery*, while his after-dinner speeches, meticulously prepared, were delivered in Churchillian style. Yet his contemporaries, and his students, remembered him as a courteous, majestic figure, with a twinkle in his eye, and his trademark pince-nez dangling from its black cord or nonchalantly twirled in his right hand.

Robert William Johnstone was born a son of the manse in Edinburgh, educated at George Watson's College and Edinburgh University, graduating MA, and then MB ChB with honours. Having decided on a career in obstetrics and gynaecology, he spent some months in Vienna, where he observed Wertheim's practice, and in Prague, where he attended von Franque's clinic. His research from this period resulted in 1906 in an MD with honours. In that same, eventful year he became a Fellow of the College, a member of the Royal College of Physicians of Edinburgh and private assistant to Sir John Halliday Croom (q.v.). There is no doubt that much of Johnstone's prowess as an orator and teacher was derived from Croom. He adopted the same technique of preparing a speech or a lecture – writing, rewriting, learning by heart, then annotating and delivering with a relaxed spontaneity.

During the First World War, he became Medical Officer to the Royal Victoria (Red Cross) Hospital, going on to a commission in the Royal Army Medical Corps and becoming a surgical specialist to the No. 3 General Hospital in France. Towards the end of the war he was recalled to Britain to become Commissioner at the headquarters of the Ministry of National Service in London. In recognition of his war service he was awarded the CBE in 1920. After the war he lectured in the School of Medicine of the Royal Colleges and shortly thereafter was appointed Physician to the Royal Maternity Hospital and Gynaecologist to the Royal Infirmary of Edinburgh. In 1926 he succeeded Sir John Halliday Croom as Professor of Midwifery and Diseases of Women at the University of Edinburgh. A Foundation Fellow of the Royal College of Obstetricians and Gynaecologists, he was elected its Vice President in 1936. During the Second World War he served as President of the Royal College of Surgeons of Edinburgh.

His *Textbook of Midwifery*, first published in 1913, became a standard work throughout the English-speaking world and ran to 21 editions before he passed on the authorship. After the war he became Chairman of the Central Midwives Board for Scotland and President of the Edinburgh University Graduates' Association. The University awarded him an honorary Doctor of Laws (LLD) in 1950.

Many of his students and trainees remember him for his impeccable command of written and spoken English. His lectures were lucid and were delivered with authority and with style, laced with illustrative stories and anecdotes. To patients, he was immaculately dressed and courteous, and his ward rounds were grand events at which even the simplest task could be undertaken with great ceremony and ritual. Several of his trainees went on to become professors of obstetrics and he was held by them, and by others, in a degree of awe, but remembered with esteem and affection.

Roll number: 1851

R. W. Johnstone (1879–1969).

Sir Henry Holland (1875–1965)

In an increasingly secular post-imperial Britain, there is a tendency to belittle the work of medical missionaries in various countries that at one time were parts of the British Empire. Their great humanitarian achievements are ignored or forgotten, but they deserve to be commemorated and there can be few surgeons anywhere or at any time whose dedication and skill benefited more people than Sir Henry Holland, who spent most of his long life as a medical missionary in what is now Pakistan.

Henry Tristram Holland, the son of a canon of the Church of England, was born in Durham. He was educated at Loretto and at Edinburgh University, from which he graduated MB ChB in 1899. One year later he joined the staff of the Anglican Church Missionary Society hospital at Quetta, Baluchistan, and, having in 1907 obtained the Fellowship of the College, he was, in that year appointed medical superintendent.

By then his surgical prowess, especially in the treatment of two common but disparate conditions – cataract and urinary calculi – had gained for him an impressive reputation extending widely over the northern parts of the Indian sub-continent.

Sir Henry Holland (1875–1965).

He began to concentrate increasingly on ophthalmic surgery, but his hospital commitments made it necessary for him to maintain his wider skills and he remained a true general surgeon in the old-fashioned sense of that term.

In 1911 an Indian philanthropist built at Holland's request a hospital at Shikarpur in Sind, on the condition that he spent six weeks there every year doing cataract surgery. The Shikarpur Ophthalmology Clinic established by Henry Holland was soon attracting patients from most of the northern provinces of British India and from regions even further afield such as Afghanistan and some of the central Asian provinces of the Russian Empire. Holland realised early on that poverty, geographical isolation and rudimentary or non-existent communications made it impossible for more than a tiny fraction of those in need of his skills to make the journey to Shikarpur. Accordingly, he and his surgical team travelled, often on horseback or on camels, to remote tribal areas, where, usually under the most primitive conditions, they carried out successful cataract surgery on large numbers of patients. He was fluent in three of their indigenous languages and could maintain a simple conversation or take a medical history in four others. His respect and affectionate regard for the peoples of the wild, rugged and often lawless regions to which he brought his skills owed nothing whatsoever to colonial paternalism and everything to the Christian principles which guided him throughout his life.

During the First World War Holland served in the Indian Medical Service with the rank of Lieutenant Colonel and during most of this period he acted as Chief Medical Officer for Baluchistan.

In the 1920s and early 1930s his workload increased steadily, and in response to this the Church Mission Hospital at Quetta was considerably enlarged only to be completely destroyed by the catastrophic earthquake of 1935. Holland, on duty at the hospital at the time of the disaster, was buried in the ruins, from which he was rescued by his own son. Thanks largely to his Herculean efforts, funds were raised for the building of a new hospital, which, on completion, was amalgamated with the Church of England Zenana Hospital for women.

Between periods of duty at Quetta and at Shikarpur, Holland travelled to many remote and almost inaccessible places in various parts of the Indian sub-continent, where he and his team of assistants set up 'eye camps'.

Each 'eye camp' remained in its location for several weeks, during which many hundreds of ophthalmic operations were carried out with incalculable benefit to impoverished rural populations, for whom loss of vision was the worst of all personal disasters. There is no doubt that this work, which he regarded as practical Christianity, was, for him, the ultimate fulfilment of his life's purpose.

Henry Holland retired officially in 1948 and settled in England but from time to time he accepted invitations to return to Quetta and Shikarpur. Often substantial contributions to his travel expenses were made by tribal chiefs and other influential persons in the newly independent Republic of Pakistan. In his 85th year he ran an 'eye camp' in Sind, assisted by his two medical missionary sons, one of whom, Dr R. W. B. Holland, had become a Fellow of the College in 1946 (roll number: 4981).

It has been estimated that teams led by Henry Holland restored sight to well over 150,000 patients, of whom at least 10,000 underwent operation at his hands. However, throughout his life he considered this achievement to be of less importance than his work as a Christian preacher. This in no way diminished the respect and affection in which he was held by his mostly Muslim patients, who recognised in him a truly virtuous and benevolent man of faith.

His honours were supremely well deserved. He held the Kaiser-I-Hind silver and gold medals and in 1929 was made a Commander of the Order of the Indian Empire (CIE). He was knighted in 1936 and soon after retirement he was awarded the Lawrence of Arabia Medal. Two other honours which gave great satisfaction to his friends and former colleagues were the 1960 Ramon Magsaysay Award for Public Service from the Philippines, which he shared with his younger son, Ronald, and in 1961 the Sitara-I-Khidmat Award from Pakistan.

Roll number: 1879

James M. Graham (1882–1962)

The presidential portrait of J. M. Graham which hangs in the College is generally considered to be one of the finest works of the distinguished artist Sir Stanley Cursiter, President of the Royal Scottish Academy. It was presented to Mr Graham on the occasion of his retirement by his former house surgeons and it is a touching tribute to a chief whose character and personality, no less than his professional achievements, earned for him the respect and affection of all whose lives he touched.

James Methuen Graham was the son of Captain Dugald Graham, Master of the Northern Lighthouses Commission's vessel *Pharos*. He was educated at George Watson's College, Edinburgh, and at Edinburgh University, from whence he graduated MB ChB in 1904. As a student he was a notable athlete and represented the University at the high jump, the long jump and at shot putting; in addition, he held his place over several seasons as a forward in the Watsonian rugby XV, at a time when it was one of the best in Scotland. He was also an enthusiastic member of the Royal Medical Society, of which he was elected Senior President in the year after his graduation.

In later life, with the exception of the College presidency, none of the honours that he received gave him greater pride or pleasure than the presidency of the Watsonian Club in 1935 and the invitation to be the guest of honour at the first Royal Medical Society dinner to be held after the end of the Second World War.

By the time he graduated, James Graham was committed to surgery and after holding various junior hospital posts, he obtained the Fellowship of the College in 1907. He then became University and private assistant to Professor Alexis Thomson (q.v.), and nothing in his life had a greater influence upon him than his association with this extraordinary man, of whom he became a fervent admirer and a most devoted acolyte.

In 1919 Edinburgh University awarded him the degree of Master of Surgery (ChM) with the gold medal for his thesis and the Chiene Medal for the highest distinction in the examination. That same year he was appointed to the honorary staff of the Edinburgh Royal Infirmary as Assistant Surgeon and nine years later was promoted to Surgeon in charge of wards. In those days, a chief's tenure was limited to 15 years, but when Sir John Fraser (q.v.) resigned from the Regius Chair of

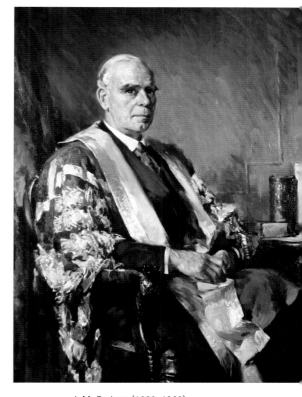

J. M. Graham (1882–1962).
Portrait by Sir Stanley Cursiter RSA.

Clinical Surgery in 1944 to become Principal of the University, Graham was called upon by the Infirmary Board of Management to take charge of Sir John's wards until such time as a new Regius Professor was appointed. This responsibility, which he held for nearly three years, gave him great professional satisfaction; he had always been sympathetic to surgical innovation and he exploited with enthusiasm and considerable success many of the new techniques which were being evolved at that time. In addition, it afforded him the opportunity of giving help and authoritative guidance to young surgeons returning from military service to the uncertainties of civilian practice at a time when the whole structure of hospital medicine in the United Kingdom was about to undergo radical change.

In 1949 he was appointed Chairman of the Edinburgh Postgraduate Board for Medicine, over which he presided with energy, wisdom and an abundance of down-to-earth common sense for nine years. There are doctors in many different parts of the world who still remember with gratitude the wise counsel they received from him while they were postgraduate students in Edinburgh.

James Graham was a tall, well-built, dignified man of imposing presence, totally devoid of personal or professional ostentation, and his modesty, courtesy and kindliness endeared him to his colleagues, his students, his nursing staff and, above all, to his patients. His clinical acumen and operative expertise were impressive and he was an excellent teacher, equally popular with both students and postgraduates.

He was one of the pioneers in Scotland of blood transfusion and his interest in this area, which persisted throughout his career, was appropriately recognised by his appointment in 1959 as Chairman of the Edinburgh Blood Transfusion Services Committee. His other great interest was thyroid surgery and he was one of the first Scottish surgeons to acquire a national reputation in this field. This was largely due to the consistently good results which he achieved in the operative treatment of hyperthyroidism at a time when this was considerably more hazardous than it is today. He also had a well-earned reputation in the surgery of pharyngeal carcinoma, and even in this field where outcomes were often disappointing he had some remarkable successes.

Junior posts in James Graham's wards were eagerly sought by young aspiring surgeons, and among his many pupils who went on to highly acclaimed careers were Norman Dott (q.v.), Ian Aird (q.v.), Maurice Ewing and James Lister, all of whom occupied professorial chairs of surgery with high distinction. It was fitting that such an inspiring teacher should be honoured by his alma mater in 1947 with the award of its honorary Doctor of Laws (LLD).

James Graham, a Fellowship examiner for many years, was highly respected by candidates for his kindly manner and his fairness. While his co-examiner was asking the questions, he would often make a rapid pen and ink drawing of the candidate under interrogation and the College retains a small collection of these impromptu sketches, among which are several recognisable likenesses of young doctors who subsequently became well-known surgeons.

For James Graham there could be no greater honour than election as College President and in his presidency (1945–7) he discharged his duties with dedication, dignity and profound respect for the College's history and traditions.

His wisdom, prudence, quiet efficiency and practical common sense were of inestimable benefit to the College during the difficult transitional period between the end of the Second World War and the introduction of the National Health Service. For this, no less than for his remarkable personal and professional qualities, his memory deserves to be honoured.

Roll number: 1889

Sir David Wilkie (1882–1938)

The widely held stereotype of the surgical leader as ruthless, domineering, cold and aloof seems to owe more to fiction than fact. While the capacity for hard work and the ability to organise and inspire are essential, many of the great figures in surgery have been notable for their warmth, charm and generosity. David Wilkie had all these characteristics and was one of the great, some would argue the greatest, surgeon produced by Edinburgh in the 20th century.

By any standards he was a surgical giant – an innovator who created, out of very little, a prestigious department which could vie with the best research facilities outside America. His 14 years as Professor of Surgery in Edinburgh saw surgical thinking transformed from the anecdotal, case-report style of the 19th century to the analytical, science-based style of the 20th. Yet to those who knew him – colleagues, assistants and students – the overriding memory was of his quiet and courteous charm.

David Percival Dalbreck Wilkie ('D.P.D.' to friends and colleagues) was born in Kirriemuir, the Angus village immortalised as 'Thrums' by J. M. Barrie. They were not contemporaries (Barrie was 22 years older) and they came from very different backgrounds: Wilkie was the son of a wealthy jute merchant while Barrie was the ninth of ten children, living in a small three-room cottage. Both achieved eminence in later life, when they became friends. When Barrie was appointed Chancellor of Edinburgh University in 1930 the friendship developed, strengthened no doubt by the bond of common threads in childhood. But there were differences. Barrie never escaped the influence of his formidable mother and part of him always wanted to remain the adored small boy, a part of his character that he drew upon in the creation of Peter Pan. Wilkie on the other hand was blessed with a less complex personality and a kindly nature. His friend and colleague, Henry Wade (q.v.), wrote 'never once did I hear him speak a hard or unkind word of anyone'.

From Kirriemuir, Wilkie moved to Edinburgh Academy and would speak fondly of his schooldays there. Graduating from Edinburgh University in 1904, he became a Fellow of the College in 1907 and two years later had obtained the degrees of MD and ChM. During house appointments in Edinburgh he worked under Sir Harold Stiles (q.v.) and Professor Francis Caird (q.v.), whose influence helped to mould his ideals and ambitions. Thereafter, as an aspiring surgeon, he travelled to three great European centres: Bonn, Bern and Vienna – before returning as private assistant to Francis Caird. Caird was a disciple of Lister (q.v.) and an advocate for experimental research in surgery. This time with Caird saw Wilkie's ambition to become a surgical scientist develop further.

Sir David Wilkie (1882–1938).

His first appointment was as Surgeon to Leith Hospital. Leith at that time was a bustling seaport whose prosperous business community helped foster a spirit of civic pride. Indeed at that time, Leith was a separate municipality, independent from Edinburgh. The surgical wing of the Hospital, built as the Queen Victoria Jubilee extension and opened in 1903, had wards constructed in the new Nightingale style, filled with light and more spacious to reduce the risk of infection. Wilkie came to a busy and modern surgical practice with Henry (later Sir Henry) Wade and John Struthers (later President of the College) as his colleagues. His time at Leith introduced him to the pleasures and responsibilities of an independent charge and saw the start of his contributions to the surgical literature. Before long he made his mark on the national scene. The Chirurgical Club (later the Moynihan Chirurgical Club), a travelling club founded by Lord Moynihan and containing many of the foremost surgeons of the day, required a representative from Edinburgh. In 1913 they chose Wilkie – then only 30 years old.

After war service as a naval surgeon, he returned to Edinburgh, where his genius as a teacher became increasingly apparent. His students would describe his eloquence, simplicity and clarity of presentation and his ability to make the dullest topic come alive. He joined Sir John Fraser (q.v.) in the extra-mural school. In 1923 when Professor Alexis Thomson (q.v.) resigned the Chair of Surgery, Edinburgh saw the need for a full-time Professor and a Rockefeller Foundation grant made this possible. Wilkie was appointed to the Chair of Systematic Surgery in Edinburgh in 1924.

He travelled to the United States as visiting professor at the Peter Brent Brigham Hospital in Boston, where he saw and liked American attitudes of discipline, criticism and forthrightness, and these he passed on to his pupils. In his 14-year tenure of the Chair, he was to make major contributions to the understanding of a variety of abdominal, particularly acute abdominal, problems. He clarified the natural history of acute appendicitis and of acute cholecystitis. He wrote on peptic ulcer, on intestinal obstruction and on surgery of the spleen and the biliary tree. He attracted around him a group of young surgeons, many of whom went on in turn to become professors of surgery. One of them, Sir Charles Illingworth (q.v.), described how, as House Surgeon under Sir Harold Stiles, he first came under Wilkie's influence: 'In the summer Stiles took a long vacation, so for three rapturous months in the absence of that formidable master, I basked in the sunshine of Wilkie's easy charm. Soon afterwards he invited me to be his assistant in private practice, and I can still recall the ecstasy, the heart-throb, the feeling of walking on air which his letter brought.'

Wilkie had recognised at an early stage the value of experimental research in surgery. He established a major research department next to the Reid School of Music in a building previously used for the teaching of anatomy to female students. This new facility included laboratories, an operating theatre, an X-ray department, a photography department and was adjudged the best equipped outside the USA. Appropriately, after his death it became known as 'The Wilkie'.

Wilkie's tireless energy and his ability to organise allowed him to combine a busy clinical practice in the Royal Infirmary, to head a series of research programmes, to teach and yet to maintain a large private practice. His private practice was inevitably criticised from some quarters. Yet its proceeds were used for some remarkable acts of philanthropy, usually without attendant publicity. Wilkie's surgical research department flourished to the extent that another floor was added, funded by an anonymous benefactor. In 1933 he bought the old Roxburgh Cinema in Edinburgh and after reconstruction presented it anonymously to the University Settlement, a charitable arm of the University. Renovated as Kirk o'Field College, it was formally opened by J. M. Barrie to offer skills training to unemployed people during the depression. Perhaps the childhood days in Thrums had instilled into Wilkie and Barrie a deep instinctive sympathy for those less fortunate. Barrie left all the royalties from *Peter Pan* books and plays in perpetuity to Great Ormond Street Hospital – surely one of the greatest acts of philanthropy in literary history. The true extent of Wilkie's beneficence only became known after his death. He had indeed been the anonymous benefactor who had paid for the extension to 'The Wilkie'. Beneficiaries of his considerable estate included the University Settlement, the Kirk o'Field College, the University and the children of Kirriemuir.

Wilkie's main legacy to surgery was the establishment of a scientific tradition of discipline and criticism in surgical research and clinical practice. These were attributes which passed to his pupils, who included Illingworth, Wilson and Aird. Hugh Dudley was later to point out that 'no fewer than 19 holders of chairs in the United Kingdom and Australia between 1955 and 1970 passed through the hands of these four men'.

Wilkie was to die from gastric cancer while only 56. The manner of his passing gives us insights into the difficulties and inadequacies of diagnosing and treating gastric cancer at that time. After a haematemesis and with continuing dyspepsia no fewer than four barium studies failed to show the tumour. It was eventually diagnosed by Wilkie himself feeling the mass in his abdomen as he lent across the operating table.

Perhaps the most fitting epitaph was written by his protégé, Sir Charles Illingworth: 'His greatest contribution lay in the influence he exerted among his colleagues and assistants. His genius lay in his ability to foster cooperation and inspire enthusiasm.'

Roll number: 1907

David Wilkie at the Peter Brent Brigham Hospital in Boston, Massachusetts.

Professor Sir David Wilkie in the lecture theatre.

Sir Samuel Irwin (1877–1961)

There can be very few men or women in any country at any time who after attaining eminence in their chosen profession in the course of their biblical quota of 'threescore years and ten' have then gone on to gain further distinction in the field of politics. This was the remarkable achievement of Sir Samuel Irwin, a notable Fellow of the College, who, at the age of 71, became a Member of the Parliament of Northern Ireland and brought to that legislative assembly the same wisdom, sincerity and integrity which had characterised his successful surgical career.

Samuel Thompson Irwin was born at Cool, County Derry, where his father farmed 80 acres of poor farmland, but spent his late childhood and adolescence at Bovally, near Limavady. He was educated at the Old Academy in Londonderry (later to become amalgamated with Foyle College), where he had an excellent record both in the classroom and on the sports field. In 1897 he entered the medical faculty of Queen's College, Belfast (later to become Queen's University), from whence he graduated BA in 1900 and MB BCh, BAO with honours and the award of the Coulter Exhibition two years later. He was elected President of the Students' Representative Council and of the Students' Union Society, but the main source of his undergraduate celebrity was his sporting prowess. Throughout his time as a student he played as a front-row forward in the Queen's College and Ulster rugby XVs and he was also an excellent cricketer and golfer. Between 1900 and 1903 he won nine Irish international rugby caps playing three times each against England, Scotland and Wales, and, in the 1901 game against England, it was his goal kicking that secured victory for Ireland. Irwin's rugby career was cut short by serious illness requiring major surgery, from which his convalescence was prolonged. However, he never lost his enthusiasm for the game, to which he gave devoted service off the field, and this was worthily recognised by his appointment as President of the Irish Rugby Football Union in 1935–6.

After serving as House Surgeon in the new Royal Victoria Hospital, Belfast, Irwin, now committed to a career in surgery, went to London, where, at St Peter's Hospital, he worked for two world-famous urological surgeons, Sir Peter Freyer and J. Thomson Walker. In spite of this, he found London uncongenial and was glad to return to Belfast, where he was appointed Surgical Registrar at the Royal Victoria Hospital. In 1906 he gained his Masters degree in Surgery (MCh) and two years later he became a Fellow of the College. However, his promotion to what would now be regarded as 'consultant status' did not come until 1911, when he was appointed Honorary Assistant Surgeon to the Ulster Hospital for Women and Children. There he had ample scope and stimulus for the further development of a special interest in orthopaedic surgery, which had been aroused by his association as registrar and as private assistant with A. B. Mitchell, a senior Belfast surgeon.

When war came in 1914, Irwin's previous serious illness rendered him medically unfit for military service overseas. Having joined the Queen's College Officers' Training Corps when it was founded in 1911, he did, however, hold the honorary rank of Captain in the Royal Army Medical Corps and throughout the war he served as Surgeon to the Ulster Volunteer Force Military Hospital in Belfast. Trauma and orthopaedic surgery formed the largest part of his work at the UVF Hospital. It was there that he first met Sir Robert Jones (q.v.), then Consultant in Orthopaedic Surgery to the British Army. From this meeting a warm long-lasting friendship developed and Irwin was one of the earliest members of the club founded by Sir Robert Jones which was to become the British Orthopaedic Association.

In 1918 Samuel Irwin was appointed Surgeon to the Royal Victoria Hospital, where he steadily enhanced his reputation as a clinician and teacher and coincidentally his private practice grew rapidly. Orthopaedic surgery was his main interest, but he remained a general surgeon in the old-fashioned sense of that term and, although not a spectacular or a particularly rapid operator, he achieved consistently good results without fuss or ostentation and his calmness and equanimity in the operating theatre were seldom, if ever, disturbed.

During the Second World War he was Chairman of the Northern Ireland Medical War Committee and Consultant Surgeon to the Forces in the province, in recognition of which, in 1947, he was appointed Commander of the Order of the British Empire (CBE).

Before and immediately after retirement from hospital practice he did much to facilitate the introduction of the National Health Service in Northern Ireland and rendered notable service to it as Vice Chairman of the Northern Ireland Health Services Board and as a member of the Northern Ireland Hospitals Authority. Outstanding among his extra-professional activities at this time were his presidency of the Central Presbyterian Association and his valuable services to his alma mater as a member of the Senate of Queen's University.

In 1948 Samuel Irwin stood as Unionist candidate in a by-election for one of the Queen's University seats in the Northern Ireland Parliament and was returned with a substantial majority. At Stormont, those same qualities which were the bedrock of his professional reputation earned for him the trust, respect and goodwill of his fellow Members and constituents of all parties. He held his seat through three further elections until his death in 1961, which occurred the day after he had been taken ill in Parliament.

In recognition of his impressive record of professional, public and legislative services, he was, in 1951, appointed Deputy Lieutenant of the City and County of Belfast and six years later he received the honour of knighthood.

Sir Samuel Irwin's life of high achievement as a sportsman, as a surgeon, as a leader of his profession and as a parliamentarian entitles him to an honoured place among the most distinguished alumni of Queen's University, with which he had an association extending over three generations. The Royal College of Surgeons of Edinburgh is no less proud to salute his memory. Sir Samuel's eldest son, J. W. S. Irwin, and one of his grandsons, S. T. Irwin, became Fellows of the College, and this family connection is probably unique in College annals. All three were or are surgeons on the staff of the Royal Victoria Hospital, Belfast. Like his father, J. W. S. Irwin also played rugby for Ireland and became President of the Irish Rugby Football Union.

Roll number: 1998

Sir Samuel Irwin (1877–1961).

The Irish Rugby Union XV, 1900.
Samuel Irwin is fourth from the right in the back row.

Professor John Fraser in the wards of
the Royal Infirmary of Edinburgh.

Sir John Fraser Bt (1885–1947)

The third and fourth decades of the 20th century are widely regarded as a golden age for Edinburgh surgery, largely because of the distinction of two remarkable men, Sir David Wilkie (q.v.) and Sir John Fraser, who, during most of that period, occupied respectively the University Chair of Systematic Surgery and the Regius Chair of Clinical Surgery. Their personalities were different but each of them in his own way, Wilkie the Lowlander and Fraser the Highlander, embodied in his character all the virtues and none of the vices of the stock from whence he sprung.

John Fraser, whose forebears on both sides of his family were farmers in Easter Ross, was born in Tain. His father died a few months later and he was brought up as an only child by his widowed mother. He always retained a deep affection for his birthplace and no honour that he received in later life gave him greater pride than the Freedom of the Royal Burgh of Tain. He was educated at Tain Academy and entered the medical faculty of Edinburgh University in 1902, gaining the class medal in clinical surgery as well as the Allan Fellowship. He graduated MB ChB with honours in 1907.

After holding resident posts in Edinburgh Royal Infirmary, Fraser was appointed House Surgeon to Harold Stiles (q.v.) at the Royal Hospital for Sick Children, and this was the start of a long association which was to be the single most important influence upon his career. He later became Stiles' assistant in private practice and at Chalmers Hospital and in 1910 he obtained the Fellowship of the College, the degree of Master of Surgery (ChM) with honours and the Lister Prize for his thesis on inguinal hernia.

With the encouragement of Harold Stiles, Fraser then embarked on his classic study of bone and joint tuberculosis in children, which was to make his surgical reputation. He showed that, in Scotland, the bovine form of the tubercle bacillus was the causative agent in 60 per cent of cases and this finding led to the introduction of legislation which, by ensuring the elimination of tuberculous infection from milk supplies, dramatically reduced the incidence of this form of the disease. In 1912 Fraser was appointed Assistant Surgeon to the Sick Children's Hospital and graduated Doctor of Medicine (MD) with the Gold Medal for his thesis on bone and joint tuberculosis. A number of his papers on the same subject received international acclaim, which, in 1913, resulted in him being invited to lecture in the United States and being made an honorary Fellow of the American Medical Association.

On the outbreak of the First World War, Fraser was commissioned in the Royal Army Medical Corps and served in France, in a casualty clearing station close to the front line. In 1916 he was wounded and awarded the Military Cross. During this period, his surgical reputation was further enhanced by his outstanding clinical and operative skill, by his important original observations on the pathophysiology of traumatic shock, by his work on blood transfusion and on the use of plasma substitutes and by his classic report (written jointly with Hamilton Drummond) on the treatment of penetrating wounds of the abdomen.

After demobilisation he resumed his work at the Sick Children's Hospital, where he was promoted Surgeon in charge of wards and was also appointed to the surgical staff of the Royal Infirmary. His adult practice increased rapidly but he remained best known as a paediatric surgeon, and his position as an international authority in this field was consolidated by the publication of his celebrated magnum opus *The Surgery of Childhood* (1926).

John Fraser's worldwide reputation made him the obvious successor to his mentor Sir Harold Stiles when that redoubtable surgeon retired in 1924 from the Regius Chair of Clinical Surgery, and, over the next 19 years, he enhanced its fame in a manner worthy of his great predecessors.

He was undoubtedly one of the most inspiring clinical teachers ever produced by the Edinburgh medical school and was a master of the art of the formal lecture. The educational impact of his teaching whether in the classroom or the out-patient clinic or on the wards was reinforced by the warmth of his personality, and by his ability to illuminate his discourse with blackboard sketches and diagrams of real artistic quality.

As a surgical diagnostician he was unsurpassed and in the operating theatre he was a master craftsman of supreme quality. Although a rapid operator, he never seemed to be hurried.

John Fraser was a true general surgeon in the original sense of that term, but besides paediatric surgery he had other special interests, among which were the surgery of the breast and of the autonomic nervous system. Surgical pathology was always one of his greatest enthusiasms and scattered through his publications are many original observations on the pathology of a wide variety of surgical conditions. Having as an army surgeon successfully sutured a gunshot wound of the heart, John Fraser maintained a perennial interest in the possible role of surgery in the treatment of cardiac disease at a time when medical orthodoxy held this to be virtually unthinkable. He was particularly interested in the surgical relief of angina, for which he carried out left cervical sympathectomy with some encouraging results, but his experience with O'Shaughnessy's operation of cardio-omentopexy was disappointing.

In 1940 he became the first surgeon in Scotland and the second in the British Isles to carry out ligation of a patent ductus arteriosus.

As Regius Professor, John Fraser's academic and professional distinction was recognised by the award of many honours. He was made an honorary Fellow of the Royal Australasian and the American Colleges of Surgeons and, in 1935, he was appointed Surgeon to HM the King in Scotland. Two years later he was made a Knight Commander of the Royal Victorian Order (KCVO) and, in 1942, he was created a Baronet.

Sir John Fraser throughout his life had always driven himself hard and the exigencies of the Second World War greatly increased his workload to the detriment of his health.

In 1944, he was invited to become Principal of Edinburgh University and although this meant giving up his life's work and taking on a host of new and unfamiliar responsibilities, his sense of duty and his loyalty to his alma mater compelled him to accept the invitation. Sir John's term of office as Principal was interrupted by illness and cruelly cut short by his untimely death but, under his guidance, the University's transition from wartime to peacetime conditions was smoothly accomplished, a number of important academic reforms were effected and several major developments postponed by the war were successfully inaugurated.

As Principal, Sir John's character and personality no less than his services to the University endeared him to the entire academic community, from which he received the same respect and affection that he had so worthily earned from his patients, students and colleagues during his 19 years as Regius Professor of Clinical Surgery. He gave the College devoted service and, throughout a career of the highest distinction, by precept and example, he enhanced its fame and prestige.

Roll number: 2071

Sir John Fraser Bt (1885–1947).

Sir Lancelot Barrington-Ward (1884–1953)

Rugby Union enthusiasts who have no personal recollections of the game when it was played only by amateurs must find it hard to believe that during the 15 years before the outbreak of the First World War, the Edinburgh University rugby team was one of the strongest and most consistently successful in the British Isles.

The XV of 1907–8 is arguably the best ever to have represented Edinburgh University and it was captained by an English medical student who subsequently became a Fellow of the College and who, in addition to winning even greater celebrity upon the rugby field, went on to a professional career of the highest distinction.

Lancelot Edward Barrington-Ward, born at Worcester, was the second of five sons of an Anglican clergyman, all of whom were King's (or Queen's) Scholars at Westminster School and all of whom were destined to make their marks in their respective callings.

After a classical education at Westminster and Bromsgrove Schools and Worcester College, Oxford, Lancelot Barrington-Ward entered the medical faculty of Edinburgh University, from which he graduated MB ChB with honours in 1908. Throughout his undergraduate course he played rugby for the University and in his final year was captain of a truly great XV, more than half of whom were current or future internationalists or international trialists. Four members of this team, which won all its matches and the Scottish Club Championship, went on in later life to achieve the honour of knighthood. Barrington-Ward also boxed for the University as a middleweight.

After holding resident hospital posts in Edinburgh and in London, he gained the Fellowship of the College in 1910 and, two years later, the Fellowship of the English College. In 1913 he proceeded to the ChM of Edinburgh University with honours and with the award of the Chiene Medal in Surgery.

In 1910 he became House Surgeon at the Hospital for Sick Children, Great Ormond Street, London, and this was the start of an association with that famous institution which lasted for the whole of his career and which was crowned 30 years later by his appointment as its Senior Surgeon.

After moving from Edinburgh to London, he continued to play first-class rugby and in 1910 his prowess was recognised by the award of four English international caps. He had the distinction of playing in the very first international match played at Twickenham and the England team of which he was a member were Five Nations Champions with three victories and one draw. Barrington-Ward is reputed to have been the smallest and lightest forward ever to play for England and to compensate for his slight physique, he must have had exceptional playing skills combined with speed and supreme fitness.

The English Rugby Union XV, 1910. Barrington-Ward is second from the right in the back row.

In December 1914 he was appointed Assistant Surgeon at Great Ormond Street, but by this time the First World War was raging and he volunteered for duty as Surgeon-in-Chief to Lady Wimburne's Hospital at Uskub in Serbia. For his distinguished services in this capacity he was awarded the Serbian Order of St Sava. Later he worked as a surgeon in British military hospitals and in 1918 he operated on HRH Prince Albert (later King George VI) for appendicitis.

Following demobilisation, Barrington-Ward returned to civilian surgery at Great Ormond Street, where he soon established his reputation as a paediatric surgeon. In 1919 he was appointed Surgeon to the Royal Northern Hospital, Holloway Road, London, and this enabled him also to build up a substantial adult practice.

During the 1920s and 1930s he achieved international recognition in the field of paediatric surgery and his book *The Abdominal Surgery of Childhood* (1928) became a standard didactic text. His contributions to adult abdominal surgery were scarcely less distinguished and many of them were embodied in the chapters he wrote for *Royal Northern Operative Surgery* (1939), the first two editions of which he edited.

In 1935 he was made a Knight Commander of the Royal Victorian Order (KCVO) and, in the following year, was appointed Surgeon to the Household of HRH the Duke of York, who, as Prince Albert, had been his patient 18 years previously. Following the Duke's accession to the throne as King George VI, Barrington-Ward became Surgeon to the Royal Household and, in 1952 after his retirement from active surgical practice, he was honoured by HM Queen Elizabeth II with the appointment of Extra-Surgeon to Her Household.

In the course of his professional career, he operated on three other members of the Royal Family, including Queen Maud of Norway, who honoured him with the award of the Grand Cross of the Order of St Olav.

He was President of the section of children's diseases of the Royal Society of Medicine and Hunterian Professor at the Royal College of Surgeons of England barely a year before he died. For several years he was an external examiner in surgery for the Universities of St Andrews and Edinburgh, and the renewal of his links with his alma mater afforded by the latter commitment was a source of great pleasure to him.

Barrington-Ward's reputation in paediatric surgery owed as much to his innate gentleness and kindliness as to his intellect and his clinical and operative skills. His remarkable ability to gain the confidence of his young patients and to establish a close rapport with them made a profound impression on colleagues, nurses and students and, most importantly, gave immeasurable comfort and reassurance to anxious parents.

Lancelot Barrington-Ward was a man of many parts who, in every aspect of his life, brought honour to the Edinburgh University medical school and the College is proud to salute his memory.

Roll number: 2121

Sir Lancelot Barrington-Ward (1884–1953).

William Anderson (1886–1949)

The characteristics of the inhabitants of north-east Scotland are, perhaps, best described in Lewis Grassic Gibbon's trilogy *A Scot's Quair* – down to earth, unpretentious, industrious, hard-headed and warm-hearted. 'Willie' (as he was universally known) Anderson exemplified the best of these characteristics. 'From an early age,' wrote his *Lancet* obituarist, 'toil and sweat were familiar and almost congenial companions, and the habits of industry, application and attention to detail, early acquired, became ever more deeply ingrained.' His professional life was dominated by two world wars, and he would look back on his experience in the First World War as the most formative of his career.

William Anderson (1886–1949).

Willie Anderson was born the eldest of a large farming family in rural Aberdeenshire. After schooling at Fordyce Academy, he graduated with distinction from Aberdeen University in 1909 with gold medals in both medicine and surgery. He went on to become House Surgeon in Aberdeen Royal Infirmary to Sir John Marnoch and Sir Henry Gray, and the latter was to become a major influence in the early stages of his career, an influence which he was always happy to acknowledge. After studying in Edinburgh, in Tübingen and in Berlin, he became FRCSEd in 1912 and the following year was appointed to the staff of Aberdeen Royal Infirmary as an anaesthetist, a recognised stepping stone to a surgical career at that time.

During the First World War he served as a regimental medical officer in France and went on to command the surgical division of a field hospital. He regarded this experience as one of the most important parts of his life, and during this time he acquired a vast surgical experience, was mentioned in dispatches and was appointed Officer of the Order of the British Empire (OBE).

Returning to Aberdeen Royal Infirmary in 1919 as Assistant Surgeon, he again found himself in the service of Sir Henry Gray. Here he built a reputation as a skilled surgeon, characterised by zest, enthusiasm and a huge capacity for hard work, but endowed also with the humanity of his native Aberdeenshire. He had the gift to put patients at their ease, talking to them in their native Doric, which he was to use to great effect throughout his life.

Despite the demands, by any standards, of a heavy surgical workload, he made time for both research and teaching. His research at the Rowett Institute allowed him to claim proudly in later life that he had 'even been Surgeon to the pigs at the Rowett'.

He was a natural teacher and his enthusiasm for teaching endeared him to a generation of students and young surgeons in the Aberdeen medical school.

In the period before specialisation in surgery, he remained a general surgeon to the end. Yet, he was at the forefront of the establishment of two major surgical specialties in Aberdeen – neurosurgery and thoracic surgery. He was the first to practise thoracoplasty in Aberdeen, which was to become a common surgical treatment for pulmonary tuberculosis with persistent cavitation. He was a founder member of the Society of Thoracic Surgeons and went on to become its President. In 1941 he was elected President of the Association of Surgeons of Great Britain and Ireland.

During the Second World War he was appointed Director of the Emergency Medical Service for North and North-East Scotland and then went on to become Consulting Surgeon, Scottish Command, with the rank of Brigadier. He died while still working and was remembered by contemporaries with affection, a companion with a seemingly inexhaustible fund of stories, an inspiring teacher, an industrious surgeon held in affection and respected by patients and colleagues alike.

Roll number: 2249

J. C. B. Grant (1886–1973)

From the First World War to the end of the 20th century, medical students around the world studying anatomy became familiar with the name (and initials) of Dr J. C. B. Grant, and most had cause to be grateful. His was to become one of the best-known names in the world of anatomy teaching. Blessed with a gift for a clarity and simplicity in writing and in drawing, he simplified apparently hopelessly complex anatomical relationships, and his textbooks became best-sellers. Grant's *Method of Anatomy*, Grant's *Atlas* and his *Handbook for Dissectors* all ran to multiple editions, and helped generations of medical students and doctors throughout the world to learn anatomy.

John Charles Boileau Grant was born in Edinburgh a son of the manse. His family were descended from Huguenot stock and he claimed descent from a mayor of Paris. As a medical undergraduate in Edinburgh, he won the anatomy medal in Professor Cunningham's class and this early achievement decided him to pursue a career in anatomy. He worked as a demonstrator first in Cunningham's department and then in the University of Durham under Professor Howden, the editor of *Gray's Anatomy*. This early introduction to the authors of the two major English language texts of anatomy set the stage for his own work as a writer of anatomy texts. After a post in ear, nose and throat surgery in Bristol, he took the Fellowship of the College and was posted, on the outbreak of the First World War, as medical officer to the Grenadier Guards and thereafter to the Black Watch. During this time he won the Military Cross and bar for attending to wounded soldiers under fire. At the end of the war he emigrated to Canada, initially to the Chair of Anatomy in the University of Manitoba in Winnipeg. Eleven years later he became Professor of Anatomy at the University of Toronto. He was by any standards an outstanding teacher with an encyclopaedic knowledge and a flare for illustration.

Grant's *Method of Anatomy, Descriptive and Deductive* (1937) enjoyed a huge success which ran to many editions and continued to be published after his death. Its strength lay in the clarity of the text, which brought logic to the learning of the body's structure and brought anatomy alive for medical students the world over. Grant's *Handbook for Dissectors* (which ran to nine editions between 1940 and 1984) and Grant's *Atlas of Anatomy*, first published in 1943 completed, the trilogy. *The Atlas* continued to be published in succeeding editions even after his death. Between them they have run to over thirty editions and been translated into five languages. After retirement, he was invited to be visiting professor to the University of California at Los Angeles, and continued actively teaching anatomy until his 84th year.

He could justly be regarded as one of the most distinguished anatomists and probably the best-known teacher of anatomy in the world in the 20th century.

Roll number: 2314

Dr J. C. B. Grant (1886–1973).

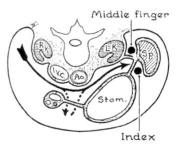

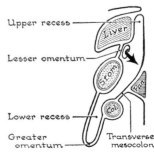

Grant's simple diagrams, which in these examples clarify the anatomy of the lesser sac and its relations.

Douglas Guthrie (1885–1975)

Most surgeons are satisfied with success in a single career. A few achieve distinguished success in two, and Douglas Guthrie was one of these. After a clinical career as an ear, nose and throat surgeon, making particular contributions to paediatric aspects of ear, nose and throat practice, he went on to a second, perhaps even more successful, career as a medical historian. His *History of Medicine* proved to be one of the most popular ever written on the subject, and he proved to be one of the most distinguished medical historians of his generation.

Douglas James Guthrie was born in Dysart, Fife, the son of a minister. After education at Kirkcaldy High School and the Royal High School of Edinburgh, he graduated in medicine with honours from Edinburgh University in 1907. The award of the McCosh Travelling Scholarship allowed him to pursue postgraduate studies in Berlin, Hamburg, Jena and Vienna. As was common at that time, he went into general practice for six years before entering specialist training. He graduated MD in 1909 and was elected Fellow of the College in 1914. During the First World War he served with the Royal Army Medical Corps and thereafter was Commandant of a hospital for Royal Flying Corps officers. Returning to Edinburgh, he was appointed lecturer to the extra-mural School of Medicine and ENT surgeon to the Royal Hospital for Sick Children. He pursued his interest in speech disorders in childhood, which resulted in a pioneering book *Speech in Childhood*, published in 1935. His eminence as an ENT surgeon was recognised by his election as President of the section of otology of the Royal Society of Medicine.

Retirement from clinical practice allowed his career as a medical historian to blossom. From 1945 to 1956 he was Lecturer in the History of Medicine at Edinburgh University, succeeding his close friend, John Comrie, author of the seminal *History of Scottish Medicine* (1927).

In 1945 his magnum opus, *History of Medicine*, was published. This was reviewed in *The Observer* by George Bernard Shaw, who pronounced it 'most readable, unique and well worth the price'. It went on to be published in German, Spanish, Italian and American editions and remains a popular work. It has since been described as the most readable, literary and witty history of the profession ever written. Yet at the same time Guthrie managed to retain accuracy and academic credibility.

His book *Janus in the Doorway*, published in 1963 (the Roman god Janus was depicted as having two faces, one looking back and one looking forward), was an eclectic collection of his papers and lectures. Other published works included a biography of Lister, entitled *Lord Lister: His Life and Doctrine* (1949) and histories of the Royal Hospital for Sick Children and of extra-mural medical education in Edinburgh.

To further his researches, Guthrie travelled widely and this resulted in his election as Chairman of the Council of the Royal Scottish Geographical Society. He founded the Scottish Society for the History of Medicine and became its Honorary President. He was also President of the section of the history of medicine of the Royal Society of Medicine and President of the British Society for the History of Medicine, which he had also helped to found.

His lasting contribution was to stimulate interest in medical history through his writing, which remains to this day both readable and authoritative.

Roll number: 2365

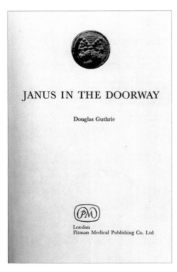

Douglas Guthrie (1885–1975).

JANUS IN THE DOORWAY

Douglas Guthrie

London
Pitman Medical Publishing Co. Ltd

Janus in the Doorway.
A collection of Guthrie's papers and lectures published in 1963.

John Kirk (1881–1959)

The motives of the medical missionaries are criticised by some who suggest that the missionary seeks to impose a religious creed on a captive audience in return for medical care. That criticism could certainly not be levelled at John Kirk, a deeply religious man who spent 20 years working in south China, where he was influential in establishing formal medical education.

John Kirk, son of the Rev. John Kirk of Edinburgh, was educated at George Watson's College and Edinburgh University. After graduation he went to New Zealand and from there to China, where he was to spend the next 20 years of his life, initially under the aegis of a New Zealand Presbyterian mission. He took the Fellowship of the College while on home leave in 1914. In 1920 he visited Canada and the United States as a member of a small delegation, which had been funded by the Rockefeller Foundation, whose aim was to organise support for formal medical education in south China. As a result of this visit the first university medical schools were founded in China. When the medical school in Canton was opened in 1924 he was given charge of the Department of Anatomy going on to become Chairman of the Department. In 1923 he was elected President of the China Medical Association.

Returning to London, he became a demonstrator in anatomy in University College, where his skills as a teacher of surgical anatomy influenced students from all over the world. His own undergraduate training in Edinburgh had been under two outstanding teachers of anatomy, Sir William Turner (q.v.) and Professor Cunningham of textbook fame.

Kirk was able to combine a love and detailed knowledge of anatomy with long experience as a surgeon, which made his anatomy classes for surgical trainees among the most popular of their day.

A tall man with natural dignity and courtesy, John Kirk was motivated throughout his life by a deep religious conviction.

Roll number: 2388

Alice Hunter (1889–1973)

Alice Hunter (1889–1973).

For the first 415 years of its existence, the Incorporation, and then the College, reflecting the practice of the day in society, admitted only men to its Fellowship. It was not until 1876 that legislation was enacted to enable women to attend medical schools and graduate in medicine in Britain. In 1911 Eleanor Davies-Colley became the first woman Fellow of the Royal College of Surgeons of England. Prejudice persisted, however, until after the First World War when further legislation paved the way towards equality of opportunity. Alice Mabel Headwards Hunter was the first woman to become a Fellow of the Royal College of Surgeons of Edinburgh. She spent her professional life in India, caring mainly for women and children.

Alice Hunter was born in India, where her father was an officer in the Indian army. After qualifying in medicine from Dublin, she returned to India serving as a Captain in the Royal Army Medical Corps in the British Troop Hospital in Bombay. On leaving the army, she worked in Peshawar Municipal Hospital for Women and Children, becoming the doctor in charge.

The Parliamentary Qualification of Women Act of 1918 allowed women to stand for Parliament and in 1919 the Sex Disqualification Removal Act was passed in Great Britain making it illegal to exclude any woman from employment because of her gender. In the months following the passing of this Act, Nancy Astor became the first woman Member of Parliament to take her seat in the House of Commons and on 20 October 1920 Alice Mabel Headwards Hunter became the first woman to be admitted as a Fellow of the Royal College of Surgeons of Edinburgh.

She returned to the north-west frontier of India to work before going to Calcutta, where her surgical practice was largely devoted to caring for women and children. She was also Divisional Surgeon to the Calcutta Brigade of the St John's Ambulance, an organisation that she was to support throughout her life. She became President of the Young Women's Christian Association (YWCA) in Calcutta and later President of the all India YWCA.

In 1933 she went as a front-line St John's Ambulance doctor to the area which had been devastated by the Monghyr earthquake. The Second World War saw her practice intensify particularly when fighting reached the Indian–Burmese border.

In 1942 she was one of the first women to go into Nepal when she was invited to attend a member of the Nepalese royal family at a time when Nepal remained a closed country. The following year, during the Bengal famine, she was asked by the Bengal government to set up a temporary hospital for child famine victims. After the war her services were recognised by the Indian government by the award of the Kaiser-i-Hind medal, which was presented to her by the Governor of Bengal. She was made an honorary life member of the St John's Ambulance Association, an honour which gave her great pleasure. In the post-war years, she served in Karachi among women refugees.

Her historic achievement in becoming the first woman Fellow of the Royal College of Surgeons of Edinburgh was acknowledged by the College in 1970 on the 50th anniversary of this achievement.

Roll number: 2655

Francis Robert Brown (1889–1967)

At a time when surgery was emerging from a craft practised by generalists to one where specialists were to dominate, a few general surgeons had the skill, the courage and the vision to take on new specialist procedures. F. R. Brown was one such, introducing cardiac and neurosurgery in Dundee.

Frank Brown, as he was always called, was born in Jedburgh, in the Scottish Borders, where his father was a farmer and he was one of a family of seven. After graduating in medicine in 1913, he went on to house posts in Glasgow Royal Infirmary and then in the Royal Hospital for Sick Children in Edinburgh, where he was influenced by the magisterial Sir Harold Stiles (q.v.). His surgical training continued until 1915 when he was called for service in the Royal Army Medical Corps, serving with distinction in Salonika as a surgeon. He was mentioned three times in dispatches, made an Officer of the Order of the British Empire (OBE, Military division, then a new decoration), and also received the Imperial Russian Order of St Stanislaus. Returning to Edinburgh armed with the rich experience of the war surgeon, he obtained the Fellowship of the Edinburgh College in 1920, and was appointed an assistant in the Department of Surgery in University College, Dundee, then part of St Andrews University. Following the death of Professor Price, he became Surgeon in Dundee Royal Infirmary and Senior Surgeon after the retiral of Professor R. C. Alexander in 1951.

In 1938–9 he was President of the Dundee division of the British Medical Association, a senior Fellow of the Association of Surgeons in 1956, and an active member of the Moynihan Club. At various points in his career he was an examiner at the universities of Edinburgh, Glasgow and Newcastle. He retired from the Eastern Regional Hospital Board Service in 1959 but continued in private practice. After retirement from the NHS and University, he had the unusual honour of being appointed Honorary Reader in Surgery at St Andrews University. Predeceased by his wife in 1952, he died after a long illness just before his 78th birthday.

These are the calendar events of Frank Brown's career, outlining the more important aspects of his life and status as a surgeon. Yet, it was as a thinking surgeon and superb technician that he is remembered by all who came into contact with him and fell under his spell.

His successor, Stanley Soutar, captured his surgical vision in a *British Medical Journal* obituary: 'The expanding horizons of surgery attracted him,' he wrote. 'New methods were constantly introduced, and once mastered, a search for new virtues began.' And so he carried out the first significant neurosurgery in Dundee, performing leucotomies, and was the first to undertake cardiac surgery when he ligated a patent ductus. Professor D. M. Douglas (q.v.), on his appointment in late 1951, was happy to assist Frank Brown and learn from him. It is certainly worth speculating that had Brown been younger and had become a cardiac surgeon, cardiac surgery might have flourished in Dundee.

It was his surgical technique which made him unique. In the words of Stanley Soutar, he was 'a supreme technician, unhurried and unruffled, bringing to each operation the scrupulous skill he had learned from Sir Harold Stiles'.

The most important of his scientific interests was referred pain, a topic on which he wrote several papers. On the social side he was a keen golfer, once having a handicap of 10 at the Royal and Ancient Golf Club. But

F. R. Brown (1889–1967).

shooting and fishing were his real passions, and on his beloved South Esk he would instruct and entertain his juniors, aided by a bottle of whisky, on a day's fishing they would not forget. His support for his juniors was unstinting, and it was not surprising that four of them became professors of surgery in due time.

A strong opponent of boxing, he wrote regularly to the press arguing against it in his own name. He also enjoyed writing highly witty retorts to the press on a variety of subjects under the pseudonym 'Ad Astra'.

However, he was also a heavy smoker all his life and used to smoke while scrubbing up. He would discard the last pre-operative cigarette after he had finally cleansed his hands with spirit.

In the words of his son, David Brown: 'My father was a kind man and a good father. He would only speak when he had something interesting to say. The biggest thing he wanted in people was to be truthful.'

Author: John Blair

Roll number: 2683

Gertrude Herzfeld (1890–1981).

Gertrude Herzfeld (1890–1981)

Before becoming the first woman to take her seat as a Fellow of the College, Gertrude Herzfeld had initially to overcome many of the barriers and the prejudices which still existed against women doctors in the years before and after the First World War. She went on to become a paediatric surgeon in Edinburgh, the first woman to hold such an appointment in Scotland.

Gertrude Marian Amalie Herzfeld was born in London, to where her parents had emigrated from Austria. She had decided early on in life to become a doctor, despite the widespread prejudice which prevailed against women in medicine at that time. As an undergraduate in Edinburgh, she was one of the earliest winners of the Dorothy Gilfillan Prize for the best woman student of the year, at a time when men and women had to attend lectures separately. She graduated in 1914 and was the first woman House Officer appointed by Sir Harold Stiles (q.v.). During the war she worked as a surgeon in the Royal Army Medical Corps Hospital in Aldershot, and on her return to Edinburgh she became Assistant Surgeon at the Royal Hospital for Sick Children and later Surgeon to the Bruntsfield Hospital for Women and Children. In 1920 she became the first woman to take her seat as a Fellow of this College (although Alice Hunter (q.v.) was the first to pass the Fellowship examination). In 1925 Mr (later Sir) John Fraser (q.v.) was appointed to the Regius Chair of Surgery, creating a vacancy to which Gertrude Herzfeld was appointed, along with Norman Dott (q.v.), as Surgeon to the Royal Hospital for Sick Children, making her the first woman surgeon in Scotland. Over the next 30 years she developed a growing practice which encompassed the full range of paediatric surgery, but in particular the developing sub-specialty of neonatal surgery. A contemporary described her as 'large in every best sense of the word – large in heart and in mind'.

Throughout her life she promoted the cause of women in medicine, latterly becoming President of the Women's Medical Federation.

Roll number: 2686

Sir Walter Mercer (1890–1971)

In the second half of the 20th century, the major improvements in the results of surgery, brought about by the advance of clinical science, tended to obscure, if not actually to downgrade, the importance of operative craftsmanship in the total care of surgical patients. Technical expertise is, however, regaining its former status among the attributes of a successful surgeon and time spent in a surgical skills laboratory has become an essential component of training at both basic and advanced levels. It is appropriate, therefore, to celebrate the career and salute the achievements of a great Scottish surgeon whose astonishing clinical versatility and supreme operative dexterity became legendary.

Sir Walter Mercer (1890–1971).

Walter Mercer, the son of a tweed mill-owner, was born at Stow, Midlothian, and educated in Edinburgh at George Watson's College and at Edinburgh University, from which he graduated MB ChB in 1912. During the First World War he served with the Royal Army Medical Corps on the Western Front, mostly as a regimented medical officer in some of the bloodiest battles fought there. Part of his time in the trenches was spent with the battalion of the Royal Scots Fusiliers, commanded for several months by Winston Churchill. Towards the end of the war, he was seconded to the surgical division of a field hospital and this was the start of what was to become a brilliant surgical career.

In 1921 Mercer obtained the Fellowship of the College and four years later he was appointed to the staff of the Royal Infirmary of Edinburgh as Assistant Surgeon in the wards of Professor (later Sir) John Fraser (q.v.). There he took responsibility for the management of all fractures and most of the orthopaedic cases, which, in those days, long before the full development of the specialties, were treated in the general surgical wards. He did not, however, restrict himself to fractures and orthopaedics, and soon developed a reputation for outstanding technical skill in other areas of surgery.

In 1932 he published his famous magnum opus *Orthopaedic Surgery*, which ran to six editions in his lifetime and was translated into several foreign languages. For many years this was the foremost British didactic text in orthopaedics and its success was an impressive achievement for a single author.

Mercer was a popular and effective teacher at the bedside or in the out-patient clinic and his instructional imitations of the abnormal gaits associated with various orthopaedic conditions acquired a celebrity which many a professional entertainer might have envied.

The spread of his reputation far beyond the limits of Edinburgh brought him a large and steadily increasing private practice, but the demands of this were never allowed to encroach upon the time he devoted to his work for the Royal Infirmary and for other voluntary hospitals.

In the 1930s and early 1940s he extended his activities to include most of the thoracic surgery in south-east Scotland. Having, in 1938, been appointed to the charge of wards in the Royal Infirmary, he became one of the first surgeons in Scotland to achieve the successful operative treatment of congenital cardiac disease.

Sir Walter Mercer in the operating theatre.

During the Second World War, with many of his younger colleagues serving abroad with the armed forces, Mercer's workload was prodigious and covered most of the surgical specialties. In modern times there can have been few 'general' surgeons who more thoroughly deserved that descriptive term but such was his orthopaedic reputation that in 1948 Edinburgh University appointed him to be the first incumbent of the newly established Law Chair of Orthopaedic Surgery. Until 1951 he continued with his general surgical activities, but thereafter devoted himself solely to his professional specialty and to the development of a new Edinburgh academic Department of Orthopaedics.

He was President of the College from 1951 to 1956 and there is no doubt that he was one of the greatest holders of this office in modern times. He initiated changes and reforms which led to the transformation of the College from a somewhat introverted institution concerned almost entirely with examinations into a vigorous, innovative centre of higher surgical education with an international influence which has expanded progressively since then. The 450th anniversary of the College's foundation occurred during Mercer's presidency and he was largely responsible for the planning and organisation of the outstandingly successful celebrations which marked this notable occasion.

He was knighted in 1956 and many other honours and distinctions came to him but none gave him greater satisfaction than the vice presidency of the British Orthopaedic Association and the presidency of the Watsonian Club.

'Wattie', as he was known throughout his life to his friends, colleagues and students, was a slightly built, trim figure with a brisk manner and a well-developed dry, pawky sense of humour. He inspired the utmost loyalty and devotion of all who worked for him and many young surgeons whom he trained went on to achieve highly successful careers.

He was a keen curler and golfer, a skilled fisherman and a good shot but the sport at which, in his younger days, he excelled was tennis. He was a serious philatelist with a valuable stamp collection built up over many years and also a recognised authority on Scottish postal history, to which, following his retirement in 1958, he devoted much of his time right up to his death in 1971.

Wattie Mercer earned his place in Scottish surgical history and the fame that he enjoyed during his lifetime through the highest technical virtuosity, but he was also a caring, compassionate doctor with the gift of inspiring his patients with total confidence and they held him in the same high regard as did his colleagues and students. His name will be long remembered in the Edinburgh medical school and by the College for which, as its President, he did so much.

Roll number: 2716

Norman Bethune (1890–1939)

There are few famous surgeons even among those of the highest professional and scientific distinction whose achievements have won for them general, popular acclaim in their own countries, and fewer still have gained widespread international celebrity. Only one has ever become a posthumous national hero and nearly seven decades after his death he not only retains his heroic stature, but is held up as a role model to the schoolchildren of the most populous nation on earth.

Henry Norman Bethune, the son of a Presbyterian minister of Scottish ancestry and the grandson of Norman Bethune (q.v.) was born in Gravenhurst, Ontario. After graduating from high school, he worked as a teacher and as a newspaper reporter before entering the medical faculty of the University of Toronto in 1912.

On the outbreak of the First World War, Norman Bethune immediately volunteered for military service and was posted to a Royal Canadian Army Medical Corps field ambulance for duty as a stretcher bearer. His unit went to France early in 1915 and he was wounded in action later that year. As a result of this, he was invalided out of the army. Having returned to Canada, he completed his medical training at the University of Toronto, from which he graduated in December 1916. He then went back to England and was commissioned as a Surgeon Lieutenant in the Royal Navy, from which he was demobilised early in 1919. It was at this stage that he decided to become a surgeon and, after holding various junior posts in England and Canada and attending a postgraduate course in Edinburgh, in 1922 he obtained the Fellowship of the College as his grandfather had done before him.

Bethune started his surgical career in Detroit, where he sought to establish himself in private practice. However, in 1926 he contracted pulmonary tuberculosis and had to spend many months in a sanatorium, where his treatment included artificial pneumothorax. This experience inspired him to devote himself to thoracic surgery, a specialty then in its infancy. He obtained the necessary training in the professorial surgical department of the Royal Victoria Hospital, Montreal, where his 'Chief' was Dr Edmond Archibald, Professor of Surgery in McGill University and a pioneer of thoracic surgery in Canada.

In 1930 he was appointed first assistant to Dr Archibald and although carrying a heavy clinical workload, he became actively involved in research and published several original papers. He also invented a number of ingenious instruments and appliances, some of which featured in medical suppliers' catalogues and were widely used.

Bethune was inherently a man of independent spirit and although his surgical abilities were impressive, this characteristic, combined with impetuosity, a contempt for established convention and an idiosyncratic temperament, conspired to make him a 'difficult' colleague. His relationship with his chief, Dr Archibald, which had originally been cordial, became strained beyond breaking point and, in 1932, he resigned his post at the Royal Victoria Hospital.

Soon afterwards he was appointed Surgeon to the tuberculosis unit of the Sacré Coeur Hospital on the outskirts of Montreal, and it was at this stage that he began to express publicly his radical opinions on the provision of health care. His Scottish Presbyterian roots and his family's long tradition of service to those less fortunate were probably responsible

Norman Bethune in the Trudeau Sanitorium, 1927.
He is smoking, showing a
characteristic defiance of the rules.

Norman Bethune in Spain in 1937.
He was made Director-in-Chief of the
Canadian Medical Unit, which acted as
a mobile blood transfusion service.

'… utter devotion to others without any thought of self … We must all learn the spirit of absolute selflessness from him.'

Mao Tse-tung writing about
Norman Bethune in 1939.

for his highly developed social conscience. He was deeply concerned with the medical implications of poverty and deprivation, and over the next three years, he became a vehement and sometimes strident advocate of the establishment in Canada of a comprehensive National Health Service. A visit to Soviet Russia in 1935 powerfully reinforced his beliefs and in the following year he joined the Communist Party in Canada.

When the Spanish Civil War broke out in July 1936, Norman Bethune resigned his hospital appointment in Montreal and went to Spain, where he was enrolled in the Republican military medical services with the rank of Major. He was stationed in Madrid, which was then under almost constant air and land attack by the rebel Nationalist forces, but, although there were heavy casualties to be dealt with, he was not given the opportunity of exercising his surgical skills.

On his own initiative, and with the help of other Canadian volunteers, he set up a blood transfusion service which, within a few weeks, was supplying blood not only to hospitals in the beleaguered capital, but also to field surgical units on the other battle fronts.

The Republican medical bureaucracy, which Bethune considered to be both incompetent and corrupt, sought to impose increasingly restrictive control upon his activities and this created what was, for him, an unacceptable situation. He resigned his commission in May 1937 and returned to Canada, where he received a hero's welcome from all who dreaded the prospect of a fascist victory in Spain. He engaged actively in fundraising on behalf of the Spanish Republican cause, but later in 1937 his attention became focused on the Japanese invasion of China. Bethune regarded this as a major extension of the worldwide struggle between democracy and fascism, and he was determined to be personally involved in it as a military surgeon with the Chinese communist forces.

He travelled to China in January 1938 and made his way to Hankow, which, since the Japanese capture of Peiping (Beijing) and Nanking, had become the temporary capital. Here, he informed the Chinese military authorities that he had come to serve in the communist 8th Route Army and would not go elsewhere.

After an extremely hazardous journey, during which he only narrowly avoided capture by the Japanese, Bethune reached 8th Route Army Headquarters in the mountains of Shansi province, where he outlined his plans for establishing a base hospital. Soon after his arrival, he was summoned to meet the communist leader, Mao Tse-tung, who opposed this project on the grounds that there was a much greater need for mobile field surgical units capable of functioning close to the battlefield. Bethune was in no position to argue with Mao. Over the next 20 months the volume and scope of his operative and organisational activity was prodigious, but such was his energy and dedication that, in addition, he was able to establish a field hospital with an associated medical training school. Later, he planned and set up a special school of military surgical practice and wrote a training manual entitled *Organisation and Techniques for Divisional Mobile Operating Units* (1939).

Bethune's charismatic personality combined with his selfless devotion to duty and his operative skill to make him an almost legendary figure throughout the Chinese communist forces. In spite of the appalling problems which confronted him daily, it is clear from his letters that this was the happiest time of his life, during which he felt for the first time that he was fulfilling his destiny. Constant intense surgical activity without respite under primitive and often highly dangerous conditions took its toll and, in November 1939, having accidentally cut one of his fingers while operating on an infected patient, he developed septicaemia, from which, a few days later, he died.

His funeral was attended by more than 10,000 people and one month later the essay 'In memory of Norman Bethune' by Mao Tse-tung was published. After China became a communist state 10 years later, this essay became one of 'the three most read articles' that all Chinese were urged to study and the story of Norman Bethune's life was made part of the elementary school curriculum. Postage stamps bearing his image were issued, statues of him were erected and in the 21st century he is remembered and revered in China as the personification of 'selflessness, dedication and responsibility'.

Roll number: 2778

The statue of Norman Bethune in Shih-chi-chuang, the Cemetry of Martyrs. Across the street, beside the Bethune museum, is the Norman Bethune International Peace Hospital.

Norman Dott (1897–1973)

The factors which determine success in any one surgical career can be difficult to analyse. A compassionate concern for patients and a meticulous attention to detail are two which most would regard as essential. Norman Dott had both of these in abundance, his compassion for patients sharpened by his own experiences, and his attention to detail the result of his training in and aptitude for engineering.

While a teenage engineering apprentice, a motorcycle accident had brought him into contact with surgeons and decided him on a career in surgery. His engineer's flair for design and invention continued throughout his life. Norman Dott trained under Harvey Cushing, the father of modern neurosurgery, and went on to establish neurosurgery in Edinburgh. He was the first doctor since James Young Simpson and Joseph Lister (q.v.) to be awarded the Freedom of the City of Edinburgh.

Norman McOmish Dott was born in Colinton on the southern outskirts of Edinburgh. His forbears were Huguenots, originally called D'Ott, who had settled in Fife. His grandfather, Aitken Dott, had founded the firm of Art Dealers, Aitken Dott and Son, which still trades in Edinburgh. His father, Peter Dott, developed the firm and in his early days was a supporter and patron of the Scottish colourists, particularly Samuel Peploe and William McTaggart.

After attending George Heriot's School, sited literally across the street from the old Royal Infirmary of Edinburgh, Dott became an engineering apprentice. Riding his motorcycle home to Colinton, he was involved in a collision which resulted in multiple fractures of the left leg. In the Royal Infirmary he was under the care of Henry Wade (q.v.), who decided not to amputate the leg, but the incident left him with a permanent limp. The following year, enthused and inspired by this encounter, he determined to be a surgeon and enrolled as a medical student in Edinburgh, graduating in 1919, and becoming a resident in the Royal Infirmary. After obtaining the Fellowship of the Royal College of Surgeons of Edinburgh, he worked as a lecturer in physiology under Professor Sharpey-Schafer, who had marked him out as an outstanding student. Here his researches included a study of

Norman Dott. Caricatured by Emilio Coia on the occasion of his receiving the freedom of the City of Edinburgh.

Norman Dott (1897–1973).

Norman Dott. A characteristic pose
with the ever-present pipe.

the effects of pituitary ablation. This led to the award of a Rockefeller Fellowship with Harvey Cushing, in Boston. If Godlee (Joseph Lister's nephew and biographer), Sir William Macewen and Sir Victor Horsley were the British pioneers, it was Cushing who refined and made safe modern neurosurgery. Working with Cushing inspired the young Dott – both were perfectionists, original thinkers and tireless workers.

Returning to Edinburgh in 1924, Dott embarked on a career in surgical neurology. The facilities did not exist for this fledgling specialty and he was required to improvise. His initial appointment was to the children's hospital, where he established the equipment. Adult neurosurgery was performed in nursing homes, to where the equipment and instruments were taken by car and taxi. In those early days his repertoire encompassed much of paediatric surgery and he would later commend this to young surgeons as valuable training for any branch of surgery. His observations on the malrotation of the intestines in the neonate, published in 1924, and illustrated with his own drawings, helped both the understanding and management of this condition and the paper remains a classic to this day. It was Sir David Wilkie (q.v.) who offered him adult beds in the Royal Infirmary, which led to the establishment of the Neurosurgical Unit in Ward 20, largely funded by the Rockefeller Foundation and the Scottish industrialist Sir Alexander Grant.

As a result of his drive, the Department of Surgical Neurology at the Western General Hospital was established and he was largely responsible for the design. His pioneering spirit resulted in some notable innovations. He was the first person in Britain to demonstrate an arteriovenous malformation in the brain using angiography. He pioneered the operation for treating aneurysm of the middle cerebral artery by wrapping the lesion with muscle. Throughout his life he retained his engineer's love of design and invention. His clamps for intestinal anastomosis remained in use in Edinburgh until the end of the 20th century; he designed retractors, traction callipers and operating tables, all with an engineer's precision and care for detail. Well into retirement, he responded to the challenge of a colostomy by establishing Edinburgh's first stoma clinic, inevitably designing and producing his own stoma appliances and devices.

He was the first holder of the Chair of Neurological Surgery in Edinburgh and was instrumental in establishing the British Society of Neurological Surgeons with Sir Geoffrey Jefferson in Manchester and Sir Hugh Cairns in Oxford, two other pupils of Harvey Cushing. He became President of that Society, Vice President of the Royal College of Surgeons of Edinburgh and was made a Companion of the Order of the British Empire (CBE).

Of the many honours that came his way, that which gave him greatest pleasure was being made a Freeman of his native City of Edinburgh in 1962.

His philosophy of 'do what is best for the patient' endeared him to the lay public. Perhaps this was the result of his life-long experiences as a patient: saved from an amputation (which might have prevented his surgical career) by Sir Henry Wade; a chronically painful hip fused by Sir Harry Platt; leg shortening by Sir Walter Mercer (q.v.); a cordotomy for chronic pain by his friend Sir Geoffrey Jefferson and a colostomy by Tom McNair (q.v.). Experiences of life as a patient undoubtedly contributed to his greatness as a surgeon.

Roll number: 2862

Ernest C. Fahmy (1892–1982)

E. C. Fahmy was, in his day, one of Scotland's most eminent obstetricians and gynaecologists and also a considerable all-round sportsman, but, although his nickname 'Fighter' was bestowed with total respect and admiration, he never once stepped into a boxing ring.

Ernest Chalmers Fahmy, the son of an Egyptian father and a Scottish mother, was born in Amoy, China, where his father, an Edinburgh graduate, was a medical missionary. He was educated at a school for the sons of missionaries (now Eltham College, Kent), which he entered a few years before another Edinburgh-trained missionary's son, Eric Liddell, the famous Olympic sprinter, whose athletic achievements are so vividly commemorated by the film *Chariots of Fire*.

The Scotland Rugby Union XV, 1920. Ernest Fahmy is seated on the ground on the right.

Fahmy entered the Edinburgh University medical faculty in 1911 and gained undergraduate fame as a rugby player, as a track athlete and as a gymnast. He played in the University rugby team at a time when it was one of the strongest in the British Isles and was given a Scottish trial in 1913.

On the outbreak of the First World War in August 1914, he immediately joined the army and served with the Royal Artillery on the Western Front from 1915 to 1917, where he was wounded three times. After sustaining his third wound, he was invalided out of the army and resumed his medical studies at Edinburgh University, from whence he graduated MB ChB in 1918.

After holding a resident hospital post in Edinburgh, he spent three and a half years conducting a large general practice in the mining town of Abertillery, south Wales – a community where rugby football enjoyed almost the status of a surrogate religion. There he won the admiration, respect and friendship of his patients, not only for his professional competence and dedication but also as a brilliant fly-half for the famous Abertillery Rugby Club. He was given a Welsh trial and might have played for Wales but the Scottish rugby selectors remembered that they had given him a trial in 1913 and in 1920 he was chosen to play for Scotland in a team which won three of its four international matches that year.

His general practice experience stimulated his interest in obstetrics and gynaecology to such an extent that he decided to make his career in that specialty. In 1922 he returned to Edinburgh as House Surgeon to Dr Haig Ferguson (q.v.) in the Royal Infirmary and later as resident obstetrician in the Royal Maternity and Simpson Memorial Hospitals.

He obtained the Fellowship of the College in 1923 and was appointed to the University Department of Midwifery and Gynaecology, first under Professor B. P. Watson (q.v.) and later under Professor R. W. Johnstone (q.v.). In this capacity he laid the foundations of his future reputation as a dynamic and inspiring teacher of both students and postgraduates. He also had responsibility for the department's histopathological service, and, through his painstaking application to this exacting task, he acquired the encyclopaedic knowledge of gynaecological pathology for which he later became famous.

Ernest C. Fahmy (1892–1982).

In 1926, Fahmy was appointed a clinical tutor and senior clinical assistant to Dr Haig Ferguson in the Royal Infirmary, and one year later he transferred in the same capacity to Professor R. W. Johnstone's unit. This was the start of his long and happy association with Professor Johnstone, to whom he gave unstinting clinical and academic support for the next 12 years. During this period he acquired his reputation not only as a supremely skilled obstetrician and gynaecological surgeon, but also as a gentle, kindly and compassionate doctor. He built up a large private practice which included patients from all over Scotland. Furthermore, there could be no more impressive testimony to both his professional expertise and the warmth of his personality than the large number of doctors' wives whom he attended.

In 1930 Fahmy became a member of the Royal College of Physicians of Edinburgh (MRCPEd) and was advanced to its Fellowship (FRCPEd) eight years later. He was a foundation member of the British College (later the Royal College) of Obstetricians and Gynaecologists, of which in 1936 he became a Fellow (FRCOG).

In 1944 he succeeded to the charge of wards in the Royal Infirmary and the Simpson Memorial Maternity Pavilion. The advent of the National Health Service in 1948 increased his clinical and teaching commitments in the Royal Infirmary, but, in spite of this and the demands of his private practice, he involved himself extensively in extra-curricular medical activities.

He was an examiner in his specialty for three universities, for the two Edinburgh Royal Colleges, for the Royal College of Obstetricians and Gynaecologists and for the Scottish Central Midwives Board. He also served on several College and University committees.

From 1948 to 1951 he was President of the Edinburgh Obstetrical Society, which a few years later conferred on him the honour of its honorary Fellowship. Ernest Fahmy was not a prolific writer, but his publications, like his teaching, were lucid, trenchant and stimulating. During the 1950s he was a notable contributor to that famous Scottish compendium, the *Combined Textbook of Obstetrics and Gynaecology*.

Soon after winning his four international caps for Scotland, he gave up rugby and thereafter confined his sporting activities to golf and salmon fishing.

In 1942 his only son, a pilot in the Royal Air Force, was lost on a flight from Gibraltar to Malta and until well after the end of the Second World War he retained the hope that his son might have been taken prisoner and would eventually return safely. The realisation that he would not see his son again affected him very deeply, but his personal faith and his professional dedication helped him to bear his burden of grief. In the immediate post-war years he took on a clinical and teaching workload which increased steadily right up to his retirement in 1958.

Ernest Fahmy's character and achievements won for him the respect and affection of all who knew him. He was a man of strong opinions and high principles; the former he might change if convinced by rational arguments but the latter were unshakeable, and it was his vehement steadfastness in their defence that earned him his nickname 'Fighter'.

Roll number: 2909

Thomas Porter McMurray (1887–1949)

The tradition of excellence in orthopaedic surgery in Liverpool was maintained by T. P. McMurray, an orthopaedic surgeon in the direct line of Hugh Owen Thomas and Sir Robert Jones (q.v.). His textbook of orthopaedic surgery became a classic, and he achieved eponymous fame with rotation osteotomy of the femur, but above all his pupils remembered him as a supreme master of the craft of operative orthopaedics, and a modest, unassuming personality with an impish sense of humour.

Born in Belfast, Thomas Porter McMurray graduated from Queen's University in 1910 and went to Liverpool the next year as House Surgeon to Sir Robert Jones. For a young doctor coming under the magnetic charm of such an influential figure it was understandable that he set out to devote himself to orthopaedic surgery. During the First World War he was Surgeon to the Military Orthopaedic Hospital at Alder Hey, where his mentor Sir Robert Jones had responsibility for training English, Canadian and American surgeons.

He obtained FRCSEd in 1923, and after clinical appointments at the David Lewis Northern Hospital in Liverpool and the Royal Liverpool Children's Hospital, he became Director of Orthopaedic Studies in Liverpool in succession to Jones in 1933. When the first Chair of Orthopaedic Surgery was established in Liverpool in 1938 he was the obvious choice. Those fortunate enough to work with him remembered him as a supremely gifted orthopaedic surgeon, and a skilled and speedy operator. As the years went by, he operated less and developed the Liverpool tradition for conservatism in orthopaedic surgery. He developed the original Lorenz osteotomy for malunion of femoral neck fracture and developed displacement osteotomy for osteoarthritis of the hip, the widespread adoption of which further enhanced his reputation. Those who came to observe him were always impressed by his dexterity as an operator and the skill and artistry of his technique.

His hero was Hugh Owen Thomas, whose principles he practised and taught throughout his life. He could be dogmatic and intolerant if Thomas' principles were denied. He wrote the *Life of Hugh Owen Thomas* in 1935 and followed this shortly afterwards with *A Practice of Orthopaedic Surgery*, written in clear and simple English.

In personal terms he could be as brusque and outspoken as Hugh Owen Thomas, yet as charming and kind as Robert Jones. He was essentially shy, unassuming and disliked pomposity.

McMurray truly succeeded to the most famous tradition in British orthopaedics when he joined Hugh Owen and Robert Jones and his name appeared below theirs in the famous practice at 11 Nelson Street. During an air raid in 1941 this famous house was destroyed and with it his records and memorabilia.

Away from surgery it was his vitality and his sense of fun that endeared him to friends. He was valued by many as a companion and his perpetual appearance of youth allowed him a boyish sense of humour.

His legacy was to develop the great postgraduate school of orthopaedics in Liverpool, which he maintained and fostered in the tradition of Hugh Owen Thomas and Robert Jones.

He died suddenly in 1949 and was buried in Denbigh. He had been President of the British Orthopaedic Association and at the time of his death was President elect of the British Medical Association.

T. P. McMurray (1887–1949).

Surgeons' Lives: An Anthology of Biographies of College Fellows over 500 Years

Roll number: 2913

Sir Gordon Bell (1887–1970)

Among the students entering the medical faculty of Edinburgh University in 1905 were no fewer than 17 from New Zealand and one of them, the bearer of an illustrious surgical name, was to achieve professional fame comparable to that of any of his distinguished namesakes who also feature in this book.

Francis Gordon Bell, the grandson of a sheep farmer from Annandale, Dumfries, who had emigrated to New Zealand in the early 1860s, was born at North Bank Station on the Wairau river, Marlborough, in the South Island. He was educated at Marlborough High School, where he did not shine academically but became captain of rugby and vice captain of cricket.

From school, Gordon Bell went to Edinburgh University for medical training and after having won the Vans Dunlop Prize for anatomy in 1908 he graduated MB ChB in 1910. By this time he was determined to become a surgeon, but, instead of immediately acquiring clinical experience in junior hospital posts, he took the unusual course of becoming a demonstrator in the University anatomy department and held this appointment for the next four years. Influenced and encouraged by the famous Edinburgh neurologist Dr Alexander Bruce, he conducted research on the cellular structure of the cerebral cortex and this formed the basis of the thesis for which, in 1913, he was awarded the degree of Doctor of Medicine (MD).

In 1912 Bell started his clinical career in the Royal Infirmary as House Surgeon to Professor Alexis Thomson (q.v.) and, having obtained the Fellowship of the Royal College of Surgeons of England, he went on to hold Resident Surgical Officer (RSO) posts in Liverpool and in Salford. A visit to Professor August Bier's department at the Charité Hospital in Berlin was followed by time spent in the United States at the Mayo Clinic, where the quality of his work earned for him not only the commendation but also the friendship of both Dr Will Mayo and Dr Charlie Mayo.

When Bell returned to Britain in 1915, the First World War was raging and he immediately joined the Royal Army Medical Corps and was sent to France with the 20th General Hospital. In 1916 he was posted to No. 21 Casualty Clearing Station (CCS) as a surgical specialist and gained his first experience of military surgery during the four and a half months of the Battle of the Somme. He was then transferred to No. 48 CCS and, with this unit, he was heavily involved in the treatment of casualties from all the major Western Front battles of 1917 and 1918. For his distinguished services to the wounded, he was awarded the Military Cross and mentioned in dispatches.

After demobilisation in 1919, Gordon Bell returned to Edinburgh and from 1920 to 1923 he was Clinical Tutor in the Royal Infirmary under his old 'Chief', Alexis Thomson, who influenced him greatly and for whom he had profound admiration and respect. It was during this period that his classic study of the pathology of testicular tumours was published in the *British Journal of Surgery* (1925) and this received international acclaim. In 1924 he was appointed Assistant Surgeon to the Royal Infirmary, which made it necessary for him to become a Fellow of the Edinburgh College and he passed the examination later that year.

A few months later the Chair of Surgery at the University of Otago in his native land became vacant and Gordon Bell's application for appointment to it was successful. He took up his duties in Dunedin in March 1925 and soon established his reputation as an inspiring clinical teacher and as a skilful and versatile operator. To begin with he had to be a truly 'general' surgeon in the old-fashioned sense of that term, but he was in no doubt that increasing specialisation in surgery was both desirable and inevitable and he actively promoted the establishment in Dunedin of units devoted to separate surgical specialties and their integration into the University Department of Surgery.

During the Second World War his academic staff was severely depleted by the absence on military service of several of its members and this, combined with a substantial increase in the intake of medical students, laid a heavy teaching burden on Bell's shoulders, which was made even more onerous by much heavier clinical commitments.

The founders of what was then called 'the College of Surgeons of Australasia' met in Dunedin in 1927, with Gordon Bell an enthusiastic supporter of the new institution. He was a Foundation Fellow of what would become the Royal Australasian College of Surgeons and from then on he played an increasingly active part in its affairs both in New Zealand and in Australia. He served 10 years on the Australasian College Council, during which he was Vice President (1943–7) and President (1947–9).

Gordon Bell retired in 1952 with the title of Emeritus Professor and, in her Coronation year (1953), HM the Queen appointed him a Knight of the Order of the British Empire (KBE).

He was succeeded by Mr Michael (later Sir Michael) Woodruff (q.v.), who, in 1957, was appointed to the Chair of Surgical Science at Edinburgh University. There was a hiatus of some months between Professor Woodruff's departure and the arrival of his successor, and during this period Sir Gordon Bell acted as full-time head of his old Department of Surgery.

His autobiography *A Surgeon's Saga*, published in 1968, is a fascinating and modest account of a remarkable career which contains vivid reminiscences of his early surgical training in Edinburgh and of his experiences as an army surgeon during the First World War. His last public appearance before his death was his attendance at the University of Otago centenary celebrations in 1968 as the official representative of his beloved Edinburgh College.

Roll number: 2959

Sir Gordon Bell (1887–1970).

T. McW. Millar (1894–1970)

To be asked to take on the professional care of a colleague or a member of a colleague's family is, for any surgeon, a very special accolade and, among the Fellows of the College who feature in this book, there is none with a better claim to be remembered as 'the surgeon's surgeon' than T. McW. Millar.

Thomas McWalter Millar, known throughout his life simply as 'Tommy', was born one of a family of eight children in Tranent, East Lothian, where his father was a draper. He was educated in Edinburgh at Broughton School, where he shone academically and was made a 'pupil-teacher' with the responsibility of giving tutorials to junior classes.

In 1913 he entered Edinburgh University and for a year studied mathematics, physics and chemistry with the intention of taking a science degree. When war broke out in August 1914 he immediately volunteered for military service and was commissioned in the 16th Battalion of the Royal Scots regiment.

He first saw action at the Battle of the Somme in 1916, and, badly wounded in the chest by a shell splinter, he lay on the battlefield for nearly 36 hours before being picked up by stretcher bearers. After a lengthy period of hospital treatment in England, he returned to front-line active service and in 1918 sustained a bullet wound of the left leg which caused damage severe enough to make him a candidate for amputation. The injured limb was successfully preserved, but he was left with a life-long limp.

After demobilisation, he returned to Edinburgh University as a medical student, inspired perhaps by his experiences as a battle casualty and as a surgical patient. He graduated MB ChB with honours in 1922 and later that year he was elected Senior President of the Royal Medical Society.

After holding junior surgical posts in Edinburgh and Carlisle, he obtained the Fellowship of the College in 1924 and became Clinical Tutor in the Royal Infirmary to Professor (later Sir) John Fraser (q.v.). In 1928 he was appointed Assistant Surgeon to the Royal Infirmary and for the next nine years held charge of its surgical out-patient department, and was also Surgeon to Chalmers Hospital and to the Vert Memorial Hospital, Haddington. In 1938 his career was interrupted by several months of sanatorium treatment for pulmonary tuberculosis.

He resumed full surgical activity not long before the outbreak of the Second World War when he was appointed Surgeon to the Emergency Medical Services Hospital, Bangour, West Lothian, but in 1941 he returned to the Royal Infirmary as a senior assistant surgeon working in close association with Professor (later Sir) James Learmonth (q.v.). From the start this was an outstandingly happy relationship and there is no doubt that Tommy Millar's contribution to the professorial surgical unit as teacher and clinician did much to maintain its high academic reputation when this might easily have been compromised by the effects of wartime staff shortages. With the combination of the Chair of Systematic Surgery and the Regius Chair of Clinical Surgery under the direction of Sir James Learmonth in 1947, his supporting role became even more important and Sir James delegated to him the clinical charge of half of the hospital beds in the joint professorial unit. This association came to an end in 1951 when Tommy Millar was appointed Surgeon in charge of his own wards in the Royal Infirmary of Edinburgh, but his warm friendship with Sir James continued and was enhanced.

T. McW. Millar (1894–1970).

Over eight years as a surgical 'Chief' in the Royal Infirmary, he was an outstandingly successful leader who set the highest standards of surgical practice and clinical teaching. Although a 'general surgeon' in the original sense of that term, he had, over the years, developed a special interest in colorectal surgery and his expertise in this field earned for him a reputation appropriately recognised in 1956 by his appointment as Chairman of the section of proctology of the Royal Society of Medicine.

His diagnostic skills and clinical judgement were widely acclaimed and he was a calm, precise, gentle operator, devoid of technical flamboyance, who achieved consistently good results with a minimal incidence of complications.

In spite of a heavy NHS workload, a considerable teaching commitment and the demands of an extensive private practice, he found time to give notable service to his alma mater as General Council assessor on the Edinburgh University Court and to the College as a Fellowship examiner for many years and as a member of its Council from 1950 to 1957.

After retirement from surgical practice in 1959, he was appointed a member of the South East Scotland Regional Hospital Board and served as its Vice Chairman for seven years, during which he had charge of a number of important committees and was heavily involved in hospital planning. In this capacity his integrity, dedication, wisdom and abundant common sense made a contribution to Scottish medicine as valuable and distinguished as that of his surgical achievements.

His son, Geoffrey Millar, who became a distinguished ophthalmic surgeon in Edinburgh, has contributed several biographies to this book.

Tommy Millar was a modest, gracious, kindly man whose character and personality earned for him the loyalty, devotion and affection not only of the surgical team which he led so admirably, but also of colleagues nationwide and most importantly of his patients from all walks of life, whose well-being was always his prime concern and whose trust and confidence he never failed to inspire.

Roll number: 2969

Surgical clinical tutors at the Royal Infirmary, Edinburgh, 1926. T. McW. Millar is front right. Charles Illingworth is front left. Bruce Dick is in the centre of the back row.

Angus Hedley Whyte (1897–1971)

Many of the graduates of the University of Durham medical school in the first two decades of the 20th century were inspired by the teaching of Professor James Rutherford Morison (q.v.) and a remarkable group of his academic disciples went on to surgical careers of the highest distinction. One of these was Angus Hedley Whyte, who became the doyen of Newcastle surgery and one of the best-known provincial surgeons in England.

Angus Hedley Whyte was the only son of Dr John Whyte, a much respected general practitioner in South Shields and a native of Easdale, near Oban, who was one of the most notable Gaelic scholars of his generation and famous for having brought into print the orally remembered poems and songs of Mary Macpherson (Mairi Mhor nan Orain), the celebrated Skye bardess. His mother, Helen Hedley, was a Northumbrian who did not speak Gaelic and he had scant knowledge of his father's native tongue.

Angus Hedley Whyte (1897–1971).

He was educated at Ackworth School and at the University of Durham College of Medicine, from which he graduated MB BS in 1919 with honours and the Philipson Prize as the best student of his year. After graduation, he held junior hospital posts in London before returning to Newcastle and became a Fellow of the College in 1924. In the same year, he obtained the Fellowship of the Royal College of Surgeons of England and one year later the degree of Master of Surgery (MS) with honours from the University of Durham.

In 1926, at the unusually early age of 29, he was appointed Honorary Assistant Surgeon to the Royal Victoria Infirmary, Newcastle, where, 12 years later, he became Honorary Surgeon, a position which he held until his retirement in 1962. Between 1926 and 1947 he was also Honorary Surgeon to four of the smaller hospitals in the Newcastle area, including the Fleming Memorial Hospital for Sick Children.

In 1927 Hedley Whyte was granted a Territorial commission in the Royal Army Medical Corps and 10 years later was appointed to command 149 (Northumbrian) Field Ambulance. When war broke out in 1939 he took this unit to France, but early in 1940 he was transferred to the command of the surgical division of No. 8 Field General Hospital. In June 1940 the hospital was taking casualties from British forces sent to France after the Dunkirk evacuation but which, after the French capitulation, had, with much difficulty and danger, to be evacuated from Cherbourg and St Nazaire. For his 'distinguished leadership and gallantry in face of the enemy at Rennes and St Nazaire', Hedley Whyte was awarded the Distinguished Service Order (DSO) and also mentioned in dispatches.

In 1941 he was appointed to command a general hospital and in the following year he became Consulting Surgeon to Northern Command with the rank of Brigadier. During this period, in collaboration with Major General P. H. Mitchiner, he wrote a useful and popular handbook of war surgery.

Before the Second World War, he was heavily involved in the work of the British Medical Association and was a member of its Council from 1936 to 1940. He served on various important BMA committees and became President of the North of England branch in 1948 and Chairman of the Newcastle division in 1952. Having been Secretary of the North of England Medical Society from 1924 to 1927 he was elected President in 1950 and he was also an enthusiastic member of both the Moynihan Club and the Surgical Travellers' Club.

He was a member of the Court of Examiners of the Royal College of Surgeons of England from 1942 to 1948, and in 1952 was elected to the English College Council, on which he served for eight years. During that time, he served as Chairman successively of the Nominations Committee, the Jacksonian Prize Committee and the Conjoint Examining Board of the English College and the Royal College of Physicians of London. On behalf of the Conjoint Board he visited the University of Khartoum in 1947 and the University of Baghdad in 1949. He served for several years on the editorial boards of the *Annals of the Royal College of Surgeons of England* and the *British Journal of Surgery*, as well as on the Council of the Medical Defence Union.

Although predominantly committed to the activities of the English College, Hedley Whyte maintained his links with the Edinburgh College as a Fellowship examiner and greatly enjoyed his examining excursions north of Hadrian's Wall, not least for the opportunity they gave him of making new friendships and renewing old ones.

His clear didactic teaching, together with his clinical wisdom and his operative versatility, ensured his recognition over more than 25 years as a major figure in British surgery. Through his staunch maintenance of the principles inculcated by his great mentor Rutherford Morison, he enhanced the reputation of the Newcastle medical school and earned for himself an honoured place among its greatest surgical alumni.

Roll number: 3005

John Burton (1888–1962)

In a world increasingly conventional, conformable and uniform, many older doctors (and patients) look back, usually with affection, to an era where medical 'characters' added leaven to a largely serious, staid and conservative profession. Lamenting the passing of one such character, his colleague, Sir Charles Illingworth (q.v.), was to write: 'Pop Burton stood out in a class by himself – original, eccentric, egregious, provoking, perverse, and altogether loveable. Short of stature, stout, his square head set low between massive shoulders, bowler-hatted and with deceptively aggressive stance, he was the complete antithesis of the popular idea of a surgeon, and gloried in the fact. His build, his appearance and, above all, his puckish impression, earned him the affectionate nickname Pop.'

John Burton (1888–1962).

John Adam Gib Burton was born a son of the manse and educated at George Watson's College Edinburgh, Glasgow High School and at the University of Glasgow, where he gained a rugby blue and excelled at tennis. After graduation and house appointments, he served in the First World War in the Royal Army Medical Corps, in France, Gallipoli, Egypt, Mesopotamia and India, for which he was awarded the Military Cross. Returning to Glasgow Royal Infirmary, he combined the study and practice of pathology with surgery to the advantage of both. In particular, he was a pioneer of blood transfusion, where his skills as a pathologist were invaluable in the days before a blood transfusion service was established. In 1935, he was elected to the St Mungo-Notman Chair of Surgery in Glasgow, a post which he held until his retirement.

Illingworth went on to write: 'most of Pop's idiosyncrasies arose from his loathing for pretentiousness. He loved to rail at authority, to mock at self conceit and to jibe at those who pretended to plan a new world. Constituted as he was, Burton could not make any great contribution to medical science or education and he took good care to avoid being embroiled in administration or planning.'

For all of his working life, he lived for, and almost literally lived in, the Glasgow Royal Infirmary, where he knew everyone and knew everything that was going on.

After retirement, he took on the formidable task of arranging and cataloguing the Glasgow Hunterian pathology collection. He was remembered by those who knew him as an avuncular figure with a wealth of stories, a warm personality and one of a now rare breed of surgical characters.

Roll number: 3033

Sir Charles Illingworth (1899–1991)

The modern professor of surgery is tasked to produce research of the highest quality and undergraduate teaching which conforms to the most stringent standards, whilst at the same time maintaining a reputation as a master surgeon and a leader of the surgical community. An important subsidiary function is to train, to stimulate and to inspire young surgeons to follow an academic path. Theodor Billroth famously achieved this in Vienna, but there is no better example in British surgery than Charles Illingworth. It was Sir David Wilkie (q.v.) who inspired him to an academic career and to develop the scientific basis of surgery. As Regius Professor of Surgery in Glasgow, he established a department of surgery which was second to none in attracting, training and producing academic surgeons. A further great legacy was his influence in the promotion of the Royal Faculty of Physicians and Surgeons of Glasgow to Collegiate status.

Charles Illingworth was born the son of a Halifax businessman. He began medical studies in Edinburgh in October 1916 but the following year, on his 18th birthday, he joined the Royal Flying Corps. After flying training, which took a mere seven hours of flying time, he was posted as a pilot to the war front in the Somme. Crash landing behind enemy lines, he was taken prisoner, and spent the rest of the war incarcerated in Bavaria. At the end of the war he travelled across Europe, still wearing his oil-stained flying jacket, by now ragged, arriving back in Halifax on Christmas morning.

Sir Charles Illingworth (1899–1991).

Resuming his studies in Edinburgh, he became House Surgeon to Sir Harold Stiles (q.v.) and then assistant to Professor David Wilkie (q.v.), and was elected FRCSEd in 1925. His delight at being offered the post as assistant to Wilkie is recorded on page 184 and Wilkie proved to be an inspiring role model. Under his tutelage Illingworth flourished as a surgeon and as a scientist. Wilkie had established the first surgical research department outside the United States, stimulated by visits to Boston. At his suggestion Illingworth in turn visited the USA and, like his mentor, found the experience a stimulating one. He was inspired by Allen Whipple's first pancreatectomy in the USA, and became one of the pioneers of that operation on his return to Britain. After working with Evarts Graham in St Louis, he carried out the first clinical studies of cholecystography in the UK.

With his friend Bruce Dick (q.v.), he ran a very successful 'cram class' for the Fellowship examination. On the basis of this course they jointly wrote a *Textbook of Surgical Pathology* in 1932, which went on to become a surgical classic, running to 12 editions. His interest in surgical pathology was further enhanced by his appointment as Conservator of the Museum of the Royal College of Surgeons of Edinburgh, in succession to David Middleton Greig (q.v.). Illingworth's *Short Textbook of Surgery*, first written in 1938, went on to nine editions and became a standard work.

In 1939 he was appointed Regius Professor of Surgery in the University of Glasgow and with the support of the Principal, Sir Hector Hetherington, developed his department as a world leader in research and training. He saw his task as 'picking winners to infuse them with the spirit of inquiry and give them a diversity of training to enable them to meet the challenge of future developments in the surgical craft'. He had the happy knack of presenting complex matters in a simple, characteristically restrained manner. The young surgeons whom he trained were berated if they failed to live up to the high standards that he set.

Illingworth abhorred idleness. On weekends after an early morning ward round, his staff were expected to join him hill climbing in Glencoe or the 'Argyllshire Alps'. Each summer he would sail his yacht around the west coast of Scotland – crewing for him would be some of the young surgical trainees destined to become the next generation of British academic surgeons.

In later years his formidable intellect was directed towards other interests, including history. He became President of the Scottish Society of the History of Medicine and produced the definitive biography of the Glaswegian William Hunter, arguably the greatest British physician, surgeon and obstetrician of his day. In 1971 he published *University Statesman: Sir Hector Hetherington*, a biographical account of his academic supporter in his early days at Glasgow University.

Although Charles Illingworth had little time for pomposity or privilege, honours were inevitably heaped upon him. He was to a large extent responsible for the promotion of the Royal Faculty of Physicians and Surgeons of Glasgow to Royal College status and he became President from 1962 to 1964. Numerous honorary degrees were conferred: DSc from Sheffield and Belfast; LLD from Glasgow and Leeds. He was made an honorary Fellow of an astonishing number of surgical Colleges – of America, England, Ireland, Glasgow, South Africa and Canada. In 1963 he received the Lister Medal in recognition of his work on peptic ulcer and biliary disease. He was Surgeon to the Queen in Scotland from 1961 to 1965, and, having been awarded CBE in 1946, he was knighted in 1961.

His energy continued unabated in retirement but he went on to found Tenovus in Scotland, a charity that continues to raise significant funds for medical research.

Roll number: 3041

The Illingworth Surgical Club.

The Illingworth Tree

Arguably Illingworth's greatest legacy was the stream of professors of surgery appointed from his department to all parts of the United Kingdom and around the world. The pupils of Theodor Billroth had in the same way, a century before, become surgical leaders throughout Europe and compiled 'The Billroth Tree'. This traced the origins of the greatest European surgical dynasty. An 'Illingworth Tree' would be equally appropriate. Among those pupils whom he names in his biography are:

Sir Andrew Kay
Professor in Glasgow

David Johnston
Professor in Leeds

Sir Robert Shields
Professor in Liverpool

Sir Herbert Duthie
Professor in Sheffield

George Smith
Professor in Aberdeen

Sir Patrick Forrest
Professor in Edinburgh

Ron Clark
Professor in Sheffield

William Burnett
Professor in Brisbane

Adam Smith
Wade Professor RCS Edinburgh

W. T. Irvine
Professor in St Mary's London

Iain Gillespie
Professor in Manchester

James Elder
Professor in Keel

Nelson Norman
Professor in Abu Dhabi

Iain Ledingham
Professor of Intensive Care Medicine in Glasgow

Jack Stevens
Professor of Orthopaedics in Newcastle

James Lawrie
Professor in Zairia, Nigeria

Bruce Dick (1900–67)

Bruce Dick (1900–67).

Surgery in Edinburgh has been fortunate to enjoy several golden ages. One of these was in the 1920s when David Wilkie (q.v.), John Fraser (q.v.), Henry Wade (q.v.) and J. M. Graham (q.v.) between them provided a stimulating, inspiring surgical milieu from which many talented surgeons emerged. Among these was Bruce Dick, who was to pioneer thoracic surgery in the west of Scotland, was to become an authority on surgical pathology and who generously bequeathed to the College a valuable X-ray teaching collection which bears his name in the College to this day.

Bruce Mackenzie Dick was born in Kendal, Westmorland, and studied medicine at Edinburgh University, graduating MB ChB with honours in 1922. He had an outstanding undergraduate academic career, winning the Beaney Prize in surgery and anatomy, the Buchanan Scholarship, the Grierson bursary in materia medica and the Allen Fellowship in Clinical Medicine and Surgery. Shortly after graduating, he took up a Fellowship in Surgery from the Rockefeller Foundation which allowed him to travel to St Louis, where he trained in thoracic surgery with Evarts Graham. After taking the FRCSEd in 1925 he was appointed a lecturer in clinical surgery at the University of Edinburgh. Here he devoted himself to the emerging specialty of thoracic surgery. During this time, Sir John Fraser, Sir David Wilkie, Sir Henry Wade and J. M. Graham were at the height of their surgical prowess and in the stimulating environment which they created, Bruce Dick flourished. He developed an early interest in surgical pathology which was to remain with him throughout his life, and in which he was to become a national authority.

At the start of the Second World War he was seconded out of the services to set up a thoracic unit at Gleneagles Hotel, which had been set up as an emergency medical services hospital in 1939. This unit was transferred to Hairmyres in 1941 to become the first fully operational thoracic unit in Scotland.

In 1947 he treated a famous patient who became a significant benefactor of the unit. George Orwell (admitted under his real name Eric Blair) had apical tuberculosis with a cavity in the right lung. The standard treatment of the day – bed rest, artificial pneumothorax and a right phrenic nerve crush – resulted in modest improvement. Bruce Dick was aware that Streptomycin, which had been discovered in the United States in 1944, had been used to treat tuberculosis in a few American patients with apparent success. Because of currency restrictions it was not possible to purchase the drug in the UK, at the time, but at Dick's suggestion Orwell arranged for his American publisher to pay for a supply. The purchase was approved by Aneurin Bevan, the Health Minister. Orwell was given daily Streptomycin and initially appeared to be making a clinical response but because he developed a reaction to the drug it had to be stopped. The remainder of the supply was given to two other patients, who did well. Orwell, who completed his novel *1984* during his stay in Hairmyres, made a generous donation which enabled Dick to purchase thoracic surgery instruments from the United States, through Orwell's American publisher.

As one of the pioneers of thoracic surgery in Britain, he was a founder member of the Society of Thoracic Surgeons of Great Britain and Ireland and went on to become its President.

He continued to develop his interest and expertise in surgical pathology, an interest which was not confined to the thoracic cavity, and he became an authority on the subject. With Sir Charles Illingworth (q.v.), he wrote *A Textbook of Surgical Pathology* in 1932, a book which was to become obligatory reading for a generation of surgeons in training.

Over his lifetime he had amassed a huge collection of teaching X-rays, which he left to the College. A generous bequest from his estate allowed this collection to be catalogued and presented for surgical teaching, and the collection was then made available for study to postgraduate students in the Bruce Dick Room in the College. Dr Bill Copland further improved the collection, adding to the descriptions of the films to enhance their teaching value. The collection of over 2,000 images has now been converted to a digital format. In this way, the Bruce Dick collection of radiographs is available through the College's website to new generations of surgeons around the world.

Roll number: 3062

John Chassar Moir (1900–77)

Among the greatest contributions to obstetrics in the early 20th century was the isolation of ergometrine and its introduction into clinical practice. John Chassar Moir was jointly responsible for that innovation, which greatly improved the safety of childbirth.

John Chassar Moir was born in Montrose and graduated from Edinburgh University in 1922. He began training in obstetrics and his thesis on internal rotation was awarded an MD with gold medal, and he went on to become FRCSEd in 1926. After studying in Vienna and Berlin and at the Johns Hopkins Hospital in Baltimore, he worked at University College Hospital in London, going on to become a reader in obstetrics and gynaecology at the newly established Royal Postgraduate Medical School at Hammersmith Hospital, London. His research into ergometrine dated from his observation during these Hammersmith years, of the potent effects of a liquid extract of ergot. This led to the isolation, jointly with the biochemist Harold Dudley, of ergometrine and its subsequent introduction into clinical practice. This was widely regarded as one of the major contributions to obstetric practice in the 20th century, and one which dramatically reduced the incidence of postpartum haemorrhage.

He was appointed Nuffield Professor of Obstetrics and Gynaecology at Oxford at the age of 37. Over the next thirty years, he built up a department which made a number of important contributions, including work on the effect of oxytocin on uterine muscle, and on prostaglandins. His own research interest was on vesicovaginal fistula, on which he became an international authority. His textbook *The Vesico-vaginal Fistula* (1961) became the standard work on the topic. Well after retirement, he continued to see and advise patients with this distressing condition from all over the world. He also took on the editorship of the seventh edition of Munro Kerr's *Operative Obstetrics* (1964).

His many contributions received wide recognition. These included the DM of Oxford University, and the honorary DSc of the University of Ontario and of his alma mater Edinburgh University. He went on to become President of the section of obstetrics and gynaecology of the Royal Society of Medicine.

Roll number: 3145

John Chassar Moir (1900–77).

Ralston Paterson (1897–1981).

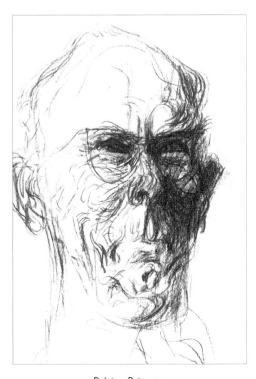

Ralston Paterson.
A caricature by Feliks Topoloski.

Ralston Paterson (1897–1981)

Radiotherapy as a specialty in its own right began in the early 20th century and Ralston Paterson was a dominant figure in the development of the specialty in Britain. He brought scientific order to radium dosage with the Paterson–Parker rules. From an early stage he had the vision to appreciate that radiotherapy would be best delivered from a single regional centre with peripheral clinics, and he established this system in Manchester. It was to prove a template for the development of radiotherapy services elsewhere.

James Ralston Kennedy Paterson (widely known to colleagues and friends as 'R.P.') was born in Edinburgh, a son of the manse. After education at George Heriot's School, Edinburgh, he served in the First World War with the Argyll and Sutherland Highlanders and was awarded the Military Cross. After graduation with honours from Edinburgh University in 1923, he took the FRCSEd in 1926 and was awarded an MD with commendation the following year. Having established an early career interest in radiology, he obtained a Fellowship in Radiology to the Mayo Clinic. Thereafter, he was able to gain experience abroad in Chicago, Toronto and South Africa. On his return to Edinburgh, he was made acting Director of the radiology department in the Royal Infirmary and, shortly thereafter, was appointed Director of Radiotherapy in Manchester when the Christie Hospital and the Hope Radium Institute were amalgamated. Within a very short time he had developed this institute into one of the leading radiotherapy centres in the world and was generally recognised as the leader of the relatively small group of British radiologists who were developing the specialty of radiotherapy.

One of his earliest contributions was the development of a system for ensuring precise and reproducible dosimetry in radiotherapy which became known as the Paterson–Parker rules. Recognising the crucial importance of accurate dosage, he realised that this was best delivered in a single regional centre with peripheral clinics and this template was widely adopted. The concept of the optimum dose and the 'Manchester method' of treatment for cervical cancer were milestones in the development of radiotherapy, and he was largely responsible for both of these.

Under his leadership, two fundamental research groups flourished in Manchester, one under the direction of his wife, Edith Paterson, and their research work led to the building of the Paterson Research Laboratories. Perhaps his early influences in Scotland had made him realise the importance of education and he pioneered a programme for public education on cancer.

R.P. went on to become President of the British Society of Radiotherapists and President of the Royal College of Radiologists, the first radiotherapist to hold this post. His many honours included the appointment as Commander of the Order of the British Empire (CBE) in 1950, the Gold Medal of the Society of Apothecaries and the Gold Medal of the Faculty of Radiologists.

His success was the result of his intellect, his energy and his organisational skills. He proved to be an inspiring leader in radiotherapy, both in Manchester and nationally. On retirement, R.P. and Edith retired to Moffat, where the same skills and energies which had proved so successful in Manchester proved equally successful when applied to sheep and cattle farming.

Roll number: 3148

Sir Alexander Gillies (1891–1982)

Sir Alexander Gillies was a pioneer of orthopaedic surgery in his native New Zealand. After war service, a scholarship took him to Edinburgh to study medicine, and he went on to work under Sir Robert Jones (q.v.) in Liverpool and at the Mayo Clinic with Dr William Mayo. He was prominent in the foundation of the New Zealand Orthopaedic Association, becoming its first President and was President of the New Zealand Red Cross Society for many years.

Alexander Gillies was born in Dunedin, New Zealand, of Scottish parents, and began preliminary medical studies at Otago University, where he was awarded a blue for rugby. His studies were interrupted by the First World War, where he served with the New Zealand forces in Egypt, Palestine and Syria. He won a scholarship to study medicine at the University of Edinburgh, from where he graduated in 1923. During his time at Edinburgh, he played rugby for Melrose, a leading Scottish Borders team, and would later recall how the team was accommodated in temperance hotels for away matches.

He went on to become Assistant Orthopaedic Surgeon to Sir Robert Jones in Oswestry, and the Royal Southern Hospital in Liverpool. In 1927 he spent a year at the Mayo Clinic in Rochester, Minnesota, working under Dr William Mayo, before becoming Orthopaedic Surgeon at the Lockwood Clinic in Toronto. Returning to New Zealand in 1929, he became Orthopaedic Surgeon at Wellington Hospital, a position that he held until 1950.

In 1932 he became a fellow of the newly founded Royal Australasian College of Surgeons and returned to Liverpool four years later to take the Master's degree in Orthopaedics. From 1940 to 1941 in London he acted as resident commissioner for the British Red Cross Society and the Order of St John of Jerusalem. During this time, he worked with the pioneers of plastic surgery Sir Harold Gillies (who was no relation) and Sir Archibald McIndoe.

He was one of the first to perform hip arthroplasty in New Zealand. In 1950 he was a founder member of the New Zealand Orthopaedic Association, becoming its first President. He was also instrumental in forming the New Zealand Crippled Children's Society and he became its President in 1966.

Knighted in 1959, he is remembered for his commitment to humanitarian causes and for the significant role he played in the establishment of orthopaedics in New Zealand.

Authors: A. W. Beasley CNZM, OBE and Iain Macintyre

Roll number: 3168

Sir Alexander Gillies (1891–1982).

David Band (1901–88).

David Band (1901–88)

Urology as a specialty came of age in the middle of the 20th century, an era which saw surgeons exclusively practising urological surgery for the first time. David Band, who was inspired to a career in urology by Sir Henry Wade (q.v.), was the first Edinburgh surgeon to become a specialist urologist, and went on to become President of the British Association of Urological Surgeons, and a member of the team which performed the first successful British renal transplant.

David Band was born in Edinburgh and educated at George Watson's College. He went on to graduate in medicine from Edinburgh University in 1923 and became a Fellow of the Royal College of Surgeons of Edinburgh three years later.

It was the influence of Sir Henry Wade which inspired him to a career in urology. Wade had been appointed Surgeon to Leith Hospital and after the First World War had begun to develop urological surgery in the Royal Infirmary of Edinburgh. David Band similarly became Assistant Surgeon to Leith Hospital and developed valuable experience of gynaecological surgery in the Hospital for Diseases of Women in Archibald Place.

Moving to the Royal Infirmary to work with Sir Henry Wade, he was able to develop a wide clinical experience in urology and began active research. Wade was pioneering the development of urological radiology and David Band contributed to this work, writing papers on excretion urography. He was appointed Consultant Urological Surgeon to the Western General Hospital and Reader in Urology in the University of Edinburgh.

Tuberculosis of the uro-genital tract was a common problem at this time and Sir Henry Wade's expertise had attracted a large number of patients with this condition to his clinic. In the years after the Second World War, Edinburgh was at the forefront of the introduction of chemotherapy for tuberculosis into clinical practice, and David Band was to adapt these chemotherapy regimens for uro-genital tuberculosis, beginning with streptomycin and defining the role of triple therapy. It was an interest which he was to follow throughout his professional career. In 1956 as President of the section of urology of the Royal Society of Medicine he was able to look back to his Honeyman Gillespie Lecture on urogenital tuberculosis in 1942 and to compare the remarkable improvements in the outlook for patients with this disease over such a short period.

While urologists of the 21st century are increasingly sub-specialising, Band's interests encompassed all of urology. He was an early exponent of cystometry, and his work on the neurogenic bladder was to lead him to become the urological specialist in the spinal unit which was established in Edenhall Hospital, Musselburgh, just outside Edinburgh.

He was the first urological surgeon in Edinburgh to confine himself exclusively to that specialty. In that capacity he attended the inaugural meeting of the British Association of Urological Surgeons in 1945, becoming a foundation member. He served the British Association of Urological Surgeons in various capacities over many years, serving as editor of the *British Journal of Urology* from 1949 until he retired in 1966, as a member of Council, as Vice President and as President in 1959. The prestigious St Peter's Medal is awarded to British surgeons who are judged to have made the greatest contribution to urology each year and in 1962 David Band was awarded this medal. He was elected a Fellow of the Royal Society of Edinburgh in 1950.

One episode which he regarded as a high point of his clinical career was his membership of the team, led by Sir Michael Woodruff (q.v.), which carried out the first successful renal transplant in the United Kingdom in 1960.

David Band also served his alma mater. In 1939 he succeeded Sir David Wilkie (q.v.) as Chairman of the Edinburgh University Settlement, a charity which Wilkie had espoused and generously supported. David Band had become Honorary Secretary of the Edinburgh University Graduates' Association between 1934 and 1955 and President in 1966. He retired in that year as one of the most distinguished British urological surgeons of his generation.

Roll number: 3195

Ion Simson Hall (1896–1991)

A sign of greatness in any innovator is the recognition that the brainchild to which he has devoted much time, thought and effort, to which he has become personally attached and which has established his reputation, has been superseded by something better.

Ion Simson Hall won international renown for his work on fenestration, yet on the introduction of stapedectomy, he was among the first to recognise the superiority of this new treatment and although it was to render fenestration obsolete, he had the magnanimity and stature to admit this.

Ion Simson Hall was born in Glasgow, a son of the manse, and was educated at George Watson's College, Edinburgh. His medical studies in Edinburgh were interrupted by the First World War and he served in the Royal Field Artillery in France, returning to graduate in 1921. He took the membership of the Royal College of Physicians of Edinburgh (MRCPE) examination, in addition to the FRCSEd, and embarked on a career in ear, nose and throat surgery. He spent time in Paris and Vienna and visited Chevalier Jackson in Philadelphia. In the years before the Second World War he was one of the first otologists to perform and develop the operation of fenestration of the lateral semi-circular canal to relieve otosclerotic deafness and among the first to use magnification techniques. This work gained him an international reputation. However, when the operation of stapedectomy was introduced some 20 years later, he was quick to recognise the benefits of this new procedure, which was to replace fenestration, and he was among the first to adopt it.

Following the Second World War, he became involved in medical politics, chairing the Edinburgh Division of the British Medical Association and becoming the first Chairman of the Consultants and Specialists Committee in Scotland. He acted as Chairman of the South East Scotland Regional Hospital Board for a year and served on the Council of the Royal College of Physicians. Well into his retirement, he held the post of Honorary Librarian of the Royal College of Surgeons of Edinburgh.

His work brought him several honours including his election as President of the otology section of the Royal Society of Medicine and Chairman of the British Association of Otolaryngologists. He wrote a textbook which was to become a classic. *Diseases of Nose, Throat and Ear* was first published in 1937 and by the year 2000 had gone on to no fewer than 16 editions.

Roll number: 3206

Ion Simson Hall (1896–1991).

William Wilson (1897–1974)

William Wilson (1897–1974).

The image of the blustering, dogmatic, overbearing, supremely self-confident surgeon is one which, thanks largely to George Bernard Shaw and James Robertson Justice, still persists to some extent even in the 21st century. There can be very few surgeons of any era who have conformed less to this unfair stereotype than Professor W. C. Wilson, whose substantial contributions to surgical science were significantly obscured by his extreme distaste for publicity in any form and whose self-effacing modesty may have done much to deny him the celebrity he undoubtedly deserved.

William Combe Wilson, a native of Fife, was educated in Edinburgh at the Royal High School. His entry into the Edinburgh University medical faculty was postponed by the First World War, throughout which he served as a private soldier. Having emerged unscathed from the conflict, he returned to Edinburgh as a medical student and graduated MB ChB in 1924.

After holding house officer posts, he joined the staff of the University Department of Surgery as a Carnegie Research Fellow and, thereafter, became one of a band of young men who, under Sir David Wilkie's (q.v.) inspiring leadership, laid the foundations of what was to become the Wilkie Surgical Research Laboratory.

He obtained the Fellowship of the College in 1927 and after a sojourn in the United States supported by a Rockefeller Travelling Fellowship, he was appointed Assistant Surgeon and then in 1935 full Surgeon to the Edinburgh Royal Hospital for Sick Children. In addition, he became a University lecturer in applied physiology and also in paediatrics. It was during this period that, in association with the distinguished biochemist Dr C. P. Stewart, he carried out what were, and are still, recognised as classical studies on the biochemical and physiological effects of burns. His investigations into the pathophysiology and treatment of shock also received wide acclaim and, in 1938, he was appointed Director of the newly established Medical Research Council unit for clinical research in surgery, which was set up in Edinburgh jointly with the University, the Royal Infirmary and the Royal Hospital for Sick Children.

In 1939 Wilson was invited to succeed Professor J. R. Learmonth (q.v.) in the Regius Chair of Surgery in the University of Aberdeen and there, in addition to taking on his professional responsibility for the organisation of undergraduate surgical teaching, he maintained and expanded the research in surgical physiology which he had pursued so successfully in Edinburgh. The exigencies of the Second World War inevitably curtailed the work of his department and having joined the Royal Army Medical Corps he was appointed to command No. 1 Medical Research Section in the Middle East with the rank of Lieutenant Colonel. In 1942–3 this unit was committed largely to studies on haemorrhagic shock and its treatment, and some of Wilson's investigations were carried out virtually on the battlefield.

Following his return to Aberdeen from military service, although continuing with his own investigative work, he chose to give priority to fostering, encouraging and guiding the research activities of younger men, and it is possible that his choice was in some degree determined by the onset of deafness, which worsened progressively over the years. Whatever the reasons for his decision to be a promoter, constructive critic and facilitator rather than an initiator and an activator, it was spectacularly successful. This is attested by the fact that between 1947 and his retirement in 1962, seven members of his academic staff were appointed to chairs of surgery in Britain and the Commonwealth.

Wilson's impressive intellect, abundant common sense and clear, analytical mind made him a formidable member of University and NHS committees in the deliberations of which he could and did sometimes employ the tactic of selective deafness with devastating effect. His influence on academic surgery in Britain is underestimated, for which his deliberate self-depreciation and the very real handicap of his deafness are largely to blame. However, Aberdeen University had no doubts about the distinction of his contributions, which, on his retirement, it honoured with the title of Professor Emeritus and conferment of the degree of honorary Doctor of Laws (LLD).

William Wilson was a gentle, kindly man who inspired great loyalty and affection and who had the gift of bringing out the best in all who worked with and for him. In this and in many other ways he was a most worthy disciple of his great mentor Sir David Wilkie.

Roll number: 3248

Sir Robert Macintosh (1897–1989)

The dramatic advances in the safety and efficacy of anaesthesia in the 20th and 21st centuries make it difficult to believe that, within living memory, anaesthetics were routinely delivered by medical students. As anaesthesia emerged as a specialty in its own right, it was Sir Robert Macintosh, the first Professor of Anaesthetics in Europe, who did much to give this new specialty the status of a university discipline. He was influential in the development of anaesthetics from a secondary service performed, often reluctantly, by students, surgical assistants or general practitioners without training, into a well-organised, scientifically based specialty in its own right. His emphasis on accurate observation, safety and simplicity did much to raise the standards of anaesthetic practice in Britain and indeed throughout the world.

Robert Macintosh was born in Timaru, New Zealand, the son of Charles Macintosh, who had been a member of the original 'All Blacks' rugby team. He was educated in Waitaki Boys' High School and in 1916 sailed for Britain taking a commission in the Royal Scots Fusiliers and then enlisting in the Royal Flying Corps as a fighter pilot. He was shot down over France and taken prisoner – an experience similar to that of Sir Charles Illingworth (q.v.). After the war he qualified in medicine from Guy's Hospital, London, in 1924, originally intending to be a surgeon, and was elected FRCSEd in 1927. As was common at that time, he began to give anaesthetics for dental procedures at Guy's Hospital with little knowledge of or training in the subject, but then, as he often said, neither did anyone else. Soon he turned to anaesthesia full time and founded a practice of peripatetic anaesthetists operating out of Harley Street which became known as the 'Mayfair Gas Company'.

Sir Robert Macintosh (1897–1989).

Through his golf club he met and became friendly with Lord Nuffield, to whom he gave advice about medical benefactions. On one occasion he anaesthetised Nuffield, who described Macintosh's anaesthetic as a pleasurable experience, which compared favourably to previous anaesthetics. When Nuffield proposed to fund chairs in medicine, surgery and obstetrics in Oxford University, Macintosh suggested he should include anaesthesia. The University of Oxford felt that there was inadequate academic status in anaesthesia to justify a chair, but Nuffield made the establishment of a chair of anaesthesia a condition of his offer to endow the two other chairs, and Macintosh was appointed the first Professor of Anaesthesia in Britain and indeed in Europe.

Among the early achievements in this new position was a classical textbook *Essentials of General Anaesthesia* (1943), written with Dr Freda Bannister. In the years immediately before the Second World War his department collaborated with physicists in the University to produce the Oxford vaporiser. This simple device accurately delivered precise concentrations of ether to the nitrous oxide–oxygen mixture and was produced in Nuffield's Cowley works. Its widespread use throughout the Second World War was a major step in safe anaesthesia. At the outbreak of the war Macintosh was appointed Consultant in Anaesthetics to the Royal Navy and the Royal Air Force, eventually being promoted Air Commodore. He frequently visited each of the RAF hospitals, where his arrival, wearing pilot's wings and First World War medal ribbons, was to prove a great morale booster for service doctors. His department at the Radcliffe Infirmary carried out a variety of research projects, which included studies on artificial ventilation, the design of lifejackets and hypoxia in airmen.

After the war, postgraduate teaching expanded and so began the long series of courses at Oxford which were to produce competent anaesthetists. In an era before the audit of clinical practice was accepted, Macintosh established the first audits into unexplained anaesthetic deaths and with Dr William Mushin persuaded the Association of Anaesthetists to establish a more formal audit of anaesthetic mishaps.

His latter years were marked by a personal campaign to improve standards of anaesthesia, characterised by safety, simplicity, detailed observation and clarity of expression. His influence was felt particularly in underdeveloped countries, where these standards were just as applicable in the absence of expensive resources.

He was knighted in 1955 and made a Fellow of the Royal Society of Medicine in 1966 but remained modest despite these and many other honours. While his name lives on with the laryngoscope blade that he designed, he wrote that he wished to be remembered 'as someone who encouraged people not to be afraid to acknowledge their mistakes'. His influence on the development of safety in anaesthesia was immense.

Roll number: 3289

224

Sir James Learmonth (1895–1967)

Almost since their foundation in 1831 and 1803, respectively, the Chair of Systematic Surgery and the Regius Chair of Clinical Surgery in Edinburgh University have been occupied by a remarkable series of illustrious professors, several of whom feature in this book. For a period of 10 years in the middle of the 20th century, these two chairs were held by one man and the University's invitation to take on this dual responsibility bears eloquent witness to his academic and professional distinction.

James Rognvald Learmonth, born in Gatehouse of Fleet, Galloway, was the son of the headmaster of Girthon School, which he attended in childhood. His early education was profoundly influenced by his father, a Scots dominie of the old school who inculcated in him the academic discipline and the intellectual rigour which were to become the driving forces of his career. For his secondary education he attended Kilmarnock Academy and then in 1913 he entered the medical faculty of Glasgow University.

James Learmonth's medical studies were interrupted by the First World War, in which, as a junior officer in the King's Own Scottish Borderers, he saw action in some of the bloodiest battles on the Western Front. In later life he seldom spoke of his war experiences, but ill-informed denigration of the British Army's commanders in the First World War never failed to arouse his wrath and, most unfashionably, he was a stout defender of the military reputation of Field Marshal Earl Haig.

At the end of the war he returned to Glasgow University and, in 1921, graduated MB ChB with honours and with the Brunton Memorial Prize. After house officer posts at the Western Infirmary, Glasgow, he was appointed assistant to the Regius Professor of Surgery in 1923. One year later he was awarded a Rockefeller Fellowship which took him to the Mayo Clinic, Rochester, Minnesota, for one year; there he worked under Dr Alfred W. Adson in the neurosurgical division and this experience had a major influence on his future career.

After returning to Scotland, he obtained his Master's Degree (ChM) with commendation in 1927 and, in the following year, he became a Fellow of the College. Then, at the invitation of Dr W. J. Mayo, he joined the staff of the Mayo Clinic as a neurosurgeon and was appointed Associate Professor in the University of Minnesota. Between 1928 and 1932 he was much involved in clinical research and his studies on the innervation of the bladder and on the physiology of micturition gained international acclaim. This period also saw the early development of his interest in the surgery of the sympathetic nervous system and its role in the treatment of peripheral vascular disease.

In 1932, he was appointed Regius Professor of Surgery in the University of Aberdeen and his seven-year tenure of this chair was for him a particularly happy and fulfilling period. He was considerably involved in the planning of the new Aberdeen Royal Infirmary and University Medical School at Foresterhill and, in 1935, he was appointed Surgeon to HM the King in Scotland. Four years later he succeeded Sir David Wilkie (q.v.) as Professor of Systematic Surgery in the University of Edinburgh, but the outbreak of the Second World War just a few months after he had taken charge of his new department meant that most of his plans for its development had to be curtailed or postponed.

Sir James Learmonth (1895–1967).

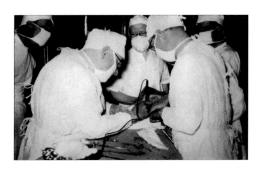

Sir James Learmonth's last operation in the Royal Infirmary of Edinburgh in 1956.

Nevertheless, he was able to establish a special unit for the treatment of peripheral nerve and vascular injuries at Gogarburn Hospital, which, over the war years, became an important clinical research centre. The activity of this unit together with his teaching commitments and the clinical demands of his wards in the Royal Infirmary constituted a heavy workload, which was made more onerous by the absence on military service of several members of his staff. In the face of many difficulties he maintained and enhanced the academic reputation of his department and this achievement was recognised by his appointment as Commander of the Order of the British Empire (CBE) in 1945.

In 1946 he was invited to fill the Regius Chair of Clinical Surgery in succession to Sir John Fraser (q.v.), who had been appointed Principal of Edinburgh University and, as holder of the two Edinburgh surgical chairs, his administrative and academic responsibilities were greatly increased. He was the driving force behind the establishment in Edinburgh, during the early post-war years, of clinical units dedicated to certain of the emerging surgical specialties and he ensured their academic integration with the University Departments of Surgery.

In 1948, he introduced the Saturday morning meetings, which provided a forum for the discussion and critical evaluation of current practice and included regular reviews of operative mortality. Within a few years, all surgical units in the Edinburgh area were participating in these meetings, which were probably the earliest example in the British Isles of systematic surgical audit.

Because of his special reputation and expertise he was called to attend HM King George VI. On 12 March 1949, he carried out in Buckingham Palace a lumbar sympathectomy, which halted the progress of ischaemia in the King's right leg and produced symptomatic relief. In the immediate post-operative period, the royal patient bestowed upon his surgeon the accolade of knighthood in the Royal Victorian Order (KCVO).

Two years later, Learmonth was made a Chevalier of the Légion d'Honneur and, in 1951, he was doubly honoured by appointment to the Medical Research Council and the award of the Lister Medal 'in recognition of his distinguished contribution to surgical science'. His reputation was further attested by the award of the honorary Fellowships of four surgical colleges, by honorary doctorates from four universities and by honorary membership of prestigious surgical societies in Britain, Europe and North America.

James Learmonth's early retirement in 1956 surprised his friends and colleagues, many of whom did not appreciate that the strain of his heavy workload was beginning to affect his health. The last years before his death were happy and tranquil, and made particularly satisfying for him by his appointment to the Court of the University of Glasgow, his alma mater, as a General Council Assessor.

As the occupant of two historic chairs of surgery and as the 'Chief' of two general surgical units in the Edinburgh Royal Infirmary, he set and maintained the highest standards in everything he did and if he was a hard taskmaster there was no one whom he drove harder than himself. To most of his students and junior staff he seemed a formidably stern and austere figure, but, behind this façade, lay a deeply emotional warm-hearted, kindly personality, which was never more apparent than when he was dealing with his patients.

James Learmonth was an excellent clinical teacher and his formal lectures, which were models of clarity, had a magisterial quality, which illuminated their subject matter and inspired his audiences at all academic and professional levels. His writing shared these characteristics and all papers written by members of his department had to meet his exacting literary standards before being submitted for publication.

James Learmonth was never a College office-bearer but he gave valuable service to it as an examiner and as a member of Council. He had strong associations with three of the four Scottish medical schools and his character and achievements have ensured that his memory is honoured not only by the College but also by the Universities of Glasgow, Aberdeen and Edinburgh.

Roll number: 3363

Bryan McFarland (1900–63)

The orthopaedic tradition in Liverpool, founded by Hugh Owen Thomas, was continued and enhanced by his pupils Robert Jones (q.v.) and T. P. McMurray (q.v.). Bryan McFarland, a son of Liverpool, was an orthopaedic teacher in that distinguished legacy. A pupil of and then assistant to Robert Jones, he succeeded McMurray to the Chair of Orthopaedic Surgery in Liverpool.

Bryan Leslie McFarland was brought up on Merseyside, graduating from the University of Liverpool in 1922 and acquiring the FRCSEd diploma in 1928. He was one of the first four candidates to gain the diploma of Master of Orthopaedic Surgery from Liverpool University. His early career was spent in Liverpool and he became Surgeon at the Royal Liverpool Children's Hospital and then to the Alder Hey Children's Hospital. It was in the Royal Southern Hospital, the hospital of Mr (later Sir) Robert Jones, that he first became a full Consultant Orthopaedic Surgeon. He worked as assistant to Robert Jones for seven years and under T. P. McMurray for two decades, succeeding McMurray to the Chair of Orthopaedics in 1951. Under his stimulating leadership the postgraduate orthopaedic school flourished, and Liverpool continued to attract graduates from around the world for orthopaedic training.

McFarland had great personal charm and warmth and was renowned as an eloquent teacher and as a raconteur. In later years he was President of the Liverpool Medical Institution, President of the British Orthopaedic Association and the International Orthopaedic Society. He served the Royal College of Surgeons of Edinburgh as Vice President from 1961 to 1963.

Roll number: 3368

Bryan McFarland (1900–63).

Eric Mekie (1902–89)

Eric Mekie was distinguished in several careers and in all of them he left his mark. Of the many distinctions he received, one was surely unique for a surgeon – that of having an orchid named after him.

David Eric Cameron Mekie was educated at George Watson's College, Edinburgh, and graduated in medicine from Edinburgh University. After obtaining the Fellowship of the College in 1928, he became Clinical Tutor under Sir John Fraser (q.v.) in the Royal Infirmary of Edinburgh before joining the Malayan Medical Service. He was appointed Professor of Clinical Surgery in the King Edward VII College of Medicine in Singapore in 1936. With the fall of Singapore in 1942, he was interred in Simod camp, where he was reputed to have performed surgical operations using a razor blade. After the war, he resumed the Chair of Clinical Surgery and was appointed in 1950 to the Chair in Surgery.

Returning to Edinburgh, he was appointed Conservator of the College Museum and his time as Conservator saw some important changes. The Museum holds a very large collection of anatomical and pathological specimens, many of great historical interest. He created a large series of teaching display boards which greatly enhanced the educational value of the specimens on which they were based. These display boards formed the basis of the textbook which he wrote jointly with Sir James Fraser *The Colour Atlas of Demonstrations in Surgical Pathology* (1984), which was published by the College.

In 1970 he became Postgraduate Dean in the Edinburgh University medical faculty, a recognition of his commitment to postgraduate medical education throughout his career.

From childhood he had enjoyed fishing and was a talented and knowledgeable gardener. The orchid named after him is regarded as a particularly attractive hybrid. 'Aranda Eric Mekie' originated in the Singapore Botanical Gardens.

Roll number: 3370

'Aranda Eric Mekie',
the orchid named after him.

Eric Mekie. Cartoon.
Artist unknown.

Eric Mekie (1902–89).

J. B. de C. M. Saunders (1903–91)

Pre-eminent among the Fellows of the College who became distinguished medical historians are Douglas Guthrie (q.v.), Arthur Logan Turner (q.v.) and Alexander Miles (q.v.), but there is another whose scholarship and historical erudition were certainly no less than theirs and whose fame, in Europe at any rate, is much less than it deserves to be.

John Bertrand de Cusance Morant Saunders was the son of F. A. Saunders FRCSEd, a surgeon in the British Army. His birthplace was Grahamstown, South Africa, and he received a classical education in that country at St Andrew's College and at Rhodes University College before entering the medical faculty of Edinburgh University, from which he graduated MB ChB in 1925. As a student, he became a demonstrator in the University Department of Physiology under Sir Edward Sharpey-Schafer and it was at this stage that he developed his life-long interest in biomechanics, neuro-muscular disorders and orthopaedics. After graduation, he held junior posts in the Edinburgh Royal Hospital for Sick Children and then joined the staff of the University anatomy department as a lecturer.

In 1930 he obtained the Fellowship of the College and later that year he accepted an invitation to become Associate Professor in the anatomy department of the University of California medical school at San Francisco (UCSF). Soon after his arrival in San Francisco, Saunders was invited to join a small faculty group which conducted a lecture course on the history of medicine and he also became an enthusiastic member of the History of Science Dinner Club of the University of California at Berkeley. As Professor of Anatomy, he conducted research into the biomechanics of the vertebral column and limb joints as well as functional and neuro-physiological investigation of normal and pathological gaits. He also published important studies on congenital abnormalities of the duodenum and on the development of the genito-urinary tract.

Saunders was Professor and Chairman of the UCSF anatomy department from 1938 to 1956, in which year he was appointed Dean of the UCSF School of Medicine. In addition, he was Chairman of the Department of History of Health Sciences from 1942 to 1975, University Librarian from 1943 to 1971, first Provost of UCSF from 1958 to 1964 and its first Chancellor from 1964 to 1966.

From his earliest days as an anatomy teacher he had an intense interest in the life and achievements of Andreas Vesalius, and in 1943 he wrote the first of his widely acclaimed papers on the contributions to medical science of the great 16th-century anatomist.

He had a felicitous collaboration with Dr Charles D. O'Malley in the writing of two classic historical works, the *Illustrations of the Works of Vesalius,* published in 1950, and *Leonardo da Vinci on the Human Body*, which appeared two years later. Among his many other historical productions, perhaps the most notable is another collaborative work *Ancient Egyptian and Cnidian Medicine,* published in 1959. His stature as a medical historian was recognised by his appointment to the Regent's Chair of History at UCSF, which, following his retirement in 1971, was renamed the 'Saunders Chair' in his honour. He continued to participate in academic activities and remained a highly active member of the American Association for the History of Medicine, for which he had delivered the Garrison Lecture in 1966.

Saunders was a notable academic statesman who gave devoted and distinguished service to the San Francisco medical school. His outstanding contribution to its high prestige was fittingly honoured on campus when the quadrangle between the Library and the School of Nursing was named 'Saunders Court'. Throughout his years in California he retained a warm affection for the College and for Edinburgh University, his alma mater. Any Edinburgh-trained doctor who had occasion to visit San Francisco could be sure of a kindly welcome from him and there are still many who have delightful memories of his generous hospitality.

Roll number: 3591

J. B. de C. M. Saunders (1903–91).

Ian Aird (1905–62).

'... for I have consciously modelled my habit of thought for years on that of my previous teachers, and if there is any good in the book it is the re-expression of their observations and opinions so far as I have remembered them. Not only did I try to learn something of the specialities which have made their own from James M. Graham, James R. Learmonth, Evarts A. Graham, Norman M. Dott, and the late Sir David Wilkie, but I endeavoured to study, understand, and copy something of their surgical philosophy, and I hope that there may be some re-distillation of their philosophy in these pages.'

Ian Aird (1905–62)

Ian Aird, the second holder of the Chair of Surgery in what is now the Royal Postgraduate Medical School at Hammersmith Hospital, London, was one of the College's most illustrious 20th Century Fellows and his death, at the age of 57 when still at the height of his powers, was a grievous loss to British surgery.

He was born in Edinburgh and educated at George Watson's College, where his academic record was mediocre apart from his aptitude for modern languages; by the time he left school he was fluent in French and had a good working knowledge of Russian, which, for a Scottish schoolboy in the 1920s, was a most unusual accomplishment.

In 1923 he entered Edinburgh University, from which, five years later, he graduated MB ChB with the Annandale Gold Medal in Surgery and the Whightman Prize for Clinical Medicine. His intelligence, industry, and exceptional memory became increasingly apparent throughout his student years and his commitment to surgery was inspired by the clinical teaching of J. M. Graham (q.v.), in whose Royal Infirmary wards he served as House Surgeon after graduation.

After visits to university departments of surgery in Paris and Vienna, he obtained the Fellowship of the College in 1930 and, in the following year, was appointed Clinical Tutor to Mr Graham. He was also appointed assistant in Sir David Wilkie's University department, where he began experimental studies on Hirschsprung's disease and on intestinal obstruction. For this work he was awarded a Rockefeller Fellowship, which enabled him to pursue his researches in the Department of Surgery of Washington University, St Louis, Missouri, under the direction of Dr Evarts Graham. His work there on the pathophysiology of intestinal strangulation formed the basis of the thesis for which he was awarded the degree of Master of Surgery (ChM) with high commendation in 1935. Later in that year he was appointed Assistant Surgeon at the Royal Hospital for Sick Children in Edinburgh and succeeded to a full charge there in 1939.

It was during these four years before the outbreak of the Second World War that Aird established his reputation as a brilliant surgical teacher. The tutorial course which, together with John Bruce (q.v.), he conducted four times a year was immensely successful and his fame as an instructor spread far beyond Scotland. The lecture notes, which he prepared for this course, were an educational masterpiece and complete bound sets of 'Aird's Notes' were regarded as treasured possessions by young doctors studying for the Fellowship examinations of all the royal surgical colleges.

When war came, Aird joined the Royal Army Medical Corps as a surgical specialist, eventually reaching the rank of Lieutenant Colonel and being twice mentioned in dispatches for his services with the 8th Army in North Africa as the surgeon in charge of a mobile surgical unit. Because of the rapid ebb and flow of the battles in the Western Desert, his unit more than once found itself behind advancing enemy forces and, on one of these occasions, it was visited and inspected by General (later Field Marshal) Erwin Rommel, the redoubtable commander of the German Afrika Korps. Rommel expressed his appreciation of the unit's care of casualties from both armies and thanked Aird warmly for his surgical efforts on behalf of a mortally wounded senior officer of one of the Panzer divisions.

Illness in 1943 caused Aird to be invalided home and then released from military service. Back in Edinburgh, he returned to his charge at the Sick Children's Hospital and, at the invitation of Sir James Learmonth, he joined the University Department of Surgery and also the professorial surgical unit in the Royal Infirmary.

Notwithstanding the demands of a heavy clinical workload, he was soon even more active in teaching and research than he had been before the war and his friends and colleagues were in no doubt that he was well set to become a major force in British academic surgery. Their high expectations were handsomely fulfilled in 1946 by his appointment to the Chair of Surgery at the British Postgraduate Medical School and by the energy and enthusiasm with which he set about the creation of a new academic surgical department at Hammersmith Hospital. In the face of all sorts of administrative and financial difficulties, he attracted to this department an impressive team of surgeons and clinical scientists whose researches gained international acclaim through their important contribution to major surgical advances, most notably in organ transplantation and in the technology of cardio-pulmonary bypass.

In 1956, Aird's pioneering operation to separate conjoined twins attracted a lot of media attention, which he found highly distasteful, and he regarded his work on the relationship of the blood groups to the incidence of peptic ulceration and of gastric carcinoma as of infinitely greater importance. He also made important personal contributions to the surgery of chronic pancreatitis and of hyperparathyroidism.

Many would regard the single-handed production in 1949 of his *Companion in Surgical Studies* as Ian Aird's most extraordinary achievement. This huge 1,000-page compendium was developed from his famous lecture notes and with every chapter supported by an extensive review of the relevant literature, it covered the whole of surgery, except for orthopaedics and fractures. Its first edition did not have a single illustration of any kind but the crystal clarity of Aird's didactic writing amply compensated for this deficiency and his *Companion* soon became a favourite reference textbook for surgeons in training throughout the English-speaking world.

Soon after his move to London, Aird was made a Fellow of the Royal College of Surgeons of England *ad eundem* and, over the next 16 years, he gave valuable service to it as a member of the College Council and the Court of Examiners. In spite of his manifold commitments in London and further afield, he maintained as a Fellowship examiner his links with his mother-College in Edinburgh, which, in 1961, bestowed upon him its highest honour, the Liston Victoria Jubilee Prize. His department at the Hammersmith Hospital attracted visitors from all parts of the world and, as guest-lecturer in many foreign universities and international surgical conferences, he was a superb ambassador for British surgery. He was one of the three co-founders and the first President of the James IV Association of Surgeons, which since its inception in 1957 has done so much to promote international surgical comradeship and its continuing success is perhaps his greatest monument.

Ian Aird's remarkable achievements are attributable to a formidable intellect combined with a prodigious capacity for hard work, a phenomenal memory and a wonderful ability to communicate the ideas which sprung in such profusion from his fertile mind. To these qualities he added great personal charm, a lively sense of humour and a warm generosity of spirit, together with a mercurial temperament and a

James IV Association of Surgeons

The James IV Association of Surgeons was founded on the night of 17 October 1957 in Atlantic City, New Jersey, USA, by Professor Ian Aird (q.v.) of London, Professor John (later Sir John) Bruce (q.v.) of Edinburgh and Dr J. William Hinton of New York, who were foregathered there for the Annual Congress of the American College of Surgeons. The two British surgeons were attending the Congress as guests and earlier that evening had been admitted to the Honorary Fellowship of the College.

In the words of Sir John Bruce: 'At the end of the proceedings the three became involved in a discussion about the lack of, and the need for a trans-Atlantic clearinghouse of information for evaluating surgical standards and practice, current research and the now voluminous literature of surgery. They were convinced of the need for closer ties between the surgeons of the two English-speaking communities than then obtained.'

As a result of this discussion it was decided to form a small association of surgical leaders on both sides of the Atlantic for the purpose of promoting close professional and social contacts between the surgeons of the United States, Canada and Britain. Membership originally by invitation was soon extended to surgeons from a number of other countries, and has been progressively augmented over the years by a process of slow and studied selection. The founders of the Association decided to give it the name of James IV King of Scots (1473–1513) because of that remarkable monarch's well-documented enthusiasm for practical surgery, and also because of the Royal Charter which in 1506 he granted to the Edinburgh Incorporation of Surgeons and Barbers – the body which in 1778 became the Royal College of Surgeons of Edinburgh.

Since its foundation, the size and influence of the Association have increased steadily and its objectives have become more clearly defined. It fulfils the purpose of its three founders by promoting and facilitating exchange visits between member countries by selected surgical travellers who individually are not members of the Association and each year, to quote Sir John Bruce again, 'the most important function of the Association is to sponsor and finance the visits of hand-picked men who not only will cross-fertilise the surgery of member countries by exchange of surgical knowledge, but also will foster the kind of friendships that have meant so much to the founders. The venture ... may help to create and to consolidate the ties that unite all who serve the cause of surgery throughout the world.'

Through funds derived from the subscriptions of its members and from charitable donations, the Association continues to make Sir John's vision an inspiring reality.

Surgeons' Lives: An Anthology of Biographies of College Fellows over 500 Years

disregard for his own health and material well-being. He worked and played hard, and it is likely that the intensity with which he drove himself both physically and mentally contributed in large measure to the tragic circumstances of his untimely death by suicide.

Roll number: 3617

Sir Brian Windeyer (1904–94).

Sir Brian Windeyer (1904–94)

The provision of radiotherapy as a specialty provided centrally from large centres in Britain owed much to the vision and the organisational skills of Ralston Paterson (q.v.) and of Brian Windeyer. Before the start of the National Health Service, radium treatment was seen as falling within the provenance of the surgeon, while X-ray treatment was mostly in the hands of diagnostic radiologists. Brian Windeyer used his energy, his enthusiasm and his imposing personality to great effect to guide the development of the new specialty in Britain.

Brian Windeyer was born and educated in Sydney, Australia, graduating in medicine from the University of Sydney. He excelled as a sportsman, rowing for his College and playing rugby for the combined Australia and New Zealand Universities' team. Early in his career he had decided on what was to be his ultimate specialty and he was appointed radium Registrar at the Royal Prince Alfred Hospital in Sydney. In 1929 he went to Paris to work for two years at the Fondation Curie and in 1930 obtained the Fellowship of the College. In 1931, he became Radium Officer to the Middlesex Hospital, with which he was to be associated for the rest of his working lifetime. He had been inspired in Paris by 'men and women of so different temperaments and talents … imbued with a single and selfless motive, the study and use of ionising radiation for the benefit of cancer patients'. He went on to become Professor of Radiology (therapeutic) at the Middlesex Hospital in London in 1942. He was an early proponent of a multi-disciplinary approach to cancer, combining with Sir Stanford Cade to carry out joint ward rounds at Mount Vernon Hospital. In a lecture to the American Medical Association in 1948 he described centralisation of treatment for cancer in Britain which envisaged the concentration of radiotherapy services into delivery from larger specialist units. This was the pattern which was followed as the specialty developed within the United Kingdom.

In 1954 he became Dean of the Middlesex Hospital medical school and with financial support from influential friends he set about the rebuilding of the medical school – later to be called the Windeyer Building. He became Chairman of the Academic Council in 1967 and Vice Chancellor of the University of London two years later.

By this stage he had established an international reputation and postgraduate students came from all over the world to train at the Meyerstein Institute of Radiotherapy.

The many offices which he held and honours which he received included presidency of the Faculty of Radiologists, membership of Council of the Royal College of Surgeons of England, Chairman of the National Radiological Protection Board and membership of the Medical Research Council. His year of office as Master of the Worshipful Society of Apothecaries in 1973 gave him particular pleasure. He received honorary degrees from the Universities of Wales, British Columbia, Cambridge and Sydney, and was knighted in 1961.

As Vice Chancellor of the University of London (1969–72) he made a public stand condemning what he saw as indiscipline and sexual permissiveness which had swept through British universities in the 1960s. He is remembered by contemporaries and his many pupils as a man of vigour, enthusiasm, strength and determination.

Roll number: 3664

Eric Farquharson (1905–70)

The single-handed production of a best-selling didactic textbook is, for a surgeon, a rare achievement, which the inexorable rise of super-specialism and the increasing complexity of surgical science and practice may have rendered almost unattainable in the 21st century. Several of the Fellows of the College whose careers are outlined in this book gained international fame through their authorship of popular textbooks and there is no more notable example of this than Eric Farquharson, whose outstandingly successful *Textbook of Operative Surgery* made his name almost a household word among surgeons in training in all parts of the world where English is the language of postgraduate medical education.

Eric Leslie Farquharson, born in Edinburgh, was the only son of a lawyer, but he had several close relatives who were doctors and from an early age his heart was set upon a career in medicine. He was educated at the Edinburgh Academy and at Edinburgh University, from which he graduated MB ChB in 1928. He obtained the Fellowship of the College in 1931 and one year later gained his Doctorate of Medicine (MD) with commendation.

In 1933 he was appointed Clinical Tutor in the Edinburgh Royal Infirmary to Mr W. J. Stuart (q.v.), with whom he had previously served as House Surgeon and for whose character and personality he had a profound admiration. It became his declared ambition to model his own professional life on that of this wise and compassionate surgeon and most of those who knew them both would agree that he succeeded in doing so.

During the 1930s Eric Farquharson visited some of the great European surgical clinics and in later years he often regaled his junior staff with fascinating reminiscences and colourful vignettes of such titanic figures as Thierry de Martel of Paris, Ferdinand Sauerbruch of Berlin and Lorenz Böhler of Vienna. He was particularly impressed by Böhler's teaching and practice in orthopaedic and traumatic surgery, which then formed a large part of the work of most general surgeons and it was probably this which inspired him to produce his first book *Illustrations of Surgical Treatment*, which was published before the outbreak of the Second World War and which ran to three editions.

When war came in 1939 he volunteered for military service and was commissioned into the Royal Army Medical Corps (RAMC) as a surgical specialist. After a period of duty in the United Kingdom, during which he obtained the Fellowship of the Royal College of Surgeons of England, he was posted overseas with the rank of Lieutenant Colonel and commanded the surgical divisions of military hospitals in East Africa, Ceylon (Sri Lanka) and India.

Eric Farquharson (1905–70).

Demobilisation from the RAMC after six years' service was soon followed by his appointment to the honorary staff of the Edinburgh Royal Infirmary as Assistant Surgeon. In 1959 he was appointed Surgeon in charge of his own wards, in which over the next 11 years he directed what came to be regarded as one of the best clinical teaching units in Edinburgh.

In 1954 he published his celebrated single-handed magnum opus the *Textbook of Operative Surgery*, which was an instant success and which soon achieved what was virtually the status of holy writ with candidates for the Fellowship examinations of all the royal surgical colleges. It owed its popularity to the clarity of its descriptive prose, to its lucid presentation of the anatomy relevant to each operative procedure and to its simple, almost conversational style, which made it a pleasure to read. It also had excellent illustrations, including many examples of the author's considerable expertise as a clinical photographer. Four editions of this remarkable book were published between 1954 and 1970, and there is no doubt that, over this period, it made an important contribution to surgical education.

He gained further widespread fame (or perhaps notoriety) through his energetic advocacy of out-patient surgery under local anaesthesia for inguinal hernia. At that time this was a revolutionary departure from surgical orthodoxy, which aroused adverse comments and even censure from many quarters, but the excellent results which he obtained in a series of more than 400 patients silenced his critics and, 45 years on, day-case hernia repair has become standard practice.

He was a skilled and enthusiastic craftsman with a well-equipped workshop in his home and a flair for gadgetry which inspired him to devise a number of instruments and appliances, of which the most successful were his widely used portable orthopaedic traction table, an ingenious ligature carrier and an ophthalmoscopic attachment for the ordinary pocket-sized pen torch.

Eric Farquharson gave long and devoted service to the College as an examiner, as a member of Council, and as Vice President from 1967 until his death. He was a member of the Court of Examiners of the Royal College of Surgeons of England from 1951 to 1957, and in 1966 he was elected to the Council of the English College. This gave him the distinction of being the only surgeon to have served concurrently on the Councils of the Edinburgh and the English Colleges.

On the wards his kindliness, consideration and courtesy in his dealings with patients from all walks of life, no less than his clinical wisdom, made a lasting impression on colleagues, nursing staff and students. As 'Chief', he was always the team captain and never a dictator or an absolute monarch, thereby earning the affection as well as the respect of all who worked in what was recognised to be one of the happiest units in the Royal Infirmary.

Nothing in his professional life gave him greater satisfaction than clinical teaching at the bedside and he could not have a more appropriate memorial in the College than the Farquharson Award for excellence in the teaching of surgery or anatomy. After his untimely death in 1970 this was generously endowed by his widow and his two daughters, one of whom, a Fellow of the College, has edited a ninth edition (2005) of her father's historic textbook.

Roll number: 3700

234

J. Roderick Cameron (1902–97)

The only President of the College in modern times who was not a university graduate is also the only one to have held a dental as well as a medical qualification.

James Roderick Johnston Cameron, known in Edinburgh medical circles simply as 'J.R.', and to his close friends always as Derick, was born in Belfast, where his father was a dental surgeon and his mother was the grand-niece of one of the most famous Scottish doctors of all time, Sir James Young Simpson.

Derick Cameron was educated in Edinburgh at George Watson's College and his original intention was to follow in his father's professional footsteps. He obtained the College's Licentiate in Dental Surgery in 1926, but then decided on a career in medicine and in 1927 he qualified in medicine as a Triple Licentiate of the Scottish Royal Colleges.

After holding junior hospital posts in Edinburgh, he spent some time in Montreal, working first in the pathology department of McGill University and later as resident to Dr Wilder Penfield in the Royal Victoria Hospital. With this renowned neurosurgeon he developed a warm and lasting friendship. Another Canadian with whom he became friendly at that time was Norman Bethune (q.v.), later to achieve posthumous fame as a hero of communist China.

Having returned from Canada and resolved to make his career in surgery, Cameron obtained the Fellowship of the College in 1931 and then became a clinical tutor in the Edinburgh Royal Infirmary. In 1938 he was appointed Assistant Surgeon at Leith Hospital and also at the Royal Infirmary, but within a few months Britain was at war and he immediately volunteered for duty with the Royal Army Medical Corps as a surgical specialist.

He was with the combined British and French force at Narvik in the ill-fated Norwegian campaign of 1940, during which, because he could ski (at that time a fairly unusual accomplishment for a Scotsman), he was seconded to act as Medical Officer to the famous French regiment, the Chasseurs Alpins. Between 1941 and 1944 he commanded the surgical divisions of various military hospitals in Egypt and Palestine, and for several months was senior surgical consultant to the British forces in Iraq and Iran (PAI Force). In 1944 he was posted to Italy and to the command of the combined surgical divisions of two base hospitals, where, during weeks of fierce fighting with heavy casualties, he had ultimate responsibility for nearly a thousand surgical beds.

J. Roderick Cameron (1902–97).

J. R. Cameron. Presidential portrait.

After demobilisation, he returned to civil practice in Edinburgh and it was during these early post-war years that, as Assistant Surgeon in the Royal Infirmary, he developed his special interest and expertise in the surgery of the thyroid gland. His appointment in 1957 as Surgeon in charge of wards was the fulfilment of a long-cherished ambition and, as such, his commitment to thyroid surgery increased steadily but not to the exclusion of other interests; among these was the surgery of malignant skin tumours and his experience of the treatment of melanoma was probably unrivalled in Scotland.

Cameron was a first-class clinician and bedside teacher, but he was neither a spectacular nor rapid operator. His meticulous technique achieved excellent results with a minimal incidence of complications, which more flamboyant surgeons found hard to emulate. He was an admirable team leader of a surgical unit which was as noted for its relaxed happy atmosphere as for its efficiency and clinical excellence.

In the 1950s and 1960s Cameron became increasingly involved in the affairs of the College and having served on Council and as Vice President, he was elected President in 1967. During his term of office, he initiated a radical and long overdue revision of the College's laws, completed under his successor, which has enabled it to function efficiently as a modern corporation without any weakening of its democratic tradition.

Mindful of his early interest in dentistry, Cameron gave special encouragement to the activities of the College's dental faculty, in recognition of which he was awarded the honorary Fellowship in Dental Surgery. During his term of office he travelled widely on College business and he was particularly proud of having led the first College examining teams to conduct Fellowship examinations in Burma (Myanmar) and in Bangladesh.

His lasting memorial in the College is the triennial Simpson Memorial Lecture, established in 1966 largely through his efforts and associated with the award of the Sir James Young Simpson Gold Medal, which is one of the highest honours which the College can bestow. He handsomely inaugurated the endowment fund which supports the lectureship and this was generously augmented by contributions from other members of the Simpson family.

Derick Cameron was a warm-hearted, kindly man with a keen intellect and an abundance of common sense, but he sometimes gave the impression of being vague, absent-minded and indecisive. It is quite likely that this image was deliberately cultivated, but, whether natural or contrived, it combined with his own special brand of whimsical humour and his benign personality to enshrine his reputation as one of Edinburgh's notable medical 'characters'.

He will be remembered as a President and as a 'Chief' whose professional excellence, wisdom, integrity and generosity of spirit commanded total respect.

Roll number: 3722

Sir John Bruce (1905–75)

Many factors can influence the choice of surgery as a career. The ambition is often nurtured from childhood, influenced by the wish to follow a parent or relative, but for many the attraction is simply that surgery offers the satisfaction of helping others through practical skills. Some are drawn to surgery by a childhood experience as a patient which provides an impression so powerful that it determines their career for life. So it was with John Bruce, who was inspired to become a doctor by a chance meeting with Sir John Fraser (q.v.) when, as a 15-year-old schoolboy, he accompanied a friend with a minor fracture to the Children's Hospital in Edinburgh. He went on to become Fraser's pupil, then colleague, eventually following his academic footsteps as Regius Professor of Clinical Surgery in Edinburgh University. Sir John Bruce became a major figure on the world stage of surgery, described by some contemporaries as the best-known surgical figure of his day.

John Bruce was born in Dalkeith, and graduated MB ChB with honours from Edinburgh University in 1928, and was elected FRCSEd four years later. As Assistant Surgeon to the Royal Infirmary, he ran, in partnership with Ian Aird (q.v.), a highly acclaimed course to prepare candidates for the Fellowship examination.

On the outbreak of war in 1939 he joined the Royal Army Medical Corps, and was posted to join the ill-fated Norwegian Expeditionary Force, which, after hurried training on the Shetlands, landed on the west coast of Norway. Within days the Germans invaded Norway and the Force withdrew under aerial bombardment from the Luftwaffe, an action which effectively marked the end of the 'phoney war'. For his actions during the evacuation of his field hospital, he was mentioned in dispatches, and his leadership qualities began to emerge. Appointment as Surgeon to the 14th Army in south-east Asia followed, and in Burma he was promoted Brigadier. Here, he developed a great admiration for his commander-in-chief General (later Field Marshal) Slim, and their friendship dating from this time was one of which he was intensely proud. After the war he took great pleasure in presenting Slim for honorary Fellowship of the College. For wartime service he was made Commander of the Order of the British Empire (CBE) and awarded the Territorial Decoration (TD).

After his move to the Western General Hospital in 1946, he founded the combined medical and surgical Gastrointestinal (G-I) Unit in partnership with Wilfred Card. This proved an innovative, visionary step, for the concept of combined patient care by physicians and surgeons was new in Britain at that time. Combined care was particularly applicable to two common G-I problems of the day – peptic ulcer and inflammatory bowel disease – and the G-I Unit developed a powerful research base and a reputation for training which was to gain international acclaim.

Brigadier John Bruce, RAMC.

Sir John Bruce – elder statesman.

Sir John Bruce (1905–75).

His appointment to the Regius Chair of Clinical Surgery in 1956, succeeding Sir James Learnmonth (q.v.), seemed a natural progression. As Regius Professor his stature grew and he became a great ambassador for Edinburgh surgery. Throughout the surgical world he came to be regarded as a 'memorial lecturer' par excellence, one who could lecture with authority on a wide range of topics including bone and joint disease, surgical anatomy, military surgery, breast cancer and surgical gastroenterology. He had huge energy and great enthusiasm for things surgical and for things Scottish. A love of company, of good food and of discussions long into the night were the hallmarks that endeared him to a circle of friends around the world. In this way he was able to foster links with the United States, Canada and the Commonwealth, links which led to his foundation, jointly with Ian Aird (q.v.) and Dr William Hinton of New York, the James IV Association of Surgeons, of which he became President,

Above all of these it was his passion for the Royal College of Surgeons of Edinburgh which was always to the fore. His short history of the College demonstrates his gift for elegant, simple prose, his depth of knowledge of Scottish history and his affection for the College. He founded the *Journal of the Royal College of Surgeons of Edinburgh* and saw it thrive in his 20 years as editor. Through the journal, he was able to foster new bonds with Fellows of the College throughout the world.

The number of honorary Fellowships which he received attests to his international standing; he was honoured by the surgical colleges in America, England, Ireland, Australasia, South Africa and Canada. He received further honours in Britain with a knighthood in 1963, appointment as Surgeon to the Queen in Scotland from 1966, and President of the Association of Surgeons in 1965. Yet most of those who met him remember him as an affable, gregarious, sociable man, who would enliven any social gathering. The tribute by Hugh Dudley, paraphrasing Kipling, is perhaps the most apt summary: 'Though he walked with kings (and in some senses was one himself), he never lost the common touch.' Many young surgeons of all nationalities had cause to be grateful for his listening ear and wise counsel.

John Bruce's character had a grandeur which placed him among the greatest names in the rich lineage of the Edinburgh Regius Chair of Clinical Surgery, of which he was so proud. Those who heard his commemorative lectures, delivered with Churchillian style and eloquence, could sense that here was a surgeon with a place in history. He brought credit to the Scottish and Edinburgh surgical tradition of which he was so proud.

Roll number: 3808

Sir Norman Jeffcoate (1907–92)

Recognition for obstetrics and gynaecology as a specialty emerged as recently as the mid-19th century. The higher specialist diploma first became available for obstetricians and gynaecologists in Britain when the College of Obstetricians and Gynaecologists was founded in 1929 by Professor William Blair-Bell and Sir William Shaw. Norman Jeffcoate was a student of Professor Blair-Bell and went on to become his greatest protégé and disciple, eventually following his mentor as President of what had by then become the Royal College of Obstetricians and Gynaecologists.

Thomas Norman Arthur Jeffcoate was educated at King Edward VI School in Nuneaton, England, and went on to study medicine at Liverpool University, where as an undergraduate he played in a successful Liverpool University rugby team. Having graduated MB ChB with first-class honours and with a clutch of distinctions and prizes, he became House Surgeon to William Blair-Bell, an association that was to prove a particularly fruitful one. He became a Fellow of the College in 1932 and received the degree of MD from Liverpool University the same year for a thesis on gonadotrophins. In 1938 he was chosen by the Royal College of Obstetricians and Gynaecologists to give the first Blair-Bell Lecture.

His outstanding ability as a communicator became evident during this time. Meticulous attention to the detail of the history and to physical signs were the hallmarks which marked him out as one of the great teachers of his generation in his specialty. In 1945, he became the first full-time Professor in Obstetrics and Gynaecology in the University of Liverpool. He followed in Blair-Bell's footsteps to become Convenor of the Gynaecological Visiting Society. His great intellectual capacity and clarity of thought, which formed the basis for his success as a teacher, also determined the success of his major text *Principles of Gynaecology*, first published in 1957. This became standard reading throughout the English-speaking world and was published in five editions. A surgical innovator, he introduced colposcopy into British gynaecological practice in 1985. As his fame spread, postgraduates from around the country preparing for the MRCOG examination were attracted in large numbers to his teaching ward rounds in Liverpool.

It was inevitable that he was in demand as a lecturer throughout the world, visiting India, Australia, the United States and Canada. He served the RCOG throughout his career and was elected President in 1969. The following year, he was knighted by the Queen. Many honours followed – the honorary Fellowship of the American College of Obstetricians and Gynaecologists, honorary Fellowship of the College in South Africa and an honorary LLD from Trinity College, Dublin.

From the time of his appointment to the Liverpool chair he took up painting and on regular holidays in the Isle of Man produced over the years a series of watercolours of Manx countryside, which were exhibited after his death.

Roll number: 3830

Sir Norman Jeffcoate (1907–92).

Isabella Forshall (1900–89)

From the perspective of a society increasingly determined to achieve true gender equality and where equal opportunity is enshrined in statute, it is difficult to appreciate the barriers which women intent on a surgical career had to overcome. Isabella Forshall was among the early women Fellows of the College and a pioneer of paediatric surgery in the United Kingdom, who did much to establish paediatric surgery as a specialty in its own right.

Isabella Forshall (1900–89).

Isabella Forshall studied medicine at the London School of Medicine for Women and became House Surgeon at the Royal Liverpool Children's Hospital, and later at Alder Hey Children's Hospital and was to work in both of these until she retired in 1965. She was elected FRCSEd in 1932. At the start of the Second World War she became Assistant Surgeon at the Birkenhead and Wirral Children's Hospitals and, as many of her male colleagues were in the forces, worked virtually single handed as a paediatric surgeon in the Liverpool region.

After the war, she was able to develop paediatric surgery in Liverpool as a specialty and it was largely due to her endeavours that the Liverpool Neonatal Surgical Centre at the Alder Hey Children's Hospital was opened in 1953. This unit, the first of its kind in the world, was able to demonstrate a reduction in surgical mortality for neonatal surgery and much of the credit for this lay with Isabella Forshall and her colleague Peter Rickham.

In the latter part of her career many well-deserved honours came her way. She was elected President of the British Association of Paediatric Surgeons in 1958 and the next year was President of the paediatric section of the Royal Society of Medicine. She became President of the Liverpool Medical Institution and in 1970 received the degree of Master of Surgery from the University of Liverpool.

Roll number: 3844

Robert McWhirter (1904–94)

In the middle decades of the 20th century the treatment of breast cancer became highly controversial, the debate centring around the relative merits of radical mastectomy on the one hand and simple mastectomy with radiotherapy on the other. At the heart of this controversy was an Edinburgh radiologist Robert McWhirter, who was one of the most ardent advocates of the latter regimen.

Over 10–15 years McWhirter was subjected to a barrage of hostile criticism from many quarters, much of it prejudiced and irrational, but he argued his case with tenacity and eventually his ideas won acceptance. It may be justifiably claimed that these ideas brought about a fundamental change in the principles underlying the surgical treatment of breast cancer and, indeed, of several other forms of malignant disease.

Robert McWhirter (1904–94).

Robert McWhirter was the second son of the village schoolmaster at Ballantrae, Ayrshire. He followed his elder brother to Glasgow University, from which, in 1927, he graduated MB ChB with high commendation and it was during the latter part of his undergraduate course that he first became fascinated by radiology.

After holding junior hospital posts, he spent four years as a general practitioner in Prestwick, during which time he persuaded his partners to install an X-ray apparatus in the local nursing home, giving him his first experience of radio diagnosis. His interest in the treatment of cancer by radiation was also aroused and he recognised that optimum results were most likely to be achieved by combining it with appropriate surgery. This prompted him to pursue surgical studies in Edinburgh, and in 1932 he obtained the Fellowship of the College.

From Edinburgh he went to Cambridge, where he took the diploma in Medical Radiology and while studying for this he was strongly influenced by the teaching of Dr A. K. Barclay, with whom he established a warm friendship. He was also inspired by Lord Rutherford's lectures at the Cavendish laboratory on the structure of the atom.

After gaining further clinical experience in the X-ray department of St Bartholomew's Hospital in London, he obtained, through Dr Barclay's sponsorship, a travelling Fellowship, which took him to the United States for a period of advanced training in diagnostic radiology at the Mayo Clinic. This was followed by a research Fellowship in radiotherapy under Dr Ralston Paterson (q.v.) at the Christie Hospital and Holt Radium Institute in Manchester. Here he saw at first hand the new system of gamma-ray dosimetry which Paterson was developing with H. M. Parker. Thereafter he returned to St Bartholomew's as chief assistant in the X-ray department. He was impressed by the unorthodox teaching and practice of a surgical colleague, Mr (later Sir) Geoffrey Keynes, in the treatment of breast cancer, particularly his advocacy of radium implantation combined with conservative surgery. This was the inspiration of the research to which McWhirter devoted the rest of his professional life and for which his name is remembered worldwide.

In 1935, when Dr Barclay was invited to take charge of the X-ray department of the Edinburgh Royal Infirmary, he accepted on condition that he could bring Robert McWhirter with him as his first assistant. Barclay stayed only a few months in Edinburgh and when he returned to his teaching and research in Cambridge, McWhirter had by then made such a favourable impression that, at the age of 31, he was invited to fill the vacancy.

Immediately he radically reorganised the Infirmary X-ray department and set about its long overdue modernisation and re-equipment, so that by the outbreak of the Second World War it had become one of the foremost centres of advanced radiology in Britain. Increasingly, he concentrated his own clinical activity on radiotherapy and he embarked on a study of breast cancer which ultimately convinced him that the scientific rationale of the classical Halstead radical mastectomy was unsound.

His ideas, although revolutionary, were well received by the Edinburgh surgeons, who, in 1938, agreed to give an extended trial to a regimen in which patients with potentially curable breast cancer were treated by simple mastectomy without axillary lymph-node excision combined with supervoltage radiotherapy.

This was widely regarded as surgical heresy and some of his critics went so far as to regard it as malpractice. For almost two decades McWhirter and those who supported his views were subjected to persistent condemnation. A crucial moment came in 1948 when he was invited to speak on the treatment of breast cancer at a meeting of the Royal Society of Medicine to a large audience, including a number of distinguished surgeons who regarded his methods with extreme disfavour. On this, and on other similar occasions, he stood his ground with calm confidence, and in due course results similar to his own began to be reported from other centres where his methods had been on trial. Eventually this led to a radical reappraisal of long-established doctrines relating to the treatment of breast cancer. He enjoyed the debate, which he conducted with oncologists and surgeons in many different parts of the world, yet his integrity earned for him the respect of even his severest critics.

In 1944 Robert McWhirter was elected a Fellow of the Royal Society of Edinburgh and two years later he was appointed to the newly endowed Forbes Chair of Medical Radiology in Edinburgh University. Soon after this, the departments of diagnostic radiology and of radiotherapy in the Royal Infirmary were separated and from then on he confined his own clinical activity entirely to radiotherapeutics. As Professor, he was the driving force behind the establishment in 1953 at the Western General Hospital of the new Radiotherapy Institute, which developed into the Department of Clinical Oncology.

McWhirter played a prominent part in the affairs of the Faculty (later the Royal College) of Radiologists, and he was its President from 1966 to 1969. In 1963 he was appointed Commander of the Order of the British Empire (CBE) in recognition of his services to radiology and to clinical oncology.

His reputation as a superb clinician and an inspiring teacher attracted many postgraduate students to his departments at the Royal Infirmary and, later, at the Western General Hospital. Twenty of his former students went on to become heads of departments of radiotherapy and oncology in the United Kingdom and overseas.

In spite of, or perhaps because of, all the controversy which it aroused, Robert McWhirter's work on breast cancer is now recognised as an important contribution to the management of malignant disease and it has assured for him a place in medical history.

Roll number: 3879

A. B. Wallace (1906–74)

During the First World War, it was recognised that battle casualties with injuries of the face and jaws required highly specialised care and this was a major factor in the development of the specialty of plastic surgery in Britain. This impetus lapsed to some extend in the interwar years, during which, in Scotland, most plastic surgery was undertaken by general surgeons with varying degrees of interest in the specialty. However, in the months before the outbreak of the Second World War, the requirement for specialist plastic surgeons was at last fully appreciated. One of the first Scottish surgeons to devote his career exclusively to plastic surgery at this time was A. B. Wallace, who went on to achieve high international distinction in his chosen specialty.

A. B. Wallace (1906–74).

Alexander Burns Wallace, who throughout his life was always known as 'Alastair' or often just simply as 'A.B.', was born in Edinburgh. He was educated at George Heriot's School and at Edinburgh University, from which he graduated MB ChB in 1929. After holding resident hospital posts, he worked for Norman Dott (q.v.) at the Royal Hospital for Sick Children and, in 1932, he obtained the Fellowship of the College. He then spent four years in the USA and in Canada engaged in research on the lymphatic system, for which, in 1936, he was awarded a Master's degree (MSc) by McGill University.

Wallace returned from North America to the Sick Children's Hospital in Edinburgh, where he was associated with W. C. Wilson (q.v.) and Ian Aird (q.v.), and it was the former's original work on the pathophysiology of burns which kindled his interest in plastic surgery. In 1938 he spent some time studying techniques of skin tissue culture at the Strangeways Laboratory in Cambridge and then he went for a period of advanced training in plastic surgery at East Grinstead under Sir Harold Gillies, Archibald (later Sir Archibald) McIndoe and T. P. Kilner.

There was an urgent need for a dedicated plastic surgery unit in southeast Scotland and when this was established in 1941 in the Emergency Medical Services Hospital at Bangour, West Lothian, Wallace was the obvious choice for appointment as Surgeon in Charge. By the end of the war the unit had become a recognised centre of excellence and, in the early post-war period, began to attract aspiring plastic surgeons from different parts of the world.

In 1945 Wallace was appointed Surgeon to the Sick Children's Hospital and in the following year Edinburgh University made him Reader in Plastic Surgery.

Wallace was a founder member of the British Association of Plastic Surgeons and, in 1948, was appointed the first editor of the newly established *British Journal of Plastic Surgery*. When he retired from the editorial chair 21 years later, it had become a highly regarded international medium for the publication of original work.

In 1941 Wallace had published a small handbook on the treatment of burns and this was to be increasingly his main interest for the rest of his career. He made many contributions to advances in the management of burnt patients and although he was by no means the first to advocate and practise the treatment of burns by exposure, he became the leading protagonist of this technique and by his lectures and writings did much to convince surgeons throughout the world of its efficacy.

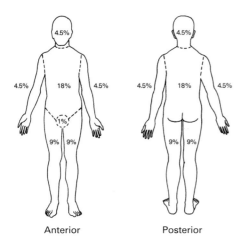

Anterior   Posterior

Wallace's 'Rule of Nine'.

In 1951 Wallace introduced his famous 'Rule of Nine' for the assessment of the extent of a burn as a percentage of the total body surface. It is so named because the head and neck constitute 9 per cent of the body surface as do each of the upper limbs; each lower limb amounts to 18 per cent (9 x 2) and the back and front of the trunk each also make up 18 per cent. The 'Rule of Nine' 53 years later is still universally applied in planning the emergency treatment of severely burnt patients and is Alastair Wallace's permanent memorial.

His work on burns earned for him international fame and he travelled widely as a visiting lecturer. His observations at home and overseas convinced him that severe burns were often preventable but that the introduction of effective preventive measures was being hindered in many countries by governmental apathy. His reaction was to work tirelessly for the creation of an international organisation of such prestige and influence that it could exert pressure on governments everywhere to legislate for the prevention of burns injuries.

Wallace organised the Second International Congress on Research in Burns in Edinburgh in 1965 and, at that Congress, the International Society for Burn Injuries was constituted with himself as its Secretary General. From an office in the College he organised the Society, which soon developed into a highly effective international pressure group. In 1974, at the Fourth International Congress on Research in Burns held in Buenos Aires, he was unanimously re-elected Secretary General of the Society for a further four years.

Wallace served on the Council of the British Association of Plastic Surgeons for 21 years and was President of the Association in 1951 and again in 1963. Throughout this period he represented the Association on the Medical Commission on Accident Prevention.

In 1965 he was elected to the Council of the College, on which he served for five years, and also in that year his outstanding clinical and scientific contributions were recognised by his appointment as Commander of the Order of the British Empire (CBE). His international stature was confirmed by the awards of the MD *honoris causa* of the University of Uppsala in 1970 and the Order of the Yugoslavian Flag and Gold Star presented to him personally by President Tito in 1973.

Following retirement from clinical practice in 1970, A.B.'s physical health declined, but intellectually he remained as active as ever. In addition to his duties as Secretary General of the International Society for Burn Injuries, he occupied himself with research into the history of plastic surgery and of the treatment of burns, for which he obtained, from St Andrews University, the degree of Doctor of Philosophy (PhD).

Wallace's work on burns overshadowed his considerable contributions in other fields, most notably maxillofacial surgery, but these were belatedly recognised by the College on the day before his death in December 1974 by the award of its honorary Fellowship in Dental Surgery.

Alastair Wallace was a genial, kindly man whose warm humanity and compassion were apparent in every aspect of his professional career, throughout which he enjoyed the respect and affection of colleagues, nurses, trainee plastic surgeons, students and patients of all ages. Clinically, technically and scientifically, he was a complete master of his specialty. However, his name will for ever be particularly associated with improvements in the prevention and treatment of burns, to which he made major contributions and which have ensured for him an honoured place in surgical history.

Roll number: 3889

James Brash (1886–1958)

The Edinburgh University Chair of Anatomy, founded in 1705, owes its illustrious place in medical history to the scientific contributions of its many distinguished incumbents. Professor J. C. Brash during his 23-year tenure, proved himself a most worthy heir to the great traditions established and maintained by the Monros, Goodsir, Turner and Cunningham.

James Couper Brash was born at Helensburgh but grew up in Edinburgh, where he received his early education at George Watson's College. In 1903 he entered Edinburgh University, from which he graduated MA in 1906, BSc in 1908 and MB ChB in 1910. The knowledge of literature, philosophy and the classics which he gained from his University arts course gave him great intellectual solace throughout his life, but in spite of heavy academic commitments, he took a full part in undergraduate affairs as Senior President of the Students' Representative Council (SRC) and, as an Office Bearer of the Liberal Association as well as of the Philomathic Society.

One year after his third graduation he joined Professor Arthur Robinson's junior staff in the Edinburgh anatomy department, from whence a few months later he was appointed Demonstrator in Anatomy in the University of Leeds.

On the outbreak of the First World War in 1914, Brash joined the Royal Army Medical Corps and most of his service was with a field ambulance on the Western Front. He attained the rank of Major and, during the Battle of the Somme in 1916, he was awarded the Military Cross.

After demobilisation, he returned to academic life and moved from Leeds to Birmingham, where, in 1922, he was appointed to the University Chair of Anatomy. Soon afterwards he also became Dean of the Faculty of Medicine and in this capacity he played a major role in the developments that led to the establishment of the new Birmingham medical school. Birmingham University awarded him its Doctorate of Medicine (MD) in 1928 and it was there that he initiated the researches on bone growth and development which gained for him an international scientific reputation and made him the obvious choice for appointment to the Edinburgh University Chair of Anatomy when his old 'Chief' Professor Arthur Robinson retired in 1931.

Brash's return to his alma mater as Professor meant that he became the departmental superior of one of his own former teachers, the world-famous Dr E. B. Jamieson ('Jimmy'), but happily their academic and personal relationships could not have been more cordial. Together they edited the seventh and eighth editions of Cunningham's monumental *Textbook of Anatomy* and the ninth and tenth editions of Cunningham's equally famous *Manual of Practical Anatomy*, both well known to generations of anatomy teachers and medical students throughout the English-speaking world.

Brash became a Fellow of the College in 1931 and a Fellow of the Royal Society of Edinburgh one year later. He continued his researches on bone growth and his 1933 Struthers Lecture to the College on this subject is regarded as a classical study. Much of his work related to the jaws and palate, and this, combined with his interest in the aetiology of dental irregularities and malocclusion, was recognised by his honorary membership of several odontological societies in Britain and abroad.

James Brash (1886–1958).

Further recognition of his scientific distinction came with his election to the presidency of the Anatomical Society of Great Britain (1945–7) and by the awards of honorary Doctorates from the Universities of St Andrews and Leeds.

In 1937 his academic eminence became widely known to the general public by his collaboration with Professor John Glaister of the Glasgow Chair of Medical Jurisprudence in the forensic investigations associated with a notoriously gruesome murder trial. Brash's meticulous studies of severely mutilated human remains, which clearly established the identity of the murder victims, were of crucial importance to the conviction of the murderer and the monograph *The Medico-Legal Aspects of the Ruxton Case* (1937), which he published with Professor Glaister, is a classic of scientific detection.

Professor Brash was not an outstanding undergraduate teacher in the mould of his celebrated colleague 'Jimmy', but his kindliness, geniality, approachability and dry pawky humour endeared him to his students. They respected his academic achievements even if they often had difficulty in understanding his somewhat discursive lectures.

He gave valuable and devoted service to his University on the Senatus Academicus and in many other capacities. At various times he acted as Deputy Dean of the medical faculty and for many years he was a member of the University Union Committee, of the Scottish Universities Entrance Board and of the University Press Committee. From 1946 almost up to his death 12 years later, he examined in anatomy for the College in the old Part I FRCSEd examination and greatly appreciated this involvement with young doctors aspiring to a career in surgery. A stringent but scrupulously fair examiner, he always did his best to put nervous candidates at their ease and he is as kindly remembered by those whom he examined as by colleagues who had the pleasure of examining with him.

Roll number: 3892

The Royal College of Surgeons of Edinburgh, President and Council (1965–7).

Ronald Macbeth
(1903–92).

Ronald Macbeth (1903–92)

Ronald Macbeth and his great friend Ion Simson Hall (q.v.) were the twin pillars of otolaryngology in Great Britain in the 1950s and 1960s. He became Vice President of a surgical college, a rare feat for an otolaryngologist in those days.

Between the time that Arthur Logan Turner (q.v.) was President of the Royal College of Surgeons of Edinburgh from 1925 to 1927, and Ronald Macbeth's election to the Council in 1952, there were no otolaryngologists among the Office-Bearers in the College. Ronald Macbeth's contemporary, Ion Simson Hall, gained his specialty qualification from the Royal College of Physicians of Edinburgh. It was Macbeth's dream to make ear, nose and throat surgery a more respected surgical specialty, especially academically and politically – and he succeeded.

Ronald Macbeth was a second-generation Englishman, but was devoted to his Scottish roots. He was born in Stevenage, Herts, and was educated at Highgate School and Oriel College, Oxford, for pre-clinical studies. From there he went to King's College Hospital, London, for clinical training and graduated BM B.Ch (Oxon) in 1928. He became a Fellow of the Royal College of Surgeons of Edinburgh in 1933, sitting the same examination as all surgeons did at that time, because the specialty option was not available until the late 1940s.

He spent almost his entire professional life as an ENT consultant in the John Radcliffe Infirmary, Oxford, being appointed after three years' training in 1931 and retiring in 1968. There can be few, if any, surgeons who could have replicated this tenure of a consultant post. But Ronald did not merely hold on to the headship. He pursued his aim of upgrading otolaryngology by building a team of specialists who made Oxford the centre of excellence of British orolaryngology in the 1950s and 1960s.

With his training in general surgery, he was more able than most other ENT surgeons to tackle head and neck surgery, and he was a skilled exponent of laryngectomy and maxillectomy for cancer, a condition which was very common in the Oxford area. Along with Dr Esme Hadfield, he identified the high risk of sinus adenocarcinoma in woodworkers in the High Wycombe area. His other seminal contribution to the specialty was the description of access to the frontal sinus using an osteoplastic frontal flap.

In 1959, he, Simson Hall and a few other enthusiasts underwrote the First British Academic Conference in Otolaryngology in London with their own money; this was no light undertaking since they all carried huge financial risks if the conference failed to attract sufficient numbers. As it was, it turned out to be enormously successful and has been a four-yearly event ever since. Ion Simson Hall was the Master of that first conference, and the honour was Ronald Macbeth's when the Conference was held in Edinburgh in 1971.

He loved Scotland. He had a caravan in the wilds of Wester Ross, where he went 'fossiking', which means 'doing nothing very special other than rummaging around on the beach'.

He had two professional disappointments. The first was his failure to have a chair established in Oxford. He had raised enough funds for the establishment of a chair, but it never came to pass. The second concerned his Oxford College, Oriel. Despite his great affection for Oriel, and despite the fact that whenever he dined, he was asked to say the enormously long College grace in Latin, he was never made a Fellow.

He was elected to the Council of the College in 1959 and in 1963 became Vice President. Such was his desire to become more involved with College affairs he even applied for a junior consultant job in the Edinburgh Royal Infirmary in 1964. This caused such alarm among the body of local ENT consultants that he was not even short-listed.

After retirement, he served on the board of governors of the United Oxford Hospitals and was University member of the City Council from 1965 to 1974.

He died shortly before his 90th birthday.

Author: Arnold Maran

Roll number: 3925

James Mason Brown (1908–64).

James Mason Brown (1908–64)

John Lauder died in 1737 during his third term of office as Deacon of the Incorporation of Surgeons and Barbers and 237 years later his lineal successor, James Mason Brown, died in the second year of his presidency of the College. When the Incorporation became a Royal College under the terms of the Charter granted by King George III in 1778, the Deacon adopted the title of President and James Mason Brown is the only bearer of that title to have died in office. Yet this tragic historical accident is the very least of the many reasons why his life and achievements are worthy of commemoration.

James Johnston Mason Brown was born in St Andrews and was educated at Edinburgh Academy. While still a schoolboy, he underwent an operation for appendicitis with peritonitis at the hands of Sir John Fraser (q.v.), and this early contact was the decisive influence upon his choice of career. He entered the medical faculty of Edinburgh University in 1926 and five years later graduated MB ChB with honours and the award of the Pattison Prize in Clinical Surgery.

His earliest graduate appointments were in the Royal Infirmary with Sir John Fraser and at the Royal Hospital for Sick Children with Mr Norman Dott (q.v.). As Clinical Tutor in the Royal Infirmary, he started his research on osteochondritis dissecans, which earned for him the Syme Surgical Fellowship. He obtained the Fellowship of the College in 1934 but, even before this, Sir John Fraser had invited him to be his private assistant, and he became successively Clinical Tutor and University Assistant.

In 1936 Mason Brown was appointed Assistant Surgeon to the Royal Hospital for Sick Children, where his senior colleague was Gertrude Herzfeld (q.v.) but at this stage he was not yet totally committed to paediatric surgery, and in 1937 he was awarded a Crichton Scholarship for his researches on peripheral vascular disease.

As a Territorial Officer in the Royal Army Medical Corps, he was immediately called up for military service when war broke out in 1939 and initially served as Regimental Medical Officer to the 7th/9th Battalion of the Royal Scots (the 'Dandy Ninth'). He served as a surgical specialist with the 31st General Hospital, after which, with the rank of Lieutenant Colonel, he commanded the surgical division of the 70th General Hospital in North Africa and Italy. His surgical division was selected to form the Vascular Injuries Centre for the British forces in the Mediterranean theatre, and for his contributions in this specialised field of military surgery, he was mentioned in dispatches and appointed OBE.

When the war ended in 1945, Mason Brown returned to the Royal Hospital for Sick Children in Edinburgh, where, after Ian Aird (q.v.) had moved to the Chair of Surgery at the Postgraduate Medical School in London and Gertrude Herzfeld had retired, he became Surgeon in Chief.

He was ideally suited temperamentally, intellectually and technically for this position, in which his ability and enthusiasm found full scope. His impressive clinical skills were immeasurably enhanced by his love of children, which enabled him rapidly to gain the complete confidence of even the most frightened and distressed of his young patients. His operative expertise covered the entire field of surgical paediatrics but his greatest special interest was neonatal surgery, to which he brought a meticulous, gentle, unhurried technique, characterised by a reverence for delicate tissues. Equally crucial to his success was the kindliness, sympathy and understanding he invariably showed to distraught parents, winning their trust and inspiring both hope and faith.

James Mason Brown was an excellent clinical teacher and his formal lectures, often liberally spiced with his own distinctive brand of gentle humour, were models of lucid exposition. The precision and clarity of his writing were equally notable and his contributions to paediatric surgical literature were as eminently readable as they were authoritative.

His greatest educational achievement was the publication of *The Surgery of Childhood* (1962), of which he was editor in chief. In this capacity he led a team of 27 distinguished authors in the production of what was the first major British textbook of paediatric surgery since the publication 18 years earlier of Sir John Fraser's single-handed magnum opus bearing the same title.

In 1948, together with Matthew White of Glasgow, James Mason Brown founded the Scottish Surgical Paediatric Society and in 1955 he was one of those responsible for the foundation of the British Association of Paediatric Surgeons (BAPS).

His close involvement in College affairs started with his appointment to the dual office of Secretary and Treasurer in 1949 and soon after this he chose deliberately to devote himself to the College rather than accept an offer of academic preferment. When the duties of the Secretary and Treasurer were separated in 1954, he continued in the latter office until 1962, by which time he had acquired an unrivalled knowledge of the College's history and laws as well as of its administrative procedures.

This was one of many factors which determined his election as President in 1962. He was the first specialist paediatric surgeon to hold the College's highest office and his international stature in his specialty undoubtedly added strength to his presidency. Whether delivering an important commemorative oration or making a light-hearted amusing after-dinner speech, James Mason Brown was an absolute master of the spoken word, and this gift, as much as his gentle charm and his warm outgoing personality, helped him to increase the College's influence and to enhance its prestige.

Soon after becoming President of the College, he was elected President of BAPS, to which over the next two years he gave inspiring leadership. Plans were made for a major international gathering of paediatric surgeons to be held in Edinburgh in 1965 under his presidency and in his honour, but fate decreed otherwise and his untimely death cruelly cut short what were clearly going to be highly successful terms of office as President of the College and of his specialty association. This tragic abbreviation of a brilliant career was a loss, not just to the College but to British surgery as a whole.

He is appropriately commemorated by the Mason Brown Memorial Lectureship, which every two years is awarded jointly by the College and by the British Association of Paediatric Surgeons.

Roll number: 4038

James Mason Brown.

David Monro (1886–1960)

The family Monro was synonymous with the teaching of anatomy and surgery in Edinburgh for much of the 18th and the first half of the 19th centuries. Monro *tertius* had not lived up to the standard of his father and grandfather, and the medical dynasty appeared to have died with him. The medical connection was resurrected with distinction in the 20th century by David Carmichael Monro, who was in direct line of succession of Monro *primus, secundus,* and *tertius*.

David Monro's illustrious forebears had occupied the Chair of Anatomy for three successive generations – 126 years – in Edinburgh, David Carmichael Monro was born in Switzerland and went to school at Wellington College, New Zealand. He was the son of Charles Monro, who introduced the game of rugby football to New Zealand, grandson of Sir David Monro (1813–77), an Edinburgh medical graduate who became speaker of the New Zealand Parliament, and great-grandson of Alexander Monro *tertius* (see Monro family tree on page 40).

Following in distinguished family footsteps, he studied medicine at Edinburgh University, and would recall his embarrassment at his first anatomy lecture, where he was publicly introduced to his fellow students as a member of the Monro dynasty. After graduating in medicine from Edinburgh University in 1911 he joined the Royal Army Medical Corps in 1914, and served as a surgeon in France and Belgium during the First World War. He was mentioned in dispatches at the Battle of Ypres. After the war he was posted to India, returning to the UK in 1931. He served at the Queen Alexandra Military Hospital at Millbank, and, at his own request, was posted to Edinburgh Castle, taking the FRCSEd in 1934 and becoming Assistant Professor of Military Surgery at the Royal Army Medical College in 1938 and Professor there two years later. He was appointed Consultant Surgeon to the Middle East forces in 1941, and it was here that he was to make his greatest contribution. Realising that modern warfare, particularly desert warfare, had become highly mobile, he developed the idea of mobile forward surgical units. These were deployed much closer to the front line than had been previously thought possible and allowed for the early resuscitation of and operation on the wounded. At this time, blood for transfusion was available in adequate quantities for the first time and peri-operative blood transfusion became possible at a very much earlier stage in treatment. 'Jock' Monro had the tact and diplomacy to implement this innovation.

Monro was twice mentioned in dispatches, awarded the CBE and promoted Major General. He was awarded the King Haakon's Cross of Liberty by the Norwegian government and made a Commander of the Legion of Merit by the government of the United States.

He was hugely popular with his troops, and Sir Henage Ogilvy, who was to succeed him as Consultant Surgeon to the Middle East forces, was to write: 'he was a great conversationalist and had the best fund of stories I have ever heard – told in the slang or dialect appropriate to the central figure'. He knew each and every one of the surgeons in the Middle East army, which at that time extended over most of North Africa.

Those who knew him remembered the precision of his surgical technique, his bonhomie, zest for life and his great contribution to saving lives in the war in North Africa.

After the war he was appointed Companion of the Bath (CB), and retired to London, where he died in 1960.

Roll number: 4073

Major General D. C. Monro (1886–1960).

Ian Smillie (1907–92)

Orthopaedic surgery began to develop as a specialty in its own right in the first half of the 20th century. Until then it was within the remit of the general surgeons, many of whom jealously guarded this area of their practice. Gradually a generation of specialist orthopaedic surgeons emerged who had realised that the demands of orthopaedics were such that surgeons required to be specifically trained for that specialty alone. One such surgeon was Ian Smillie, who went on to become the first Professor of Orthopaedics in the University of St Andrews, latterly in Dundee.

Ian Smillie (1907–92).

Ian Scot Smillie was educated at Merchiston Castle School, Edinburgh, and Edinburgh University, qualifying MB ChB in 1931. For three years from 1936 he was Clinical Assistant to Mr (later Sir) Walter Mercer (q.v.), who was to go on to become the first Professor of Orthopaedic Surgery in Edinburgh. With the outbreak of war, he became Surgeon in Charge of the Emergency Medical Service Hospital at Larbert in central Scotland. Here he was able to promote some of the concepts which were to remain a theme throughout his professional life. He developed specialist teams for the care of patients which included nurses, physiotherapists and orthotists. In recognition of this wartime service, he was made an OBE in 1946.

After the war he was awarded a Nuffield Travelling Scholarship and visited centres in the United States and Canada. He graduated ChM from Edinburgh University and was awarded the gold medal for his thesis. When the National Health Service was established in 1948, he was made Surgeon in Charge of the Orthopaedic Service of the Eastern Region of Scotland. Initially based at Bridge of Earn Hospital, he further developed the concept of the team approach to care of the orthopaedic patient. The principles of early mobilisation and intensive rehabilitation were corner stones of his philosophy of care, and they are just as applicable today. In 1967 he became the first holder of the Chair of Orthopaedic Surgery at the University of St Andrews, moving the next year to Dundee.

Smillie became a world authority on the surgery of the knee. His *Injuries of the Knee Joint*, first published in 1948, became a classic which ran to five editions and was widely translated. While this publication led to his fame around the world, he also enjoyed a reputation as a brilliant technical surgeon and surgical innovator. The meniscectomy knife which he designed came to be used throughout the world. Recognition of this pre-eminence came with his presidency of the International Society of the Knee in 1981.

Outside of medicine, Smillie pursued a full life. He had raced vintage cars at Brooklands before the war and could be seen driving in Dundee in his open two-seater Allard. He enjoyed to the full country pursuits, especially deer stalking, and published a guide to the stalking of red deer in Scotland in 1983. He owned two estates in Sutherland, where his guests could enjoy both stalking and salmon fishing. An insight into his meticulous attention to detail is shown by his insistence that any salmon caught in the river Oykell on his estate must be frozen only in water drawn from that river. Many visiting orthopaedic surgeons from around the world – and there were many – would remember him for his generosity and unstinting hospitality, combined with a style and elegance in well-tailored clothes and a wide-brim black fedora.

Roll number: 4103

William Arthur Mackey (1906–91)

The original Chair of Surgery in Glasgow University was founded by King George III in 1815. Since that time the two Glasgow University Chairs of Surgery have had many distinguished incumbents including Professor (later Lord) Lister (q.v.), Professor (later Sir) William Macewen and Professor (later Sir) Charles Illingworth (q.v.). William Arthur Mackey was in that proud tradition.

William Arthur Mackey was educated at Ardrossan Academy, Ayrshire, and came to Glasgow University as a youthful prodigy – he was 16 years old when he entered the University, and only 21 when he graduated MB ChB with honours and won the Brunton Prize as the most distinguished student of his year.

After junior hospital posts, he became an assistant to the Professor of Pathology, a post which did not involve research to the extent that became the norm a decade later. However, one interesting piece of original work from that era survives. He published with Alan Lendrum (later to become Professor of Pathology in Dundee) an early account of glomus tumour, which, with its vascular and autonomic nervous connotations, indicated his early interest in the pathology and surgery of the sympathetic nervous and vascular systems, which was to become fulfilled in later life.

In the 1930s, conditions for employment in hospitals throughout Britain for aspirants to a surgical career were difficult – there were '10 lean years' to be survived with few poorly paid posts and a slowly growing private practice to be developed. Mackey progressed through a series of posts which took him to a University lectureship in surgery. In 1935 he became a Fellow of the College and of the Royal Faculty of Physicians and Surgeons of Glasgow (FRFPSG). Shortly thereafter he set off on a Rockefeller Travelling Fellowship to the USA, to visit Dr Warren Cole, who was pioneering the new technique of cholecystography, and to see at first hand the techniques of biliary surgery in Evarts Graham's department in St Louis. Circumstances prevented him from profiting immediately from his American experience, as he returned to a Britain preparing for war. For the next six years he was to devote himself to the demands of military surgery, and he did this in a way which earned him a formidable reputation in the army. He saw service in the Middle East and Europe and left the Royal Army Medical Corps with the rank of Lieutenant Colonel.

Returning to the professorial unit of the Western Infirmary of Glasgow as Assistant Surgeon under Sir Charles Illingworth, he developed an interest in porto-caval shunt surgery. His surgical roots were different, however, from those of Sir Charles. Cast as he was in the tradition of Macewen and Learmonth, he took up the surgery of the sympathetic nervous system, as applied then to hypertension and peripheral vascular disease. He established the first vascular clinic in Glasgow. As a former army surgeon he had an appointment to Cowglen Military Hospital, where he performed some of the earliest reconstructive arterial surgical procedures done in Glasgow on soldiers who had been wounded in the Korean War. In the Western Infirmary at this stage, he began to perform open heart surgery, specifically mitral valvotomy, the prelude to the valve replacement surgery that he was to undertake a few years later as Professor in Glasgow Royal Infirmary.

The Moynihan Chirurgical Club

This society was founded by Professor Berkeley Moynihan (1865–1936), Professor of Surgery at Leeds. In July 1909 he wrote to a number of surgeons in various parts of the country: 'It has long been in my mind to suggest to a few of the provincial hospital surgeons the need for the formation of a small and informal "Society of Clinical Surgery". The object of this society would be to hold meetings, say, twice yearly of two days' duration at one of the hospitals as the guests of one or more of the staff. Operations could be performed, cases presented, and general conversation and discussion follow.

'Such meetings should ensure closer friendship amongst us and make for better work ...
I propose to arrange for operations on Friday morning and afternoon and for a series of demonstrations on Saturday morning.'

All of the surgeons whom he invited in this way accepted, and the first meeting was held at Leeds on 23 July 1909. It was the first such society to be founded in the British Isles, and such was its success that others were soon established. In 1911 the society decided that it should be named 'The Chirurgical Club', and in 1929, as a compliment to its founder, who had by then been raised to the peerage as Lord Moynihan, it became the 'Moynihan Chirurgical Club'. In his response Lord Moynihan wrote: 'I look back upon the formation of the club as one of the happiest inspirations of my life.'

Since its inception the club has met on two occasions each year, interrupted only by the two world wars, with one of the meetings held in the British Isles, and the other overseas.

This expansion of his surgical repertoire meant that he had to move, temporarily, to the Southern General Hospital, but from here he was appointed to the St Mungo-Notman Chair of Surgery at Glasgow Royal Infirmary. This was a time when full-time professors were not allowed private practice and he gained great admiration for this move since it deprived him of a fairly substantial income.

In his new department he developed open heart surgery and put his surgical team to work with physicians and anaesthetists to create facilities for cardio-pulmonary bypass and secured funds for this to be carried out in a purpose-built unit – perhaps his lasting memorial. His energy, determination and foresight ensured that the obstacles encountered in this development were effectively overcome.

Mackey was an immensely scholarly man who had visited clinics in Germany before the war and maintained membership of the Anglo-German Medical Society. Through his army service in the Middle East, which took him to French-speaking areas, he had become fluent in that language. He had an effective use too of the English language, with an entertaining and imaginative turn of phrase – he once described cancer cells as 'loitering with intent'.

Like many other successful figures, he was full of antitheses, one moment crushingly sarcastic, the next paradoxically displaying a warm sense of humour. A hostile look and a steely glance from behind his spectacles could change in a few moments to a smile of encouragement to young surgeons and nurses, but the storm first had to pass. He was widely admired for his surgical panache – some elements of which were carried on into everyday life. He was probably the last professor in Britain regularly to wear morning dress on his ward rounds. This tendency towards the dramatic helped make him a bold and decisive surgeon. His intellect, his vision and his drive played a major part in restoring the essential vigour of the Glasgow School of Surgery at the Royal Infirmary to a level not seen since the time of Macewen.

Roll number: 4149

William Arthur Mackey (1906–91).

George Scott (1907–89)

George Scott was appointed to be the first incumbent of the Forbes Chair of Ophthalmology in the University of Edinburgh in 1954. At the time he was only the second Professor of Ophthalmology to be appointed in the United Kingdom.

Educated at Edinburgh Academy during and after the First World War George Ian Scott proceeded to graduate MA and then MB ChB from Edinburgh University, qualifying in 1933. He soon chose to specialise in ophthalmology and trained at the Royal Infirmary of Edinburgh under Harry M. Traquair (q.v.). Thus he followed the succession of ophthalmic surgeons in Edinburgh who promoted the study of the visual pathway and the quantitative measurement of fields of vision which had begun when George Andreas Berry (q.v.), President of the College in 1910, trained under Jannik Bjerrum in Copenhagen in the 1880s, and continued through Arthur H. H. Sinclair and Traquair. In the course of his own training, Scott witnessed Henning Roenne testing visual fields using the same matt-black deeply panelled double door in the

George Scott (1907–89).

Rigshospital that Bjerrum himself had used. In this work on perimetry he provided valuable assistance to Norman M. Dott (q.v.), then pioneering neurosurgery in Edinburgh. This experience later led him to edit the seventh edition of the seminal textbook *Traquair's Clinical Perimetry*, published in 1957.

He proceeded to Fellowship of the Royal College of Surgeons of Edinburgh in 1937 and joined the Royal Army Medical Corps in 1939 as Ophthalmologist to Scottish Command. He was promoted to the rank of Brigadier in 1942 and became Adviser in Ophthalmology to the Middle East forces. There he worked closely and formed an abiding friendship with Sir Stewart Duke-Elder, the leading figure in the specialty during and after the war. Before going to the Middle East he had published papers on diabetic retinopathy and the systemic and topical use of sulphonamides, notably Sulphacetamide. Drawing on his wartime experiences, he published papers on neuropathy in prisoners-of-war and the localisation of intra-ocular foreign bodies.

On his return to Edinburgh he was appointed Assistant Ophthalmic Surgeon to the Royal Infirmary and in 1953 Surgeon in Charge. He continued his interest in neuro-ophthalmology and diabetes, and, in the era before sub-specialty interests became fully differentiated, also published papers on retinopathy of prematurity and the operative treatment of congenital ptosis, on the lacrimal drainage system and on chronic open angle glaucoma.

In his inaugural address on his professorial appointment in 1955, he reviewed the early pioneers of ophthalmology in Edinburgh before going on to state his ideas on the role of a clinical academic department. With the title 'A Holistic Approach to Medicine', he argued that the development of the faculty of observation was important for undergraduates in medicine, and that ophthalmology offered the opportunity to study the progress of many types of disease affecting the eye, brain and body as a whole. The study of ophthalmology also demonstrates that minute pathological changes in a delicate structure can have a disastrous effect on function.

He believed that the apprenticeship system was the only effective way of producing a competent ophthalmologist, after the trainee has had a preliminary broad exposure to general medicine, surgery and basic sciences. His view on the service versus training debate was decades ahead of its time: 'The routine duties of a registrar tend to make such demands upon his time as to be detrimental to his training. He should be given more time to read and think, and share in clinical research.' He aimed to develop discussion groups where problems of joint concern to physicians, surgeons, ophthalmologists and laboratory workers could be considered in all their aspects. At the time this was innovative thinking as ophthalmologists were tending to become isolated from other branches of medicine by often working in single-specialty hospitals and by the unique terminology which they used.

His research philosophy warned of the hazards of short-term projects by clinically inexperienced workers and called for intimate linkage between various departments of medicine and science, taking diabetes as an example. He was later to develop close links with the Department of Psychology, joint clinics within the neurology department, and links with optometry (initially about the therapeutic use of contact lenses).

He excelled at administration and added a lecturer, medical artist and photographer to his academic department. He embraced the arrival of fluorescein fundus photography as an investigative tool. Overseeing the planning and opening of the Princess Alexandra Eye Pavilion, built to allow the redevelopment of the Royal Infirmary in Lauriston Place, he was able to avoid the disruption suffered by other departments forced to work on split sites. During a busy professional life in Edinburgh, he also served as President of the Faculty of Ophthalmologists and the Ophthalmological Society of the United Kingdom. He wrote with Sir Stewart Duke-Elder the volume on *Neuro-Ophthalmology* (1971), 12th in the multivolume *System of Ophthalmology*.

His calm manner was reassuring to patients and he continued his private practice from his house in Heriot Row. As Vice President of the Royal College of Surgeons, he succeeded to the presidency on the death of the President, J. J. Mason Brown (q.v.), in 1964. Appointed Surgeon Oculist in Scotland to HM the Queen, he was the last to hold that office, and was appointed Commander of the Order of the British Empire (CBE).

Meticulous in his appearance, tall, with an aquiline nose, bowler-hatted and dark-suited, his desk was clear of clutter and he wasted few words on patients or staff. A good talent-spotter, he supported his team and in return earned a high degree of loyalty.

His enthusiasm for reforming the tendency to a narrow outlook in ophthalmology was encapsulated in the closing words of his inaugural lecture, 'It will always be my aim to foster the closer relationship of all branches of medicine, so that, as a whole, we may hope to achieve more than we could attain by our individual efforts.'

Author: Geoffrey Millar

Roll number: 4305

Professor G. I. Scott. Presidential portrait.

James Ross (1911–97)

One of the most striking presidential portraits in the College is that of James Ross painted by Alan Sutherland. Fellows who knew him are agreed that it is an excellent likeness, but, perhaps more importantly, it also reveals the warmth of its subject's personality and thus goes far towards explaining why, during his lifetime, he was held in such remarkable affection by everyone connected with the College.

James Alexander Ross was educated at Merchiston Castle School, Edinburgh, of which, many years later, he was to become a governor. From school he entered the medical faculty of Edinburgh University, where at an early stage he developed an enthusiasm for anatomy, which was to persist throughout his life. He graduated MB ChB in 1934, but before then he had decided to become a surgeon. After holding junior posts in Edinburgh and London, he obtained the Fellowship of the College in 1938. Later that year he was appointed Clinical Tutor in the Edinburgh Royal Infirmary.

With the outbreak of the Second World War, he volunteered for service with the Royal Army Medical Corps (RAMC) as a surgical specialist. In 1940 he gained his first experience of war surgery in the treatment of casualties from the Dunkirk evacuation and in 1941 he embarked for Egypt with No. 58 General Hospital RAMC. Over the next three years,

James Ross (1911–97).

James Ross treated casualties from most of the major battles fought by the 8th Army in North Africa and in the invasions of Sicily and Italy. In 1944 he was posted to the Anzio beachhead with No. 15 Casualty Clearing Station, and for his services here to the wounded during four weeks of heavy fighting he was appointed Member of the Order of the British Empire (MBE).

After demobilisation in 1945 with the rank of Lieutenant Colonel, he returned to Edinburgh and worked initially in the anatomy department. He was granted the degree of Doctor of Medicine (MD) in 1947. In that year, he was appointed Assistant Surgeon to Leith Hospital and to the Royal Infirmary and with the establishment of the National Health Service in 1948 he acquired the new designation of Consultant Surgeon.

When Professor (later Sir) Michael Woodruff (q.v.) was appointed to the Chair of Surgical Science in 1957, James Ross joined his surgical team in the Royal Infirmary and, in this capacity, played an important part in the first British renal transplantation, which was successfully carried out by Professor Woodruff in 1960.

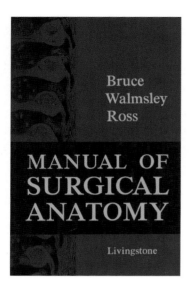

The Manual of Surgical Anatomy written with Sir John Bruce and Prof. Robert Walmsley.

In 1961 he was invited to set up a new general surgical unit at the Eastern General Hospital and the success of this from the beginning was in large measure due to his energy and his leadership. As Honorary Consultant Surgeon to the Army in Scotland from 1970 to 1976 he was particularly gratified when the unit at the Eastern General was selected by the RAMC for the training of its surgical specialists. A succession of army surgeons were seconded under his tutelage and several of these officers went on to attain high rank.

James Ross always had a special interest in urology and this is reflected in the number of his publications which relate to that specialty. Perhaps the most important of these is the monograph *The Behaviour of the Human Ureter in Health and Disease*, published in 1972, embodying the results of pathophysiological research which he and two colleagues carried out at the Eastern General Hospital. Nevertheless, he remained a general surgeon in rather more than the strict modern sense of that term and his clinical commitments in no way diminished his zeal for anatomical teaching and research. This bore fruit in his collaboration with Sir John Bruce (q.v.) and Professor Robert Walmsley as co-author of their *Manual of Surgical Anatomy*, published in 1964.

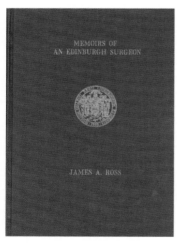

James Ross' *Memoirs*.

From his appointment as a Fellowship examiner in 1948, James Ross' College activities increased steadily. He became Secretary in 1960 and in his eight-year tenure of that office he acquired a profound knowledge of its history and traditions as well as of its laws and administrative procedures. His election as Vice President in 1971 seemed to be a natural progression, but it was felt in some quarters that although he was a prominent figure in Edinburgh surgery, his professional reputation furth of Scotland was perhaps insufficient for a holder of the College's highest office. In spite of such doubts, he was elected President in 1973, and his presidency was one of the most successful of modern times.

He was largely responsible for the establishment of the College's triennial overseas meetings, and the first of these, held in Cairo and Alexandria in 1976, was, for him, a notable personal triumph. Another major achievement of his presidency was the formulation of the College's proposals for the reform of higher surgical examinations, which were refined under his successors and which ultimately resulted in the institution of Higher Intercollegiate examinations in the surgical specialties. His visits to Fellows in many different parts of the world enhanced the College's international image and did much to strengthen its corporate spirit. He was a superb ambassador not just for his own College but for British surgery as a whole, and the honours which he received from five sister Colleges are a clear indication of his stature as a medical statesman.

When his presidential term ended in 1976, he took on the Chairmanship of the College Appeal, which raised funds for the building of the postgraduate residence in Hill Square, and its success owed much to his personal efforts. His book *The Edinburgh School of Surgery after Lister*, published in 1978, is a valuable contribution to Scottish medical history. Ten years later, his historical knowledge enabled him to play an important part in the planning of the Sir Jules Thorn Exhibition Hall in the College Museum.

James Ross was a man of strong principles, from which he never deviated, and of equally strong opinions, which he was never afraid to express. A natural extrovert of convivial disposition who enjoyed good food, good wine and good company, he was blessed with a keen sense of humour which could enliven the dullest gathering. He wore his heart upon his sleeve; he always chose to see the best in his fellow men and women, and his innate benevolence enabled him, when necessary, to suffer fools gladly.

His splendid portrait is a fitting memorial to a great President.

Roll number: 4397

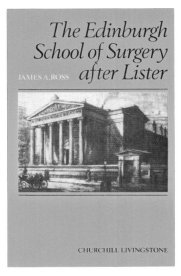

James Ross' history of
The Edinburgh School of Surgery after Lister.

John Goligher (1912–98)

Most of the leaders of British colorectal surgery in the 20th century were associated with St Mark's Hospital in London. Of those practising outwith St Mark's, John Goligher, Professor of Surgery at Leeds, was arguably the foremost British colorectal surgeon of his day. Through a combination of dedication to surgery, a prodigious operative workload and academic rigor, he was able to publish some of the most important controlled clinical trials of the day in surgical gastroenterology. His textbook *Surgery of the Anus, Rectum and Colon*, written with his authoritative and lucid style, became a classic of its time.

John Cedric Goligher was born in Londonderry and was educated at Foyle College. Following graduation from the University of Edinburgh in 1934 and junior posts in the Royal Infirmary, he became a Fellow of the Royal Colleges of Surgeons of Edinburgh and of England. He was drawn at this early stage to specialise in surgical gastroenterology and went as House Surgeon and then Resident Surgical Officer to St Mark's Hospital in London. Here the shape of his future career was determined as he trained under the leading colorectal surgeons of the time and began an association with the pathologist Cuthbert Dukes which was to last for much of his professional lifetime.

During the Second World War, having gained his paratrooper wings, he was given charge of an airborne surgical unit frequently operating behind enemy lines in Greece and Italy. Leaving the army as a Lieutenant Colonel, he returned to civilian practice as Honorary Assistant Surgeon

John Goligher (1912–98).

to St Mark's and St Mary's Hospitals in London in 1947. In 1954 he was invited to become the first full-time salaried Professor of Surgery in the University of Leeds medical school and Chairman of the Department of Surgery, following in the footsteps of Lord Moynihan.

Here over the next quarter-century, he built a department of international renown, which attracted surgeons from all over the world to observe his practice and to train. With little interest in University politics he devoted himself to operative surgery, where his meticulous technique became world-famous, and to developing academic surgery. He was an early proponent of the randomised clinical trial in surgery and under his leadership, the Leeds department produced many important clinical trials. The Leeds–York trial to assess the best operation for peptic ulcer disease was probably the most important and best conducted on that topic. Inevitably most of the trials were on colorectal surgery. These were to make important advances to surgical knowledge and their results had a major influence upon practice in gastrointestinal surgery. These included trials demonstrating that single-layer colonic anastomoses were as effective as two layer, that sphincterotomy was preferable to anal stretch for anal fissure, and that high ligation of the inferior mesenteric artery improved the results in colorectal resection for cancer. This academic zeal combined with his encyclopaedic knowledge of the literature led to the huge success of his textbook *Surgery of the Anus, Rectum and Colon* (1967). In this book he was able to combine a lucid highly readable style with academic authority. It ran to five editions and was published in Spanish and Italian.

His contributions were recognised by his election as President of the Association of Surgeons of Great Britain and Ireland and presidency of the British Society of Gastroenterology. He served on the Council of the Royal College of Surgeons of England.

His legacies to surgery are his textbook, a model of its kind, and the high standards of operative surgery and academic rigor in coloproctology, which he and his pupils promoted so effectively.

Roll number: 4474

Denis Burkitt (1911–93)

Despite opposition from some quarters, eponyms abound in medicine. Yet few British surgeons of the 20th century left the legacy of an eponymous condition. Denis Burkitt was one of the few, gaining lasting fame by defining the geographical distribution and the aetiology of the childhood lymphoma which bears his name. His energy and determination were to lead to a second major contribution in a quite different field of medicine. He was largely responsible for promoting the hypothesis that lack of dietary fibre resulted in disease in western society and for popularising the subsequent dietary change throughout the developed world.

Denis Parsons Burkitt was born in Enniskillen, Northern Ireland, the son of an engineer who became County Surveyor. His father, an amateur ornithologist, mapped out the movements and territorial activities of robins and was among the first to use bird ringing in this work. The methodology of mapping was to be used by his son to epoch-making effect years later.

He enrolled to study engineering at Trinity College, Dublin. During his early days at Trinity he became a committed Christian and was to remain so for the rest of his life, his faith becoming the dynamo of his energetic life. The first manifestation of his new commitment was a change of course to study medicine. After graduation, he applied for the colonial medical service in Africa but was rejected because he had lost an eye in a childhood accident. He was later to write: 'this was a profound disappointment, but when I eventually reached Africa, God enabled me with my one eye to see things which my predecessors had missed with two'. In 1938 he obtained the FRCSEd. Three years later he joined the Royal Army Medical Corps and was posted to East Africa, for which he formed an affection which was to last for the rest of his life. After the war he returned to Uganda as a medical officer, working first under primitive conditions as a surgeon in Lira and thereafter at Mulago Hospital in Kampala.

In 1957 Hugh Trowell, a physician colleague in Kampala, consulted him about a young patient, a consultation which was to lead to his first historic contribution. A five-year-old boy had facial tumours which were symmetrically placed. While head and neck tumours were familiar and invariably fatal, the symmetry around the face in this case was unlike other malignancies. Burkitt began to study these tumours and soon realised that they did not affect children under two and were rarely seen in adolescence. He discussed the tumours with Dr George Oettla, Director of the South African Cancer Research Unit, who was adamant that tumours of this type were never seen in South Africa. So began the detective work on the geographical distribution of the tumour. With a grant of £25 Burkitt sent out photographs of the tumour along with questionnaires to hundreds of hospitals around Africa asking about tumour incidence. The results were plotted on wall maps in his office and so emerged the 'lymphoma belt'. This extended over some 5 million square miles roughly from 10 degrees north of the equator to 10 degrees south with a tail down to the Mozambique–Natal border.

The next stage of the research took him on a 10,000-mile safari which showed that within the belt the distribution was related to temperature and rainfall. The pattern suggested an infective aetiology. The virologist Tony Epstein, who attended one of his lectures in London, postulated that the infecting agent was a virus, and so began the collaboration which led to Burkitt sending him tumour samples to see if viruses could be identified in the tumours. Some three years later, a new virus, the Epstein–Barr (EBV) was identified, the first such agent to be discovered solely by electron microscopy. This was the first demonstration of a malignancy caused by a virus, a discovery which was to have a huge impact on cancer research.

The initial hypothesis was that the virus was carried by an insect vector, but subsequent research showed that the EB virus had a widespread distribution. It was later to emerge that the lymphoma belt corresponded to those areas where mosquitoes thrived, and malaria was endemic, causing suppression of childhood immune systems which allowed the EB virus to stimulate lymphoid cells to undergo malignant transformation.

Burkitt went on to pioneer the treatment of these tumours. Mutilating surgery was rarely successful and in the absence of radiotherapy facilities in the endemic area he persuaded pharmaceutical companies to supply chemotherapeutic agents. Many of these tumours were completely cured and he was later to write that 'the most inexperienced chemotherapist in the world was getting the best results'.

Denis Burkitt with the map of Africa on which he mapped out the lymphoma belt.

Burkitt with young patients under treatment for Burkitt's lymphoma.

Denis Burkitt (1911–93).

In 1966 he returned to England as a Medical Research Council Fellow. Sir Richard Doll introduced him to Peter Cleave, a naval surgeon who had developed the hypothesis that many diseases of western society were caused by eating an excess of refined carbohydrates and insufficient dietary fibre. Burkitt immediately saw the logic of this hypothesis and realised that these diseases were rare on the staple rural African diet, which produced voluminous stools. Burkitt by this stage had a stature and credibility within the medical establishment throughout the world which enabled him to promote the hypothesis. He carried out further original studies comparing the transit time in the bowel of those on the refined western diet with those on the unrefined African diet. He measured stool weights in the two groups. Again he sent out questionnaires to hundreds of hospitals in Africa. Collaboration with Dr Alec Walker, a Scottish biochemist working in South Africa, resulted in a mass of evidence in support of the hypothesis.

This led to several classic papers and a series of lecture tours in which Burkitt promoted the fibre theory with missionary zeal. While his presentation style was simple and dogmatic, it resulted in the medical establishment accepting the need for more fibre in the western diet and changed the thinking of nutritionists and food manufacturers for ever. Inevitably with time the hypothesis has been modified and diluted – but few doctors have reached the pinnacle of two 'citation classics' in unrelated fields of medicine.

As a result of this work he received many honorary degrees, medals and prizes. These included Fellowship of the Royal Society, membership of the French Academy of Science and the Bower Prize in the United States. He was appointed Companion of the Order of St Michael and St George (CMG) in 1974.

Throughout his life his Christian values and his Irishness shone through. For all the eminence and fame which he achieved, he remained modest and never lost his innate humility. He would often sign copies of his book with the following inscription:

Attitudes are more important than abilities
Motives are more important than methods
Character is more important than cleverness
Perseverance is more important than power
And the heart takes precedence over the head.

Roll number: 4481

John Shepherd (1913–92)

While nearly all doctors write papers and articles, only a few can combine a busy clinical practice with a career as a successful author and biographer. John Shepherd was among the few who were able to achieve this.

John Alfred Shepherd was born in Edinburgh and educated at George Watson's College and Kelso High School going on to St Andrews University, where he qualified MB ChB in 1936. He had joined the Royal Naval Volunteer Reserve (RNVR) as an undergraduate and the navy was to be an important part of his life for some 25 years. After junior appointments in Oxford, he obtained a surgical post in Portsmouth Royal Hospital, graduated MD from St Andrews University in 1939 and obtained the FRCSEd in the same year.

At the outbreak of war, he was appointed to HMS *Woolwich* and went on to serve in the Royal Naval Hospital, Plymouth, from 1940 until 1942, when he joined the hospital ship *Ophir*, on which he saw active service in the Mediterranean and the Far East.

After the war he returned to Oxford as Surgical Tutor at the Radcliffe Infirmary and in 1948 was appointed Senior Lecturer in Surgery at the University of Liverpool. He was awarded the ChM degree in 1950. In 1951 he was appointed Consultant Surgeon at Broadgreen Hospital, Liverpool, Victoria Central Hospital, Wallasey, and Hoylake Hospital. He retained his affection for the navy remaining in the RNVR after the war and serving as Principal Medical Officer to the training ship *Eaglet*. He was appointed Queen's Household Surgeon in 1960 and in that same year was awarded the Volunteer Reserve Decoration (VRD) and retired with the rank of Surgeon Captain RNR.

His principal surgical interests were gastroenterology and emergency surgery. He proved both a prolific writer and a popular teacher, and these two skills were combined in his first book *The Acute Abdomen* (1961). This enjoyed great popularity among surgical trainees throughout the UK and beyond, and was reprinted three times.

His interest in literature and history and his flair for writing resulted in three important medical biographies: *Spencer Wells* (1965), *Simpson and Syme of Edinburgh* (1969) and *Lawson Tait: The Rebellious Surgeon* (1982). Each of these was destined to become a classic.

It was his last book, *The Crimean Doctors* (1991), that was to become the definitive work on the subject. His painstaking research and the wealth of original material which he drew together provide a remarkable history of this important era of medical development.

He was an enthusiastic member of the Liverpool Medical Institution, serving as Librarian, Archivist and in 1976 as President. In commemoration of its bicentenary in 1979 he published *A History of the Liverpool Medical Institution*.

His skill and charm in committee was put to good use throughout his career and he served on numerous committees, including the Liverpool Regional Hospital Board. He gave devoted service to the College on several of its standing committees, as a member of Council and from 1970–3 as Vice President.

Roll Number: 4566

John Shepherd (1913–92).

Archibald Duncan (1914–92).

Archibald Duncan (1914–92)

After a distinguished academic career in obstetrics and gynaecology, Archie Duncan embarked on a second career as Executive Dean of the Faculty of Medicine in the University of Edinburgh.

Born in Darjeeling, India, the son of a Church of Scotland missionary, Archibald Sutherland Duncan was educated at Merchiston Castle School and graduated in medicine from Edinburgh University in 1936. During the Second World War he served as a surgeon in the Royal Navy, seeing service on destroyers in the Mediterranean, and was awarded the Distinguished Service Cross.

After the war he became Honorary Consultant Obstetrician in Aberdeen and then Senior Lecturer in Obstetrics and Gynaecology at Edinburgh University. In 1953 he was appointed Professor of Obstetrics and Gynaecology in the Welsh National School of Medicine, a chair which he occupied with great distinction for 13 years. He was invited in 1966 to become the first Executive Dean of the Faculty of Medicine in Edinburgh with a personal chair in medical education. His courtesy, eloquence and willingness to listen to staff and students at all levels ensured the success of this new venture and did much to improve liaison between different parts of the Faculty, which he represented on the Medical Research Council and the General Medical Council.

In retirement he was to become consultant editor of the *Journal of Medical Ethics*, joint editor of the *Dictionary of Medical Ethics* and Chairman of the Scottish Council on Disability. He served on the Council of the College and there, as in his many other committees, he was remembered for his charm, diplomacy and gifts of persuasion.

Roll number: 4586

Andrew Lowdon (1911–65)

Among the distinguished Fellows of the College commemorated in this book are some whose lives were tragically cut short before they could reach the pinnacles of achievement to which they seemed destined by their outstanding abilities. One such was Professor Andrew Lowdon, whose contributions to surgery and to medical education are remembered with gratitude and admiration by the famous University medical school, to which over 11 years he gave devoted and distinguished service.

Andrew Gilchrist Ross Lowdon, a son of the manse, was born in Greenock. Both of his parents died before he reached the age of 14 and thereafter he and his younger brother were brought up by aunts in Edinburgh. He was educated first at Greenock Academy and then at the Royal High School, Edinburgh, of which he was Captain and Dux of the School in 1929. He then entered Edinburgh University, from which he graduated MA in 1932, with the class prizes in philosophy and political economy and MB ChB with honours in 1936. He won most of the medical class prizes and his brilliant academic career was crowned by the award of the Ettles Scholarship and the Leslie Gold Medal as the most distinguished graduate of his year. As a student, he was an active and enthusiastic member of the Royal Medical Society, of which he was elected Senior President in 1936–7.

After graduation, he spent two years in junior hospital posts, including six months as House Surgeon to Sir David Wilkie (q.v.) in the Royal Infirmary. He then spent a year in Sir David's surgical research laboratory, where he worked with W. C. Wilson (q.v.) on the biochemical effects of severe burns. In 1939 he obtained the Fellowship of the College. He was about to depart for the USA to spend a year at the Mayo Clinic when the Second World War broke out and, as the holder of a Territorial commission in the Royal Army Medical Corps, he was immediately called up for military service.

After duty in Palestine, he was appointed to command No. 4 Field Surgical Unit in the 8th Army, with which he served at the Battle of El Alamein, and throughout its victorious progress from Egypt to Tunisia and then into Sicily.

Andrew Lowdon moved back to Egypt as Surgeon to No. 6 General Hospital and when this unit returned to Britain in 1944 he was appointed to command its surgical division with the rank of Lieutenant Colonel. While in Egypt he had occasion to treat King Farouk for injuries sustained in a road accident, and for this he received the Order of Ismail from his grateful patient.

As the officer in command of the Surgical Division of No. 6 General Hospital, he served in Normandy, Belgium and Holland, and was in Germany when the war ended in 1945. In the surgical volume of the official *British Medical History of the Second World War*, there are 13 references to Lowdon, several of which are for his original work on complicated penetrating wounds of the abdomen. For his outstanding services, he was twice mentioned in dispatches and was made an Officer of the Order of the British Empire (OBE).

On demobilisation, he returned to Edinburgh, where he was invited by Sir James Learmonth (q.v.) to join the professorial surgical unit in the Royal Infirmary as Clinical Tutor and in the following year he was appointed Assistant Surgeon to the Infirmary. In 1947 when the Edinburgh chairs of systematic surgery and of clinical surgery were combined he rejoined the University Department of Surgery first as Lecturer and then as Senior Lecturer. In this capacity he established an impressive reputation as an abdominal surgeon and as a teacher of both students and postgraduates. The commitments associated with occupancy of the two chairs of surgery had greatly increased Sir James Learmonth's academic and clinical responsibilities, and it would be impossible to exaggerate the importance to him of the support he received from Andrew Lowdon. Sir James was not slow to acknowledge his debt of gratitude and their personal relationship could not have been happier, but Lowdon was clearly destined for professorial rank and in 1954 he was appointed to the Chair of Surgery of the University of Durham at King's College, Newcastle-upon-Tyne, which, in 1963, became part of the new University of Newcastle.

In this new environment Andrew Lowdon's keen intellect, warm personality and gracious kindly manner, no less than his professional distinction, rapidly won for him the respect and admiration not only of his surgical colleagues and students, but of the entire academic establishment.

He became Dean of the Newcastle Faculty of Medicine in 1960, an appointment which had the enthusiastic support of the Newcastle medical community. He took on this task with considerable misgivings because of its inevitable encroachment upon his surgical activities, but in spite of this he maintained a substantial clinical and teaching commitment and his department continued to flourish.

Andrew Lowdon (1911–65).

As Dean, he gave the lead in the development of an entirely new undergraduate medical course and together with five other senior faculty members he produced plans for a radical revision of the curriculum, whereby the basic sciences and the clinical disciplines were fully integrated throughout the undergraduate course and students were involved with patients from the very beginning of their training. It was largely through his powers of reasonable persuasion and his genius for sensible compromise that fundamental reforms were achieved without acrimony or recrimination and with preservation of what was best in the old system.

He was held in the highest regard by the Newcastle medical students for whom, quite early on, he became a father figure and, in 1956–7, he was President of the University of Durham Medical Society. Three years later he was elected Honorary President of the British Medical Students' Association.

Andrew Lowdon gave notable service to the *Newcastle Medical Journal* as a member of its editorial board and also to the North of England Surgical Society, of which he was Honorary Secretary for nearly five years before becoming its President in 1962–3. For many years he was a member of the Board of Governors of the Royal Victoria Infirmary and Adviser in Surgery to the Regional Hospital Board.

In 1961 he became a member of the General Medical Council (GMC) and his achievements as Dean of the Newcastle medical faculty made him an obvious choice for appointment to the Royal Commission on Medical Education when this was formed in 1965. On behalf of the GMC, he undertook in 1963 an extensive tour of medical schools and teaching hospitals in India.

He was a College examiner for many years before and after his move to Newcastle and as Professor he was invited to be an external examiner in surgery by several universities in the United Kingdom and overseas. In 1959 he was elected to the Fellowship *ad eundem* of the Royal College of Surgeons of England and in the following year he visited Australia as the Norman Paul Visiting Professor at the Sydney Hospital.

During his time in Newcastle, Andrew Lowdon fell in love with the Northumbrian countryside and this makes his sudden death, while walking on the moors near Blanchland, all the more poignant. Like his revered mentor Sir David Wilkie, he died in his mid-fifties at the height of his powers and when he still had so much more to give, not only to his medical school but to British surgery as a whole.

The University of Newcastle honoured his achievements by appointing him Pro-Vice-Chancellor a few months before his death, but he could have no more appropriate memorial than words taken from his obituary in the *University of Newcastle Medical Gazette*: 'The greatest tribute that can be paid to a remarkable man is that if the position of Dean of the Medical Faculty had to be filled by an election among the students, one man would have stood head and shoulders above the rest – Professor A. G. R. Lowdon.'

Roll number: 4637

264

William Michie (1911–78)

Sir Patrick Heron Watson (q.v.) was the first surgeon to treat hyperthyroidism by thyroidectomy but other surgeons who are commemorated in this book also became famous for their expertise in thyroid surgery. One of the most notable of these was William Michie, who throughout his life was known by the diminutive form of his Christian name.

Born of farming stock at Durris, Lower Deeside, Bill Michie was educated at Banchory Academy and at the University of Aberdeen, from which he graduated MA in 1930 and MB ChB in 1935. As an undergraduate, he was elected President of the University Union and gained a blue for athletics.

After holding junior hospital posts in Aberdeen and in London, he returned to Aberdeen Royal Infirmary in 1927 as surgical registrar and in 1939 he obtained the Fellowship of the College. During this period his mentor and exemplar was Gordon Bruce FRCSEng, and it was this master surgeon, for whom he had profound admiration, who not only kindled his interest in thyroid surgery but who also encouraged him to achieve supreme virtuosity in the art of salmon fishing.

With the outbreak of the Second World War in 1939, Bill Michie joined the Royal Army Medical Corps as a surgical specialist and was posted initially to West Africa. Later he served with a casualty clearing station in north-west Europe from Normandy to the Rhine crossing in 1944–5, and thereafter he commanded the surgical division of a field general hospital with the rank of Lieutenant Colonel. In recognition of his military services he was appointed a Member of the Order of the British Empire (MBE) in 1945.

After demobilisation, Michie returned to Aberdeen and in 1947 was appointed to the consultant staff of the Royal Infirmary and of the Royal Aberdeen Hospital for Sick Children, both of which he served with the utmost distinction for the next 30 years.

Although a general surgeon, in the original sense of that term, with a wide range of operative expertise, it was in the special field of thyroid surgery that his supreme technical craftsmanship combined with meticulous record keeping and rigorous audit won for him an international reputation. His clinical research was widely acclaimed, particularly in relation to the true incidence of hypothyroidism after subtotal thyroidectomy for thyrotoxicosis, to the use of beta-adrenergic blockade in the preparation of thyrotoxic patients for surgery and to the automated surveillance of patients with thyroid disease.

Bill Michie was a Fellowship examiner for several years, but his greatest service to the College followed his election to Council in 1971. His many valuable contributions to its deliberations and to those of the Finance Committee, on which he also served, were characterised by crystal clarity of thought, rigorous analytical objectivity and an abundance of shrewd Aberdonian common sense.

He was President of the Medico-Chirurgical Society of Aberdeen (1971–2) and further recognition of his professional prestige came with his election to the Council of the Association of Surgeons of Great Britain and Ireland. He was President of the Association in 1972–3 and the resounding success of its 1973 annual meeting in Aberdeen owed as much

William Michie (1911–78).

to his impressive organisational skills as it did to his surgical distinction and his natural geniality. As one of the first two United Kingdom representatives on the Monospecialist Section of General Surgery of the European Union of Medical Specialists, he was a highly effective spokesman for British surgery in the original discussions on the harmonisation of surgical training within the European Economic Community.

Bill Michie was an enthusiastic sportsman throughout his life, with a single-figure golf handicap, and his captaincy of the Royal Aberdeen Golf Club from 1967 to 1970 gave him great pride and pleasure. He was also an expert shot with rifle or shotgun, but from youth his great passion was salmon fishing, at which his skill and artistry were legendary and to watch him in action on his beloved Dee was for lesser anglers an inspiring and humbling experience.

He was admired and respected for his excellence as a teacher and clinician as well as for his operative dexterity and his important contributions to thyroid surgery, but it was his kindliness, courtesy and warm, outgoing personality that gained for him the special esteem and affection of his colleagues, junior staff and students. His death at the age of 67 when he still had so much to offer to his profession was a grievous loss to the Aberdeen medical school, to the College and, indeed, to British surgery.

Roll number: 4640

Ainslie Jamieson (1914–84)

When the young Professor Charles Illingworth (q.v.) was appointed to the Regius Chair of Surgery in the University of Glasgow in 1939, he brought R. A. Jamieson with him from Edinburgh as his assistant. Ainslie Jamieson was born in India of parents serving in the Ministry of the Church of Scotland, as his forebears had done for almost 300 years. His motivation for a career in surgery probably came from being a descendant of Robert Liston (q.v.).

Robert Ainslie Jamieson returned to Scotland for his education at the age of six and in 1932 was Dux of George Watson's College in Edinburgh. He was later to graduate MB ChB with honours from the Edinburgh medical school in 1938, and was Gold Medallist in Surgery.

His first important role in Glasgow was as an amanuensis to Charles Illingworth in the creation of a new Department of Surgery, which in those years was a small one but with a heavy teaching load. With the advent of the Second World War, he was also involved in the huge surgical workload in the Clydeside area. In his early graduate days in Edinburgh, Ainslie Jamieson had unfortunately become the victim of tetanus, and was one of the very few survivors of this condition in this country at that time. It was always understood that the chapter in the first edition of Illingworth's *Short Textbook of Surgery* (1938) had either been written by Ainslie Jamieson or that he had provided the record of the dramatic events that had directly affected him at first hand. Certainly anyone reading this account cannot help but be moved by the conclusion 'that the agony beggars description'.

Ainslie Jamieson was supported by the Medical Research Council to study blood glucose changes in shock, and the results of these studies found their way mainly into government memoranda. The need for research to have a military application, however, relaxed in the post-war years. Various clinicians had observed that in the west of Scotland the incidence of peptic ulcer-related deaths had risen in the war years. Attribution had already been made in the London area that a rise in the incidence of perforated peptic ulcer was the consequence of the stress of bombing. Ainslie Jamieson saw this phenomenon as worthy of critical study and, with a physician colleague, Laurence Scott, he organised a detailed retrospective examination of the west of Scotland data on perforated peptic ulcer. It was known that the condition had been rare until the latter part of the 19th century when it mainly affected young women and was usually located in the stomach. Jamieson now demonstrated a male predominance and the perforation was usually located in the duodenum. The peak incidence in the wartime Clydeside area antedated the main air raids and consequently was not 'stress' related. Jamieson repeated this study later, finding a seasonal and week-day variations. Illingworth made the claim that this, the first main epidemiological record of perforated peptic ulcer, had no equal.

In 1949 Jamieson was awarded a Nuffield Fellowship to the Peter Brent Brigham Hospital in Boston to work on the metabolic aspects of trauma with Dr Francis Moore. He put much of what he had learned in Boston into writing and joined forces with Mr (later Sir) Andrew Watt Kay, then a fellow Glasgow Senior Lecturer in Professor Illingworth's department, to publish *A Textbook of Surgical Physiology* (1959), which was the first of its kind in Britain.

In 1956 it occurred to Sir Charles Illingworth, with the opening of a new hospital at Vale of Leven in Dumbartonshire, that it would be advantageous to have a linkage between it and his unit, following the pattern which was already being developed in the London hospitals. This was intended to take place at a time when plans were being made to transfer the Western Infirmary to a new site at Gartnavel. Later that year, Ainslie Jamieson went to Vale of Leven to take the lead in this 'expansion' of the academic unit, remaining there until his retiral.

When it seemed that he had yet five years or more to continue in the post he became aware of a progressive lower-limb paresis and was soon confined to a wheelchair. However hard this was to bear, it was concealed by a calm and quiet philosophical acceptance. He turned to poetry and wrote verses published posthumously as *Sonnets of a Surgeon*, which reveal much of the inner nature of the man. His last days were spent in Angus, where he enjoyed the peace of the rural environment after a busy life in surgery.

Author: Adam N. Smith

Roll number: 4685

Ainslie Jamieson (1914–84).

Surgical staff, Western General Hospital, 1937.
With Sir David Wilkie in the front row are
Charles Illingworth, David Band and Bruce Dick.
Andrew Wilkinson is in the 2nd row (3rd from right)
and Ainslie Jamieson stands on the left of the picture.

Kenneth McKeown (1912–95)

Over the past 200 years, most surgeons who achieved international eminence established their reputations in great teaching hospitals; yet it should never be forgotten that major contributions to the advancement of surgical science and practice have been made by surgeons working in peripheral hospitals unassociated with academic centres of excellence. Of this there could be no better example than Kenneth McKeown, whose outstanding clinical and operative abilities attracted to Darlington and Northallerton a host of surgical visitors from all parts of the world.

Kenneth Charles McKeown was born in Belfast and educated at the Royal Academical Institute and at Queen's University, Belfast, from which he graduated MB BCh, BAO in 1935. At this stage he decided to become a surgeon and went to London for his early postgraduate training.

When the Second World War broke out in 1939 he was a Resident Surgical Officer at Croydon General Hospital and early in 1940 he obtained the Fellowship of the College. Before appearing for the examination, he attended the tutorial course conducted by Ian Aird (q.v.), with whom he was to be closely associated a few years later and whose teaching both impressed and inspired him. In the following year, his alma mater, Queen's University, awarded him the degree of Master of Surgery (MCh). Having joined the Emergency Medical Service based at King's College Hospital, he was heavily involved in the treatment of air-raid casualties during the London 'Blitz' of 1940–1. He acquired extensive further experience of trauma surgery in dealing with battle casualties from the Allied landings in Normandy in 1944 and the victims of the German 'flying bomb' and V2 rocket attacks in 1944–5.

Towards the end of the war in Europe, Kenneth McKeown was called up for duty as a surgical specialist in the Royal Army Medical Corps and served in military hospitals in Libya, Greece and Egypt, ultimately as commanding officer of a surgical division with the rank of Lieutenant Colonel.

Following demobilisation, he contacted Ian Aird, who, by then, had become Professor of Surgery at the Postgraduate Medical School and who appointed him Senior Registrar in the professorial surgical unit at Hammersmith Hospital. He subsequently became Assistant Lecturer in Professor Aird's academic department, and it was at this stage that, with his chief's enthusiastic encouragement, he developed the special interest in gastro-oesophageal surgery which was the foundation of his future fame.

Kenneth McKeown (1912–95).

The Moynihan Chirurgical Club meeting in Newcastle-upon-Tyne, 1993. Kenneth McKeown is in the front row second from left. See page 252 for a short history of the Moynihan Chirurgical Club.

In 1949 he obtained the Fellowship of the Royal College of Surgeons of England and, in the following year, with Professor Aird's support, he was appointed Senior Consultant Surgeon to the Darlington Memorial Hospital and the Friarage Hospital, Northallerton. Over the next 27 years he established, in these two institutions, a surgical service which achieved standards of care unsurpassed by any of the most famous teaching hospitals. He made important original contributions in several surgical fields but his work on oesophageal carcinoma was of the highest distinction, and it was this, above all, which earned for him his illustrious international reputation.

In addition to being a superb surgical craftsman, he was an excellent teacher in the operating theatre and at the bedside, and a lecturer of outstanding clarity. His teaching abilities were appropriately recognised by the English College when in 1963 he was appointed one of its first regional tutors. He was a prolific writer and his authoritative publications based on a wealth of personal experience progressively enhanced his reputation far beyond the British Isles. Surgeons of all nationalities visited Kenneth McKeown in Darlington and Northallerton to observe the techniques with which he achieved impressive results in the treatment of oesophageal carcinoma. In due course, he also began to travel widely as a visiting lecturer.

In 1972 the English College awarded him a Hunterian Professorship and paid him what was then the unprecedented compliment of inviting him to deliver his Hunterian Lecture in his own hospital. This was the first occasion on which a Hunterian Lecture had ever taken place outside the College.

Kenneth McKeown disliked bureaucracy in all its manifestations, but he willingly took on his fair share of committee work and gave valuable service as a member of the Central Health Services Council and the Central Council for Postgraduate Medical Education. For this and for his distinguished surgical services he was, in 1972, appointed Commander of the Order of the British Empire (CBE). He was proud also to be made a Deputy Lieutenant of the County of Durham in 1982.

Kenneth McKeown's remarkable achievements and his warm personality have their permanent memorial in the Edinburgh College – the McKeown Medal, which he endowed in 1978, is awarded to a lecturer chosen by the President and Council to deliver a College lecture in a centre outside Edinburgh.

A few months before his death in 1995, he published his autobiography, *A Tale of Two Citadels*, which, in addition to being a fascinating account of his distinguished career, contains some profound reflections upon the development of the National Health Service and the changing state of surgical training and practice in Britain in the latter half of the 20th century.

Roll number: 4709

The McKeown Medal.

Andrew Wilkinson (1914–95)

When Andrew Wilkinson became President in 1976 he made history through being the first ever holder of the College's highest office to live and practise outside Scotland. His election enhanced the College's image as a truly international body and expunged from it totally and finally any lingering stigma of parochialism that may have persisted over the years. Yet this is only one of the many reasons why he deserves commemoration in this book.

Andrew Wood Wilkinson was born in Taunton, Somerset, but his paternal forebears were Scottish and he liked to think of himself as an expatriate Scot. He was educated at Weymouth College before going up to Edinburgh University, from which he graduated MB ChB with first-class honours in 1937. After holding junior posts at the Royal Infirmary under Sir John Fraser (q.v.) and at the Royal Hospital for Sick Children under Ian Aird (q.v.), he obtained the Fellowship of the College in 1940. He then became Sir John Fraser's Clinical Tutor in the Royal Infirmary and in 1942 was called up for war service with the Royal Army Medical Corps as a surgical specialist. In June 1944 his field surgical team supported the D-Day landings and was in constant action in northern France and Belgium for the next three months. He was then posted east, where he served with the rank of Lieutenant Colonel in the campaign to liberate Burma from the Japanese.

After demobilisation in 1946, Wilkinson returned to Edinburgh, where he was appointed Clinical Tutor in the Royal Infirmary wards of Sir James Learmonth (q.v.) and, later, Lecturer in the University Department of Surgery. He was awarded a three-year Syme Surgical Fellowship and in 1949 obtained the degree of Master of Surgery (ChM) with the Gold Medal for his thesis. The research upon which his thesis was based related to fluid and electrolyte balance and to the metabolic response to trauma. Over the next five years he published a number of papers on these subjects, which were widely acclaimed, and in 1953, when he was appointed Senior Lecturer in the Aberdeen University Department of Surgery under Professor W. C. Wilson (q.v.), his work had already earned for him a substantial reputation as a scientific investigator. In Aberdeen his clinical commitment included a considerable volume of paediatric and neonatal surgery, which gave him great satisfaction and accorded well with his research interests.

In 1955 he published the small book *Body Fluids in Surgery* – a most lucid and concise exposition of a complex subject which was very favourably received and which made his name well known to surgeons throughout the English-speaking world.

In 1958 Andrew Wilkinson had the distinction of being appointed to the newly established Nuffield Chair of Paediatric Surgery in the University of London at the Hospital for Sick Children, Great Ormond Street, and thereby became the first Professor of Paediatric Surgery in the British Isles. To his new post he brought a wide experience of surgery in general as well as of paediatric surgery, together with an impressive research record, and on these foundations he built up an academic department which attracted surgical trainees from many different parts of the world.

Wilkinson was a stimulating teacher and a clear, concise, stylish writer with a profound respect for the niceties of English grammar. He was also a master of the art of the formal lecture and received many invitations to

Hospital for Sick Children, Great Ormond Street, London.

College examining team in Hong Kong. Andrew Wilkinson is seated centre with G. B. Ong on his left and W. Selby Tulloch on his right.

deliver prestigious lectures at surgical meetings in Britain and overseas. In 1959 he became a Fellow of the Royal College of Surgeons of England *ad eundem*. In addition to being a member of many foreign paediatric surgical associations, his international stature was recognised by honorary Fellowships of both the Royal Australasian and American Colleges of Surgeons.

He was an indefatigable promoter of the specialty of paediatric surgery and after long service on its executive committee, he was President of the British Association of Paediatric Surgeons in 1971 and 1972.

Andrew Wilkinson was much involved in College affairs and served on Council from 1964 to 1973, when he was elected Vice President and, although by then living and working in London, he played a full part in Council's deliberations and in the governance of the College. In 1976 he was elected President and his term of office saw the initiation of many important College developments. He vigorously promoted the College's proposals for radical reform of the Fellowship examinations (which eventually gained general intercollegiate acceptance some 13 years later!) and in spite of opposition he secured the introduction by the College of specialty Fellowship examinations taken at the end of higher training in the various specialties. He also inaugurated the College Appeal of 1978–81, which successfully raised funds for the establishment of the Postgraduate Residence in Hill Square and of the College's Symposium Hall.

Perhaps Andrew Wilkinson's greatest service to the College lay in the field of medical politics. Always supremely well briefed and with absolute mastery of the subjects under discussion, he was a very tough but not unreasonable negotiator and as its representative on intercollegiate, academic and NHS committees, he seldom if ever failed to maintain the College's independence and prestige.

Roll number: 4717

Andrew Wilkinson (1914–95).

Thomas Gibson (1915–93)

Many young surgeons embark on research inwardly hoping that it might lead to a discovery which will alter surgical history and benefit patients worldwide, but very few truly achieve that ambition. Tom Gibson was one of those who did. He went on to distinction as a plastic surgeon, described by his obituarist Ian McGregor as 'the most illustrious member of the generation that was responsible for the postwar expansion of plastic surgery'. Yet it was one brilliant observation, made while a young surgical researcher that led to our understanding of the scientific basis of organ transplantation. Peter Medawar, then a graduate student in Oxford, joined him and their subsequent collaboration led eventually to a Nobel Prize for Medawar, while Gibson went on to become one of the most distinguished plastic surgeons of his generation.

Tom Gibson was educated at Paisley Grammar School and graduated in medicine from Glasgow University in 1938. He became a Fellow of the Royal College of Surgeons of Edinburgh in 1941, and from 1942 to

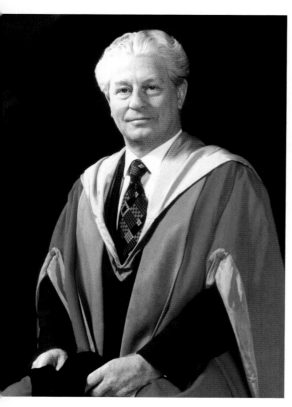

Thomas Gibson (1915–93).

1944 worked in the MRC Unit in the Burns Wards of Glasgow Royal Infirmary as Assistant Surgeon. It was during this period that he was destined to make the observation on which subsequent understanding of the science of organ transplantation was based. On two occasions he grafted skin from a father to his young daughter, who had extensive burns, and noticed that, on the second occasion, the skin grafts were more rapidly rejected. He rightly deduced that this was the result of an immune mechanism. Peter Medawar, who had been working on the same problem in Oxford, came to Glasgow and they collaborated. The results of their work were published in a seminal paper *The Fate of Skin Homografts in Man* (1943). This observation of the 'second set' reaction paved the way for Medawar's subsequent work on organ transplantation, which led to his Nobel Prize in 1960. At that time, he wrote to Gibson: 'I do want you to know how clearly I understand my deep obligation to you for giving me my first insight into the real problem we were facing and my first understanding of the nature of clinical research.'

In 1944 he served in the Royal Army Medical Corps as a maxillofacial specialist in northern Europe and in India where he commanded the No.1 Indian maxillofacial unit. After the war he was appointed Consultant to the West of Scotland Plastic and Oral Surgery Service and became its Director between 1970 and 1980.

His association with Professor Robert Kenedi at the engineering department of Strathclyde University led to the establishment of the Wolfson Bioengineering Centre, devoted to the application of engineering principles into medicine and surgery.

His love of books and reading and his gifts for writing science, history and poetry were evident throughout his career. He published widely on various aspects of plastic surgery, on tissue immunology, burns and on biomechanics. He was editor of the *British Journal of Plastic Surgery* for 10 years and was Honorary Librarian of the Royal College of Physicians and Surgeons of Glasgow, with which he maintained a close association throughout his life. He wrote a beautifully illustrated history of the College, which was published in 1963. Tom Gibson became President of the British Association of Plastic Surgeons and was President of the Glasgow College from 1976 to 1978. He went on to receive many other honours, including an honorary Doctorate of Science from Strathclyde University, honorary Fellowships of the Royal Colleges of Surgeons of Australasia and England and Fellowship of the Royal Society of Edinburgh. In 1987 he was awarded the Lister Medal for outstanding achievement by the three Royal Surgical Colleges in the United Kingdom.

For all his eminence he remained a modest, genial and affable man with a ready smile and his humour showed in his poems, many of which were included in an anthology of his poetry *Poems and Versifications,* published in 1991.

Gibson left many literary legacies, but it was the observations that he made and described whilst a young surgeon in Glasgow during the Second World War which have secured for him an honoured place in surgical history.

Roll number: 4758

Sir Ian McAdam (1917–99)

Sir Ian McAdam was a towering figure in the developing surgical services of East Africa during the latter half of the 20th century. His contributions to Makerere, Uganda, then the only medical school in East Africa, did much to enhance its international reputation.

Ian William James McAdam was the son of a South African mining engineer. After schooling in the then Southern Rhodesia, he studied medicine in Edinburgh, where his academic and sporting gifts developed and his achievements included a blue for tennis. Inspired by the surgical teaching he had received as an undergraduate – the surgical chairs were occupied at the time by Sir John Fraser (q.v.) and Sir David Wilkie (q.v.) – he went on to become Wilkie Research Fellow under Sir James Learmonth (q.v.). His training under Learmonth led him to acquire a meticulous operating technique and an analytical approach to difficult surgical problems. Learmonth schooled him in the art and technique of clinical teaching and he was to use these to good effect in the developing medical school in Uganda.

Sir Ian McAdam (1917–99).

He was made Senior Surgical Specialist to the Ugandan government in 1946, and appointed to the Chair of Surgery in Makerere University medical school in 1957. At that time surgical services were developing in East Africa and he made major contributions to their development, including the establishment of the Uganda Blood Transfusion Service and contributions to the founding of the Polio Treatment Centre and the Uganda Cancer Institute. Under his leadership, the surgical department enlarged and its reputation grew.

His sporting prowess continued unabated. He was able to win national titles at tennis, golf and motor rallying and also represented Uganda at cricket. He was instrumental in establishing the first multi-racial sports institute in Uganda, the Lugogo Sports Centre, which opened in 1959. It was here in 1970 that President Milton Obote was shot through the open mouth while addressing a political rally. McAdam operated successfully under frightening circumstances, his operating theatre being full of nervous, excited soldiers with automatic weapons.

This positive outcome, together with his activity in helping young surgeons of Asian origin to find posts abroad so that they could escape persecution by the dictatorial regime of Idi Amin, got him into serious difficulty with the government of Uganda. He was expelled without notice by Amin in 1973, and spent a year at the National Cancer Institute in Washington, but Africa drew him back. He settled in Knysna in South Africa, where he continued to teach and to operate.

McAdam received many honours. He was a founder member and later President of the East African Association of Surgeons, the forerunner of the College of Surgeons of East, Southern and Central Africa. He was knighted in 1966.

In 1995 he was awarded the Bruce Medal by the Royal College of Surgeons of Edinburgh, an award which gave him particular pleasure.

Authors: John Cook and Iain Macintyre

Roll number: 4972

Major General John Matheson (1912–2003).

John Matheson (1912–2003)

A generation of British medical students in the 1930s, anticipating the coming of war, joined the Territorial Army and subsequently went on to active war service and distinguished careers in the forces. John Matheson had a commanding presence which, combined with his natural warmth, charm and ability, destined him for a successful military career. After appointment as Professor of Military Surgery in London, he returned to his native Edinburgh as Postgraduate Dean.

John MacKenzie Matheson was born in Gibraltar, educated at George Watson's College, Edinburgh, and entered the Edinburgh University medical school. There, he distinguished himself by winning a Vans Dunlop Scholarship and becoming President of the Students' Representative Council (SRC).

After qualifying MB ChB in 1936, he obtained a research fellowship at the Royal Victoria Hospital, Edinburgh, where he worked on tuberculosis. As the prospect of war grew, he joined the 23rd (Scottish) General Hospital of the Territorial Army, being given a TA commission in 1936. He gained the membership of the Royal College of Physicians of Edinburgh in 1939.

On the outbreak of war, the 23rd General Hospital saw service in Palestine and then in Egypt. Matheson's abilities led to his appointment as Assistant Director of Medical Services (ADMS) to the Tobruk Garrison during the siege of the fortress in 1941. At the end of the siege he returned to general headquarters, occupying a series of ADMS posts during the El Alamein campaign, in Tunisia and in Italy.

His wartime service had been administrative rather than clinical and at the end of the war he had to decide whether to continue with a career as a staff officer, or return to clinical work after an absence of six years. With characteristic determination, he decided to train as a surgeon in Edinburgh Royal Infirmary and obtained the FRCSEd in 1946. In 1948 he resumed his military career as liaison officer at the British Army Mission in Washington. The US Surgeon General Leonard Heaton appointed him Assistant Surgeon at the Walter Reid Hospital, where he was able to continue with surgical and research work. At the end of this three-year posting he was appointed OBE.

Thereafter, he took charge of a number of British military hospitals, including Chester, Fayid in Egypt, Catterick, Aldershot and Cyprus. In 1963 he was promoted Brigadier and became Consulting Surgeon to the Near East land forces.

The following year he was appointed Professor of Military Surgery jointly at the Royal College of Surgeons of England and the Royal Army Medical College at the Millbank. This allowed him to direct research into missile wounds, vascular injury and the sterilisation of surgical materials. He went on to become Commandant and Director of studies at Millbank, with the rank of Major General.

He had been widely regarded as a future Director General of the Army Medical Service, but it was not to be. He left the army in 1971 returning to Edinburgh, where he became Postgraduate Dean in the Faculty of Medicine until 1978. This was a time of considerable change in postgraduate training, and his charm and gifts of communication were put to good use as these changes were introduced.

Roll number: 5016

David Waterston (1910–85)

David Waterston (1910–85).

The attributes for success in medicine vary widely, but would certainly include concern for and sympathy with patients, and clarity of expression with patients and colleagues. Success in surgery requires all of these and, moreover, a gift of technical skills and equanimity in a crisis. Greatness in surgery requires, in addition, vision and ingenuity. When dealing with the surgery of neonates, all of these qualities are needed in even greater measure. David Waterston, surgeon to the Hospital for Sick Children Great Ormond Street, London, had all of these attributes.

David James Waterston was born in St Andrews, where his father, a Fellow of the Royal College of Surgeons of Edinburgh, was Professor of Anatomy. His initial undergraduate medical education was in St Andrews University and, he retained a life-long affection for the town, remaining a member of the Royal and Ancient Golf Club. He graduated MB ChB from Edinburgh in 1933.

After junior hospital posts in Edinburgh he moved to Great Ormond Street Hospital in London, where he was to work for the rest of his professional career, interrupted only by war service. As a captain in the Royal Army Medical Corps, he served in a blood transfusion unit of the 8th Army in North Africa, where he was twice mentioned in dispatches and awarded the MBE. Towards the end of the war, serving in Europe as a surgical specialist with the rank of Major, he was with the first medical team to be exposed to the horrors of the Belsen concentration camp in May 1945.

On a hospital visit.

He became FRCSEd in 1946 and FRCSEng three years later. Returning to Great Ormond Street, he developed his interest in neonatal surgery at a time when operations in this vulnerable group of patients still carried considerable risks. His work on tracheo-oesophageal fistulae was to make him famous, particularly his innovative use of interposed transverse colon after oesophageal resection. This procedure became known as Waterston's procedure throughout the world and gained him an international reputation.

His practice extended to pioneering procedures for the correction of congenital cardiac lesions. He was among the first to realise the benefits of a holistic approach to children with such problems. With his colleague, Dr R. E. Bonham-Carter, he established the Thoracic Unit in Great Ormond Street, the first of its kind in the world, in which children with intra-thoracic disease were treated in a joint medical and surgical unit. He did, however, remain a general paediatric surgeon, and as such operated on the young Prince Charles for acute appendicitis.

His contribution to his specialty was recognised by honours at home and abroad. He became President of the British Association of Paediatric Surgeons, and was awarded the Denis Browne Gold Medal in 1970 for outstanding services to paediatric surgery. In 1972 he was awarded the CBE. Honours came from abroad – the Ladd Medal from the United States, the Copernicus Medal from Poland and honorary MD degrees from Genoa and Warsaw.

Studying an X-ray on a ward round.

Those whom he taught remember the clarity of his teaching and lectures, his superb operative skills, but, above all, his gentleness, humanity and concern for the patients under his care.

Roll number: 5025

Sir Robert Wright (1915–81)

To be elected President of the General Medical Council (GMC) is one of the greatest honours to which a British doctor can aspire and two of the Council's 19 Presidents, since its establishment in 1858, have been ordinary Fellows of the College.

Sir William Turner (q.v.) was GMC President from 1898 to 1904, but Sir Robert Wright's presidential term was cruelly cut short by his death when at the height of his powers after little more than one year in office.

Robert Brash Wright was the son of a general medical practitioner in Overtown, near Glasgow. The circumstances of his father's practice in a depressed industrial area where there was much poverty and deprivation engendered the humanitarian qualities and social conscience that characterised his entire professional life.

He was educated at Hamilton Academy and at the University of Glasgow, from which he graduated BSc in 1934 and MB ChB with honours three years later.

His plans to pursue a career in surgery were interrupted by the outbreak of the Second World War, throughout which he served with the Royal Army Medical Corps as a regimental medical officer and in field medical units in the Middle East and in Italy. He was wounded in action and for outstanding services he was made an Officer of the Order of the British Empire (OBE) in 1944 and awarded the Distinguished Service Order (DSO) in 1945.

After the war, Bob Wright, as he was known always to friends and colleagues, completed his surgical training at the Western Infirmary, Glasgow. He obtained the Fellowship of the College in 1947 and his Master's degree in Surgery (ChM) from Glasgow University in 1953. In that same year, he was appointed Senior Consultant Surgeon to the Southern General Hospital in Glasgow. It was here that, over the next 27 years, he built up his formidable reputation as a clinician, as a teacher and as a master surgical craftsman. He had a special interest in vascular and thyroid surgery but his expertise extended into a number of other areas and, together with colleagues, whom he inspired with his energy and enthusiasm, he developed at the Southern General an impressive surgical service which also provided clinical teaching of the highest quality. His own precise and authoritative didactic style, enhanced by humour and humanity, ensured his popularity as a teacher in the classroom, and at the bedside, but it was as Chairman of the Regional Postgraduate Surgical Training Committee that, through his establishment of highly successful rotational training programmes, he made his most notable contribution to surgical education. He also served for a time on the Glasgow University medical faculty, and his distinction as an educator and trainer of students and surgeons was recognised in 1981 when his alma mater awarded him its honorary degree, Doctor of Laws (LLD).

Robert Wright was appointed Treasurer of the Royal College of Physicians and Surgeons of Glasgow in 1958 and thereafter he played an increasingly prominent part in its affairs. Having been elected Visitor in 1966, he became President two years later, and there is no doubt that his presidency was one of the most effective of modern times. He was an ardent protagonist of increased co-operation between the British Royal

Medical Colleges, particularly in the fields of education and training and, in his role as President of a combined College of Physicians and Surgeons, he did much to foster the development of the MRCP (UK) examination.

For his enthusiastic promotion of intercollegiate collaboration, he was awarded the Fellowship of the Royal College of Physicians of London and the honorary Fellowships of both the English and Australasian Royal Colleges of Surgeons. In 1976 he received the honour of knighthood. By this time, he was an important and influential member of the General Medical Council, on which he had represented the Glasgow College since 1970.

Sir Robert's logical mind, absolute clarity of thought and abundant common sense made a profound impression on the Council and he was appointed the first Chairman of its new Overseas Committee and Deputy Chairman (under the President) of what was then the Disciplinary Committee. In the first of these capacities he was largely responsible for the overhaul of the regulations for limited registration of overseas qualified doctors seeking further training in the United Kingdom, which included the successful introduction in 1975 of the TRAB (Temporary Registration Assessments Board of the GMC), later to become the PLAB (Professional and Linguistic Assessments Board of the GMC) examinations. As Deputy Chairman of what was then the Disciplinary Committee, he conducted its proceedings with the utmost judicial skill, tempered with an integrity and humanity which commanded wide respect.

Sir Robert's election to the presidency of the GMC in 1980 was warmly acclaimed and he took office at a critical time not long after it had undergone radical reorganisation. He soon showed that he was more than equal to the challenges that lay ahead, but he was stricken by mortal illness before his various initiatives had time to come to fruition.

Bob Wright was a remarkable personality who will be remembered as a compassionate doctor, as an inspiring teacher and as a wise medical statesman. A life-long churchgoer, teetotaller and non-smoker, he could occasionally present an impression of dour austerity, but behind this he was a kindly, warm-hearted, quietly humorous man and, in his own home, the most generous and hospitable of hosts. His untimely death, when he had so much still to offer, was a grievous loss to British medicine.

Roll number: 5098

Sir Robert Wright (1915–81).

Douglas Clark (1917–91)

Sir Charles Illingworth (q.v.) asked each of his residents to present him with a framed photograph and each one was placed on the wall of his room. Douglas Clark had been his first resident and his portrait was first. All who subsequently shared the privilege of 'the photographs' felt that Clark's was at the top not merely because of seniority but because Illingworth felt a special kinship with him.

At school in Ayrshire and University in Glasgow, Douglas Henderson Clark excelled at sport and was awarded a blue at football. He supported himself at University with the help of a Miners' Welfare Scholarship and a bursary from the Rainy Foundation. On graduation in 1940 his first resident post was with the newly appointed Regius Professor of Surgery, Charles (later Sir Charles) Illingworth, to whom then, and in future years, he gave the utmost loyalty.

Clark had gone unhesitatingly to volunteer for war service in the Second World War just as Illingworth had done in the First. He spent six years in the army, serving in South-east Asia, India, Burma and Malaysia. He had taken part in the advance out of India into Burma towards Mandalay and saw at first hand, as one of Sir John Bruce's (q.v.) young surgeons working in support of the 14th Army, several instances of wartime brutality. One of these is worth recording, partly because of its singularity and partly because Clark's innate modesty prevented his making the episode widely known.

He had operated on a young British officer who had been tied to a tree, bayoneted, naked and left for dead. After several surgical operations and devoted medical and nursing care, the officer recovered. At that time the *British Journal of Surgery* alternated its issues with a *British Journal of War Surgery* edition. Douglas Clark submitted a case report for publication in the latter but this was prohibited by the War Office. A month later he received a letter from the House of Commons containing an apology for failure to publish his article. The letter went on 'it is my intention to use your contribution in a speech on war atrocities in the House, and hope the perpetrators will one day be brought to justice. In the mean time I wish you well and can only hope that a reference to my speech in Hansard will bring recognition to your efforts. Yours sincerely. Winston S. Churchill.'

After return to the professorial unit at the Western Infirmary of Glasgow, Douglas Clark, in 1947, became FRCSEd and a Fellow of the Glasgow Faculty of Physicians and Surgeons. Within the year he had joined the surgical staff as the first of a new breed of full-time NHS senior registrars.

About this time Sir Charles Illingworth had been collecting information on patients who had had a gastric resection for peptic ulcer disease, hoping that this would become established as the operation of choice. Douglas Clark was given the task of setting up meticulous follow-up after ulcer surgery to establish, *inter alia*, the rate of recurrent ulcer. For this work he was awarded the degree of ChM by Glasgow University.

In this way he had joined the ranks of the 'Peptic Ulcer Clinic' of Mr (later Sir) Andrew Kay. This ulcer follow-up clinic provided a consulting clinic for patients with peptic ulcer in the west of Scotland at a time when the incidence of peptic ulcer was at its height, and Glasgow had among the highest incidence of the condition in the world. Studies done in the clinic led to a further thesis on hormonal influences in peptic ulcer, for which he was awarded an MD with honours. As part of a Fulbright Scholarship to the United States, he was awarded the William Stewart Halstead Fellowship to the Johns Hopkins University Hospital in Baltimore. This proved to be an enriching experience which led to a life-long friendship with the Johns family of Richmond, Virginia, and to a long-lasting exchange programme with Glasgow.

On return to Glasgow, he was appointed Consultant Surgeon in 1954 in Mr Murray Newton's unit at the Western Infirmary. On Newton's retiral, he joined forces with Andrew Kay and took charge of wards in the Western Infirmary of Glasgow. He went on to become sub Dean in Glasgow University and later served on the University Court, for which he was awarded an honorary DSc by the University of Glasgow in 1983.

His earlier contacts in the United States resulted in frequent requests for him to return as a visiting professor. During his presidency of the Glasgow College, he visited South Africa, Hong Kong, Malaysia, Australia and New Zealand. His presidential years (1980–2) saw the award of honorary degrees from the Surgical Colleges of England, Ireland and South Africa and from the Royal College of Physicians of Edinburgh in its tercentennial year. He was also made a member of the Academy of Medicine of Singapore. A founder member of the Illingworth Surgical Club, he was also a Director of the James IV Association of Surgeons and a member of the Surgical Travellers' Club.

Like his mentor, Sir Charles Illingworth, he had no frills – he had come from a country school to Glasgow University supported by bursaries, entering medicine as a Scottish 'lad o' pairts'. When he chose surgery as a career, his diligence and innate ability gave him entry to a wider world; yet throughout he retained his humility.

All who were privileged to know him respected his integrity. He had worked with, trained, or knew all of Sir Charles Illingsworth's young professors and could hold his head high among them all. He was proud of his friendship with Sir Charles, but was equally proud to be singled out in a surgical meeting by Sir John Bruce as an old comrade of the India and Burma days. Eric Mekie (q.v.), who had known years of Japanese captivity, said of those days 'those of us in captivity had to believe that somewhere there were people like Douglas Clark coming to get us out'.

Author: Adam N. Smith

Roll number: 5175

Douglas Clark (1917–91).

Sir Donald Douglas (1911–93)

Although by the end of the 19th century the College had become truly international with many of its Fellows domiciled far from Scotland, it was not until 70 years later that, with the election of Sir Donald Douglas to the presidency in 1970, its leadership was for the first time entrusted to a Fellow from outside Edinburgh. There could not have been a more effective counterblast to any charges of narrow parochialism which might, in former times, have been brought against the College, but there are many other reasons why Sir Donald's presidency is worthy of special recognition.

Donald MacLeod Douglas was born in St Andrews and educated there, first at Madras College and later in the Medical Faculty of Scotland's senior university, which he represented at rugby football and from which he graduated MB ChB in 1934.

After junior hospital appointments in Dundee and London, the award of a Commonwealth Fellowship enabled him to travel to the USA, where from 1937 to 1939 he was a Fellow in Surgery at the Mayo Foundation, Rochester, Minnesota. He obtained the degree of MS from the University of Minnesota before returning to Britain in 1939 to become first assistant in surgery at the postgraduate medical school in London. In that year he became a Fellow of the Royal College of Surgeons of England and, soon afterwards, he was awarded the ChM *summa cum laude* by St Andrews University.

From 1941 to 1946 he served in the Royal Army Medical Corps as a surgical specialist, initially in North Africa with the 8th Army, and was involved in the Battle of El Alamein. Later he was posted to Iraq, where, by virtue of his academic distinction, he was seconded from his army duties to act as Professor of Surgery in the University of Baghdad. For his outstanding military service he was appointed MBE and, after demobilisation in 1946, he returned to the professorial surgical department of the postgraduate medical school as Senior Lecturer with consultant status in Hammersmith Hospital.

His appointment one year later to the Edinburgh medical school as Reader in Experimental Surgery and Deputy Director of the Wilkie Surgical Research Laboratory marked the beginning of his happy and productive association with Sir James Learmonth (q.v.), which influenced him profoundly, not least through the stimulus it gave to his interest in what was then the infant specialty of vascular surgery. His impressive experimental studies in gastrointestinal physiology on shock and on the use of radioisotopes in surgical research date from this period, during which he also had demanding clinical responsibilities in Edinburgh Royal Infirmary. Although his academic status and his surgical reputation would assuredly have gained for him admission to the Fellowship of the College *ad eundem*, he deliberately chose to become a Fellow by examination and did so in 1948.

When the Chair of Surgery in his alma mater, St Andrews University, became vacant in 1951, Donald Douglas was the obvious choice for appointment as its first full-time Professor. At Queen's College, Dundee (later to become the University of Dundee), he established a dynamic and vigorous academic department closely associated with the professorial surgical unit of the Dundee Royal Infirmary, which, under his direction, became a recognised centre of clinical excellence particularly in the field of cardiovascular surgery. Important research on wound healing and on surgical infection further enhanced his department's reputation and led to his involvement in the design of hospital wards and operating theatres. He played a notable part in the planning of Dundee's magnificent teaching hospital at Ninewells, and the surgical wards and theatres there are perhaps his greatest monument.

Many honours came to him during his tenure of the St Andrews/Dundee Chair of Surgery and none gave him greater pleasure than the honorary Doctorate of Science (DSc) awarded by his own University. He was President of the Association of Surgeons of Great Britain and Ireland (1963–4), President of the Surgical Research Society (1966–8), and, in 1965, he was appointed Surgeon to HM the Queen in Scotland.

Over these years he became increasingly active in College affairs as an examiner, as a member of Council and as a Vice President. This record of service combined with his professional eminence made him an ideal candidate for the highest office and his election as the first ever out-of-Edinburgh President in 1970 was received with general acclaim.

As President, Donald Douglas oversaw the adoption of new College laws, in the drafting of which he had been heavily involved. These were the end result of a revision process extending over several years and, among many other beneficial effects, they greatly improved the efficiency of the College's administrative processes without prejudice to its democratic principles.

He was one of the first senior surgeons in Scotland to appreciate the need for reform of the Fellowship examinations and the radical proposals which were so intensely debated at the 1977 College meeting were the result of studies and discussions initiated during his presidency.

Twenty-five years later the educational concepts which inspired the 1977 proposals have gained full intercollegiate acceptance and are embodied in the examinations of all the four Royal Surgical Colleges of the British Isles.

Donald Douglas had a keen intellect and an analytical mind, which, together with his tenacity and decisiveness, made him a supremely effective Committee Chairman and, in this role, he gave outstanding service not only to his University and to the College, but also to the National Health Service in Scotland.

He was an excellent teacher with absolute mastery of the art of the formal lecture, and this brought him invitations to visit medical schools and colleges in many different parts of the world. His affability and his easy, relaxed manner made him a particularly popular visitor in all these places and he was a superb ambassador not only for the College but for Scottish medicine as a whole.

The conferment of knighthood upon Donald Douglas in 1972 was hailed by the entire Scottish medical community as a worthy recognition of the achievements of a great master surgeon, an inspiring teacher, a dedicated investigator and a wise medical statesman.

Roll number: 5307

Sir Donald Douglas (1911–93).

Arthur Hodgson (1915–93)

At the beginning of the 21st century the Department of Orthopaedic Surgery in the University of Hong Kong is recognised as a major centre of excellence and it is difficult to appreciate how rapidly its illustrious international reputation was acquired or how modest and meagre were its original resources. Several distinguished and dedicated surgeons made important contributions to this remarkable success story but none more than Professor A. R. Hodgson, who may be justifiably regarded as the father of Hong Kong orthopaedic surgery.

Arthur Ralph Hodgson was born of British parents in Montevideo, Uruguay, and his mother, a Scot, was responsible for most of his childhood education in that country. For his medical training he went to Edinburgh University, from which he graduated MB ChB in 1939. For the next three and a half years he held junior hospital posts in Norwich. There he worked for two eminent orthopaedic surgeons, H. A. Brittain and G. K. McKee, and this experience undoubtedly influenced his decision to pursue a career in orthopaedic surgery. Having joined the Royal Army Medical Corps in 1943, he saw active service in India, Burma and Singapore, eventually attaining the rank of Lieutenant Colonel.

After demobilisation, he was appointed Senior Registrar in orthopaedic surgery at St Bartholomew's Hospital, Rochester, Kent, and in 1948 he obtained the Fellowship of the College. During this period he laid the foundations of his clinical and operative skills, but poor promotion prospects in the National Health Service determined his decision to seek advancement overseas. In 1951 he was appointed Senior Lecturer and Surgeon in Charge of the newly established orthopaedic and trauma unit in the Department of Surgery in the University of Hong Kong. At that time in Hong Kong, orthopaedic and traumatic surgery was dealt with by the general surgeons, but although initially his facilities were exiguous, Hodgson and two assistants eagerly took on an enormous workload and started to develop a dedicated orthopaedic and trauma service.

Spinal tuberculosis (Pott's disease), causing gross deformity and often associated with paraplegia, was then common in Hong Kong, and it would be impossible to exaggerate the importance of Hodgson's contributions to the successful treatment of this disabling and dangerous condition. He appreciated early that, with the advent of effective anti-tuberculous chemotherapy, radical surgery had an important part to play in the management of spinal tuberculosis.

His technique, using a revolutionary anterior approach to the vertebral column with extirpation of the whole area of active disease combined at the same procedure with anterior strut bone grafting in compression, was internationally acclaimed and came to be known worldwide as the 'Hong Kong operation'. His 1956 paper in the *British Journal of Surgery* entitled 'Anterior Spinal Fusion: A Preliminary Communication on the Radical Treatment of Pott's Disease and Pott's Paraplegia' remains a surgical classic nearly 50 years later.

The clinical and research activity of the orthopaedic and trauma unit was increasing rapidly and this, together with Hodgson's growing international reputation, prompted the University of Hong Kong in 1961 to create a separate department and a Chair of Orthopaedic Surgery. He was appointed Foundation Professor and held this position, along with administrative charge of the new orthopaedic department, until his retirement in 1975. Under his leadership, the department expanded progressively and acquired greatly improved facilities in the new professorial block at the Queen Mary Hospital.

In the 1950s poliomyelitis was common and the treatment of the residual musculo-skeletal effects of this disease became another of Hodgson's principal clinical and research interests. He played an important part in the foundation of the Society for the Relief of Disabled Children, which in 1956 established the Sandy Bay Convalescent Home for Crippled Children. Twelve years later this became the Duchess of Kent Children's Hospital, with 200 beds devoted to paediatric orthopaedics in which Hodgson acquired a reputation as distinguished as that which he had earned in spinal surgery. His teaching and research attracted increasing numbers of orthopaedic surgeons to Hong Kong for advanced training and the University encouraged this by the establishment in 1968 of special orthopaedic research fellowships. Further recognition of his professional stature came with his admission to Fellowship of the American College of Surgeons in 1960 and of the Royal Australasian College of Surgeons in 1974.

Inevitably he became much in demand as a guest lecturer or visiting professor and among the many prestigious lectures which he was invited to deliver in Europe, America, South-east Asia and Australasia was the Robert Jones Lecture to the British Orthopaedic Association in 1977.

Arthur Hodgson (1915–93).

In addition to an increasingly hectic travel programme and his heavy clinical and research commitments, he took on his full share of academic responsibilities and as its Dean from 1962 to 1967 he did much to enhance the administrative efficiency of the University of Hong Kong Faculty of Medicine. His remarkable achievements as a surgeon and his contributions to medical education were honoured by his appointment in 1966 as an Officer of the Order of the British Empire (OBE).

'Hoddy', as he was known to surgeons all over the world, retired from the Chair of Orthopaedic Surgery in 1975 but continued in private practice in Hong Kong for 10 years before returning to England. He was a dynamic extrovert who thrived on hard work, who enjoyed life to the full and who, as a charismatic team leader, inspired the loyalty, devotion and profound admiration of all whose lives he touched.

The surgeons whom he trained have maintained and enhanced the illustrious reputation of Hong Kong orthopaedic surgery and the high prestige which it enjoys worldwide is Hoddy's greatest monument.

Roll number: 5437

Walter Galbraith (1889–1960)

Walter Galbraith (1889–1960).

Walter Galbraith, who became Senior Surgeon to the Western Infirmary of Glasgow, played a leading part in the development of urology as a specialty in the west of Scotland.

After preclinical studies at Cambridge, Walter Weir Galbraith completed his medical training at Glasgow University, from which he graduated MB ChB in 1914 and almost immediately joined the army as a medical officer. He saw active service in France and Italy and soon became a surgical specialist. On demobilisation, he returned to Glasgow and he was elected, in 1919, to the staff of the Western Infirmary, where he remained until retirement in 1954.

Though at the outset a general surgeon, he was among the first to recognise that urological surgery was destined to develop as a distinct specialty. He allocated most of his own hospital beds to this purpose and enthusiastically set about procuring the special radiological services and instruments which were novel at that time. He also embarked on the recruitment and training of medical and nursing staff which enabled him to establish a dedicated specialist team. The urology department that he built up was regarded as second to none; under his leadership the department produced pioneering work on 'pyelography' and he became widely known as a major exponent of the Harris prostatectomy.

In the years that followed he established a reputation for himself as one of Britain's outstanding urological surgeons. In 1948 he was elected President of the British Association of Urological Surgeons (he had already been President of the section of urology of the Royal Society of Medicine). He then became the President of the Royal Faculty of Physicians and Surgeons, now the Royal College of Physicians and Surgeons of Glasgow, and almost immediately after demitting office became a Vice President of the Royal College of Surgeons of Edinburgh.

He was a natural sportsman and excelled at golf and fishing, as well as being a first-class shot – the latter skill, he averred, kept him adept at the quick visual responses needed when using the cystoscope in the interpretation and handling of problems in diagnostic urology. On retiral, he served on the Western Regional Hospital Board and was an assessor for the General Council on the Court of Glasgow University.

Walter Galbraith came from a family imbued with the spirit of service as exemplified by the career of his brother, T. D. Galbraith, who served with the Royal Navy at the Battle of Jutland in 1916 and later became an MP, a Minister of State and, after 1955, Lord Strathclyde. Walter Galbraith shared the same high ideals of service in his dedication to the Western Infirmary of Glasgow, where he is remembered with affection as a great Scottish pioneer of urological surgery.

Author: Adam A. N. Smith

Roll number: 5723a

Patrick Steptoe (1913–88)

A major scientific advance invariably requires inspiration followed by years of toil. Most advances in medical science are made in teaching hospitals, which are organised, staffed and funded with that as one of their principal aims. To achieve what was the greatest advance in fertility treatment of the 20th century from a base outside a teaching hospital attests not only to inspiration but to a diligence and determination enjoyed by few doctors. Patrick Steptoe, an Oldham gynaecologist, was a pioneer of laparoscopy, whose innovative work on in-vitro fertilisation led to the birth of the first child to be conceived outside the mother's body. He was widely regarded as the surgeon who did more than any other in the 20th century to improve the prospects for childless couples throughout the world.

Patrick Steptoe (1913–88).

Patrick Christopher Steptoe was born in Whitney, Oxfordshire. His manual dexterity was apparent early in life. As a boy he would play the incidental piano music for silent films in the local cinema, and went on to play the church organ in his local town. He trained in London at the St George's Hospital Medical School and when war broke out in 1939 he joined the Royal Naval Volunteer Reserve as a Surgeon-Lieutenant. While serving as a ship's surgeon his ship was torpedoed, and he became a prisoner of war in 1941. After the war he returned to St George's as an assistant obstetrician and gynaecologist, and in 1949 was appointed Senior Registrar at the Whittington Hospital in London.

He obtained the FRCSEd in 1950, and was appointed Consultant Gynaecologist in Oldham the following year. Here, he developed an interest in laparoscopy, then in its early stages of development. A visit to Dr Raoul Palmer in Paris further stimulated this interest and he maintained a personal and professional association with Palmer throughout his life.

As a result of Patrick Steptoe's efforts, Oldham became an important centre for laparoscopic training and in 1967 he published a seminal textbook, *Laparoscopy in Gynaecology*. In this he described the value of laparoscopy in the treatment of endometriosis, division of adhesions and in the monitoring of the suppression of ovulation by the contraceptive pill. This book, and the training which he offered, helped to spread the use of laparoscopy throughout the English-speaking world.

His interest in fertility led to a meeting with the Cambridge physiologist Robert Edwards, with whom he was to establish a pioneering collaboration. Their initial clinical research, which involved depositing ova and spermatozoa in the oviduct, was unsuccessful. They next implanted fertilised ova in the uterus but again this failed to result in a single pregnancy in the first four years. Perseverance in the face of mounting ethical criticism led to the development of in-vitro techniques, which resulted in the birth of Louise Brown, the world's first 'test tube baby' in 1978.

At the age of 65 he retired from the National Health Service, but continued to develop the technique at Bourn Hall, a clinic which he established with Edwards near Cambridge. Here, as in Oldham, each step was taken rigorously adhering to scientific principle and within the strict ethical guidelines which Steptoe had been careful to seek to establish as early as the 1960s.

Like his friend Ian Donald, he strived for the betterment of women unable to have children. As a result of their efforts, the laparoscope and the ultrasound scanner became everyday tools of practice in obstetrics and gynaecology.

Patrick Steptoe became a household name and his innovative work was acknowledged by the Eardley Holland Medal of the Royal College of Obstetricians and Gynaecologists and the Gold Medal of the British Medical Association. He was made a Fellow of the Royal Society and awarded the CBE. Even in the throes of his final illness, he travelled to San Francisco to join the American Association of Gynaecological Laparoscopists, playing the piano with a symphony orchestra in front of an audience of 3,000 admiring colleagues.

His work truly revolutionised the treatment of infertility, and gave, and continues to give, children to many couples who had thought this would be denied them.

Roll number: 5785

Aylwin Hitchin (1907–96)

Professor Aylwin Hitchin was the first dental graduate of the University of Durham in 1932. As Professor of Dental Surgery at the University of St Andrews and Dean of the Dundee Dental Hospital and School he presided over the post-war modernisation of the Dental School and did much to establish its academic reputation.

On leaving Rutherford College, Aylwin Drakeford Hitchin entered the Dental School of the University of Durham at Newcastle-upon-Tyne, where he soon achieved distinction academically, on the sports field and in the Royal Army Medical Corps Unit of the University Officer Training Corps (OTC). Indeed, it was at the OTC camp in 1928 that it was realised all was not well with his left leg, which was subsequently amputated after osteogenic sarcoma had been diagnosed. Despite this major setback, he returned to his dental studies, and he learned to cope with a dental foot pedal. He qualified LDS in 1931 and BDS the following year. He then combined private practice in Gosforth with an honorary appointment at the dental hospital in Newcastle, during which time he gained his Master of Dental Surgery degree and became an avid attender at postgraduate courses and national and international meetings.

It was at the Federation Dentaire Internationale meeting in Vienna that he first met the eminent oral surgeon Harold Round of Birmingham, with whom he established a 'master–disciple' relationship from which Hitchin emerged as a very accomplished and successful oral surgeon.

Throughout this period he maintained contact with the Territorial Army and was extremely frustrated and disappointed that on the outbreak of the Second World War, he was graded 'Medically Unfit' for call-up. He refused to accept this grading and after much argument and pressure (which according to rumour included a 'sit-in' on the War Office steps), he was accepted into the army for 'Home Service' only. He left the army in 1946, having served in London and as Dental Specialist to Scottish Command.

He resumed practice in Gosforth but clearly his time in the army had fired an enthusiasm to become involved in dental education and research.

Hence, when the Boyd Chair in Dental Surgery in the University of St Andrews tenable at the Dundee Dental School became vacant, he applied and was appointed. He took up the Chair in October 1947 and at the same time assumed the Deanship of the Dundee Dental Hospital and the Directorship in Dental Studies in the School.

In 1951 he was elected to the Fellowship in Dental Surgery which the Edinburgh College had established in 1949.

At this time the whole face of dentistry in the UK was about to change; the National Health Service had come into being on 1 April 1948, the dental schools throughout the United Kingdom were becoming schools within universities with growing numbers of full-time academic staff, and the urgent need for research within the wider field of dentistry was accepted. By any standards the facilities in Dundee fell short of the requirements of a modern university-based dental school. The curriculum required revision, equipment was obsolescent and there was virtually no research activity. Indeed, almost all the staff were part time, with practice commitments demanding most of their time.

Aylwin Hitchin (1907–96).

With vision and determination, Hitchin set about the task of bringing the school and hospital into the post-war age. Visits to other schools in the UK, Scandinavia and the USA had provided valuable insights into what was needed to put the Dundee Dental School into the forefront of academic and clinical excellence. As a result of his imaginative planning and leadership, the Dundee Dental Hospital and School, with its tower dominating the university campus, has become the centre of academic and clinical excellence that he envisaged.

Hitchin transformed the teaching and clinical programmes by personal example and effort. He was a skilled clinician and an inspirational clinical teacher. Demanding but fair, he asked most of all from himself. He was especially skilled in the introduction of young graduates to research and many have good reason to be grateful for his encouragement, patience and sound guidance as they found their way through the pitfalls of that first project. His own research was varied, ranging from in-depth studies of 'broken mouth' in sheep and the genetically based anatomical anomalies of incisor teeth of Lakeland Terrier dogs to epidemiological and clinical investigations. This work earned him a DSc degree in 1957.

In 1970 he was made Commander of the Order of the British Empire (CBE), in 1977 was given the honorary Doctorate in Odontology of the University of Lund and in 1979 the Honorary Dental Fellowship of the Royal College of Physicians and Surgeons of Glasgow. During the last decade of his career he was very active in postgraduate education and had a most productive period in office as Convenor of the Dental Council RCSEd (1971–4). He held external examinerships at most of the UK dental schools as well as the Dental Fellowships of the Glasgow and Irish Colleges. He was a former President of the Oral Surgery Club, the British Society of Dental Radiology and a Foundation Fellow of the British Association of Oral Surgeons.

Throughout his life, Hitchin was sustained by his deep Christian faith. Originally a strict Baptist, in adult life he became a member of the Church of Scotland, in which he served as an Elder, Presbytery and General Assembly member.

Author: Sir David Mason CBE

Dental roll number: 14

Douglas Roy (1925–2003)

Douglas Roy (1925–2003).

Douglas Roy had the unique distinction of heading departments of surgery in three different continents.

The son of an accountant, Douglas Roy spent his early childhood in London. When he was aged 10, the family moved to Scotland, where he attended Paisley Grammar School and Glasgow University medical school, at which he was the recipient of numerous prizes and awards, graduating with distinctions in medicine and surgery. As an undergraduate he was a member of the University XV (1945–7) and represented the Combined Scottish Universities at rugby.

After National Service for two years with the Royal Army Medical Corps, he embarked on a surgical career, obtaining the FRCSEd in 1952. Following training in Glasgow, Inverness, Aylesbury and Oxford, he was appointed Consultant Surgeon, Honorary Lecturer and First Assistant to Sir Charles Illingworth (q.v.) and subsequently to Sir Andrew Watt Kay in the University Department of Surgery, Western Infirmary, Glasgow. It was from this springboard that he launched into three consecutive, outstanding and fruitful phases of his surgical career in which he headed three university departments of surgery in three continents – Africa, Europe and Asia.

A new Faculty of Medicine was established in the University of Nairobi, Kenya, in June 1967, and the following year Douglas Roy was appointed Foundation Professor of Surgery, a post which he held for four years (1968–72). During this period, he established a dynamic and enterprising department.

At that time the East African Federation was still in existence and he played a pivotal role in enhancing co-operation and collaboration between the three universities and health services in the region.

His prime concern was to produce doctors of quality equipped to meet the diverse clinical needs of the population of Kenya. In spite of the pressures of work in Nairobi, he made time for visits with the Flying Doctor Service to remote provincial and mission hospitals, a practice which helped to develop his deep concern for community medicine in all its aspects. In this, as in many other aspects of his work, he proved to be a leader and exemplar who could inspire his students and in particular his postgraduates.

In 1973 he was appointed to the Chair of Surgery in Belfast and, as Head of the Queen's University Department of Surgery, he built up an energetic and productive clinical research team.

His willingness to delegate administrative and research responsibility contributed greatly to the strength of his department and to the excellent relationships within it between University and National Health Service staff.

He inspired a remarkable degree of loyalty in all who worked with him and, as a result of his encouragement and stimulation, there was an impressive output of scientific publications from his department during his tenure of the Chair.

His leadership as Chairman of the Surgical Training Committee of the Northern Ireland Council for Postgraduate Medical Education during an 11 year-period led to the establishment of a comprehensive rotational training scheme which brought considerable benefit to generations of aspiring young surgeons. He himself was a fine technical surgeon, dedicated trainer and respected role model in the fields of gastrointestinal, breast and endocrine surgery and the management of trauma.

He was elected to the Council of the Royal College of Surgeons of Edinburgh (1979–85) and served on a host of other committees and advisory bodies, where his wise counsel and sound judgement were greatly appreciated. He was a perceptive and popular examiner and was much in demand in university and college circles at home and abroad.

Douglas Roy was invited to lead the establishment of a new health service as Chief of Surgical Services for the Sultanate of Oman and as Professor of Surgery, Sultan Qaboos University (1985–8). There, he devoted his energy and skill to help develop surgical services in the capital and in strategic stations throughout the country. Aided by the recently acquired substantial oil revenue, he was instrumental in designing and establishing a surgical training programme in the newly opened University medical school.

His vision, enthusiasm and commitment played a significant role in the evolution of a meritorious health service that is highly regarded among the Arabian Gulf States and beyond.

Above all he was a kind, considerate, friendly and hospitable man. He retired in 1988 to Devon, where he was a non-Executive Director of a Community Trust for three years. He took up gliding, sharing a glider with a local general practitioner, and went solo on his 65th birthday.

Author: George Parks

Roll number: 5888

William MacLennan (1921–2002)

Bill MacLennan, the son of an Edinburgh dentist became an internationally renowned oral surgeon. He was the first Professor of Oral Surgery in the University of Edinburgh and he was the Convenor of the Dental Council of the Royal College of Surgeons of Edinburgh uniquely for seven years.

William D. MacLennan was born in Edinburgh, the eldest of three brothers. After school at George Watson's College, Edinburgh, he studied dentistry and medicine obtaining the triple qualifications of the Scottish Royal Colleges. He was a superb athlete, running 220 yards in 21.6 seconds. At rugby he excelled as a wing three-quarter for Watsonians, scoring 74 tries in one season alone. He played for Scotland in three Services Internationals and gained two full caps. But for the war he would probably have had many more. He joined the Royal Navy and was posted to New York for Special Duties, and here he met his wife, Millie, a volunteer at the Red Cross. After marriage in Edinburgh, he served out the remainder of the war at Portsmouth.

Following demobilisation, he continued his training in oral surgery in Edinburgh and at Bangour General Hospital, West Lothian. He also had a period of experience overseas at Columbia University, New York. In due course he was appointed Consultant Oral Surgeon within the plastic surgery unit at Bangour. This was a most productive, fulfilling and happy time for him. He enjoyed the teamwork within an internationally

William MacLennan (1921–2002).

renowned pioneering unit with eminent surgeons – A. B. Wallace (q.v.), Campbell Buchan and Alistair Batchelor. He was proud of the important place oral and maxillofacial surgery had within the team, and from this emerged new techniques and better treatment for traumatised and physically handicapped patients.

His empathy with patients was very special. Physically handicapped himself facially, with a vestigial ear from birth, he knew how much many of his patients needed understanding, encouragement and perspective. He had been teased at school about his appearance and felt disadvantaged until he started to play rugby, and he then realised that he had gifts that others did not have.

As well as communicating well with patients, he was an outstandingly good clinical teacher and lecturer, remembered by generations of Edinburgh students and postgraduates from many countries. He was also sought after as an after-dinner speaker. He was very direct and forthright, quick witted, and with a mischievous desire to surprise his audience. He was a kind but firm mentor to many now senior clinicians from different countries who came to train with him. His interest and encouragement sustained them, and their subsequent achievements meant a great deal to him. He was a true guide, philosopher and friend to many.

From his base in Edinburgh, he became internationally renowned. He was President of the Royal Odonto-Chirurgical Society of Scotland. He was a member of the Inaugural Councils of the British and the International Association of Oral Surgeons and he became the President of the British Association of Oral Surgeons. He held honorary appointments at the Royal Infirmary and the Royal Hospital for Sick Children in Edinburgh. In 1978 he was appointed to the Foundation Chair in Oral Surgery at the University of Edinburgh and built up a fine department before retiring in 1983. His main research interests were in the field of facial fractures and the treatment of facial deformities.

His commitment to the work of the Royal College of Surgeons of Edinburgh started in his student days and his contributions continued throughout his life. During his distinguished career he served as an examiner, Councillor, Secretary and Convenor of the Dental Council. When he was Convenor he acquired the incomparable Menzies Campbell Collection for the College and latterly he acted as a museum guide. In turn he was honoured by the College in 2002 when he received the Gold Medal of the Faculty of Dental Surgery for his outstanding work.

In his spare time he enjoyed music and played the organ. He also played golf, but less successfully, having a love/hate relationship with the game. Like most golfers, he was inconsistent and his psyche never came to terms with this. He could relate to Alastair Cooke's description of golf as the Scottish torture! He was captain of Watsonians' Golf Club and of Luffness Golf Club and his love of the game and his humour come through in the beautiful *Centenary History of Luffness*, which he edited.

Author: Sir David Mason CBE

Dental roll number: 65

Guan Bee Ong (1921–2004)

Hong Kong is fortunate in enjoying a standard of surgical practice as high as anywhere in the world. It is no exaggeration to say that this is to a large extent the legacy of one man – Professor Tan Sri Guan Bee Ong.

'G.B.', as he was known to friends and surgeons throughout the world, was born in Kuching, Sarawak, and went to boarding school in Singapore, where his natural manual dexterity and his determination to achieve perfection first became manifest. Appointed as school barber but with no practical experience in the art, he trained himself to the high standards that were to become his hallmark by actually paying his fellow scholars for the privilege of cutting their hair, until his skills were second to none.

He entered Hong Kong University to study medicine, but the course was interrupted by the Japanese invasion of Hong Kong in 1941. The University of Hong Kong determined to continue its activities in mainland China. G. B. Ong, in a hazardous journey lasting some three months, made his way on foot to Chungking, where he resumed his studies, graduating MD from the Shanghai medical school. Returning after the war, he graduated MBBS from Hong Kong in 1947. For the next 10 years he set about developing his surgical skills in several centres around the world. He trained in Edinburgh and in London, being awarded the Fellowship of the Royal Colleges of Surgeons of Edinburgh and England. In 1956 he was awarded the Harkness Commonwealth Fellowship to study at the Massachusetts General Hospital and Harvard University in Boston, and the Bellevue Hospital in New York City.

On his return to Hong Kong he became Surgeon in Charge of Kowloon Hospital until 1963, when he was appointed to the Chair of Surgery in the University of Hong Kong – the first ethnic Chinese to hold this post.

By this time he had already developed a reputation as a master surgeon. His surgical repertoire encompassed the full gamut of surgical specialties, including neurosurgery and cardiac surgery. His natural technical brilliance allowed him to be a courageous and innovative surgeon. He was able to develop the trans-sphenoidal approach to the surgery of the pituitary gland, the trans-oral approach to the upper cervical spine, the transhiatal dissection of the oesophagus and the construction of oesophago-gastric anastomoses in the neck. He pioneered the posterior approach to the common bile duct and developed techniques of pouch colocystoplasties and gastrocystoplasties.

In addition to his brilliant operative skills he had a formidable intellect and was a natural leader who drove himself and all who worked for him to the utmost limits in his pursuit of excellence. He encouraged and promoted the establishment in Hong Kong of all the surgical specialties and these were developed to the highest standards mostly by young surgeons whom he had trained.

G. B. Ong's surgical virtuosity was honoured and acclaimed worldwide. He was awarded an OBE in 1966, became a member of the James IV Association of Surgeons the following year and became a Governor of the American College of Surgeons (1974–9). He was President of the International Society of Surgery from 1983 to 1985.

Guan Bee Ong (1921–2004).

G. B. Ong in academic robes.

In 1979 the honour of PSM (the equivalent of a knighthood) was conferred upon him by the King of Malaysia giving him the title Tan Sri and in the same year he was awarded the honorary degree of DSc by the University of Hong Kong.

One award which gave him particular pleasure was receiving the first John Bruce Gold Medal from the Royal College of Surgeons of Edinburgh in 1970, as his friendship with Sir John Bruce (q.v.) had started during his first visit to Edinburgh.

G.B. and Sir John Bruce, with the support and encouragement of Dr P. H. Teng, the Director of Medical Services in Hong Kong, were largely responsible for initiating there in 1965 the first overseas Fellowship examinations. A few years later G.B. endowed in the College the G. B. Ong Gold Medal for award annually to the candidate with the best overall performance in the FRCS Examination in Edinburgh and overseas.

He received the Gold Medal from the College of Surgeons of Malaysia, the Abraham Colles Medal from the Royal College of Surgeons in Ireland and the Medal of the Royal Australasian College of Surgeons. He was awarded honorary Fellowships by a host of Surgical Colleges throughout the world, and was Hunterian Professor at the Royal College of Surgeons of England.

He always maintained close links with the Edinburgh College, cordially entertaining the visiting examiners at his home, even during his final illness, which he fought with characteristic courage, even defiance. In 1998 he was appointed a Regent of the College and in 2001 he paid his last visit to the College for the award of the College Overseas Medal.

G. B. Ong was one of the great, perhaps the greatest, surgeons of his day in Asia. A combination of natural aptitude for surgery, courage, decisiveness and a formidable appetite for hard work were some of the ingredients which produced this master surgeon.

Roll number: 5929

The examiners in an early FRCSEd examination in Hong Kong. James Ross, then President of the College, is seated centre with G. B. Ong standing behind him. Sir John Bruce is seated extreme left of the photograph and Sir Donald Douglas extreme right.

Sir James Fraser Bt (1924–97)

A son who chooses or is persuaded to follow in the professional footsteps of a famous father incurs a risk of emotional turmoil and stress, induced by fear of failure to emulate paternal excellence. If Sir James Fraser was ever a prey to such fear, he overcame it triumphantly, and his career and achievements can, in their own right, stand comparison with those of his father.

James David Fraser was the son of one of Scotland's greatest surgeons, Sir John Fraser Bt KCVO, MC (q.v.). He was educated at Edinburgh Academy and at Magdalen College, Oxford, from which he graduated BA in 1945, having also in that year captained the Oxford University golf team.

He then entered the medical faculty of Edinburgh University and, following his father's untimely death in 1948, he succeeded to his baronetcy a few months before graduating MB ChB. After a year in house officer posts at Edinburgh Royal Infirmary, he was called up for National Service in the Royal Army Medical Corps and, as a junior medical officer, was posted to the Far East. He had, by then, decided upon a career in surgery and his secondment to the surgical division of the British Military Hospital, Singapore, was a stroke of good fortune which afforded him valuable training and experience.

On demobilisation in 1951, he returned to Edinburgh and was appointed Registrar in the professorial surgical unit at the Royal Infirmary under Sir James Learmonth (q.v.), his father's successor in the Regius Chair of Clinical Surgery. In 1952 he obtained the Fellowship of the College and three years later he became Senior Registrar in the urological unit at the Western General Hospital.

In 1958 he surprised his friends and colleagues by resigning from his senior registrar post and returning to the Far East as surgeon to a district hospital in Sarawak, where he had sole responsibility for providing a surgical service to a large and widely scattered community. His affection for the country and its people helped him to rise splendidly to the challenge of single-handed general surgery and professional isolation did not inhibit him from producing a thesis for which, in 1961, he was awarded the degree of Master of Surgery (ChM).

In 1963 he returned to Edinburgh as Senior Lecturer in the University Department of Clinical Surgery with honorary consultant status in the Royal Infirmary. His 'Chief' was Sir John Bruce (q.v.), who had succeeded to the Regius Chair in 1956 and who, in the early 1930s, had been his father's Clinical Tutor. As Senior Lecturer, James Fraser developed impressive administrative and teaching skills which led, in 1969, to his appointment to the Chair of Clinical Science (Surgery) in the newly established medical school of the University of Southampton.

Over the next 11 years he created an impressive academic Department of Surgery and played a key role in the introduction of a new undergraduate medical training programme which was influenced by several revolutionary educational concepts. As Honorary Consultant

Sir James Fraser Bt (1924–97).

Surgeon to the Southampton Hospital Group, he won the respect and friendship of his NHS colleagues and this cordial relationship contributed, in no small measure, to the high reputation acquired by the Southampton medical school.

In 1980 he returned again to the Edinburgh medical school as Postgraduate Dean and held this post with distinction for the next nine years. He had been appointed Secretary of the College in 1968 but his tenure of this office was cut short by his move to Southampton. His 450-mile separation from Edinburgh did not, however, preclude his election in 1975 to the College Council, of which he became a highly effective member. In 1980 he became Vice President and three years later he was elected to the College's highest office – a distinction never achieved by his father.

As President, James Fraser gave dynamic leadership to the College throughout an eventful term of office, which saw the completion of the Symposium Hall and of the Postgraduate Residence in Hill Square, as well as the initiation of the Historical Museum project funded by a generous grant from the Sir Jules Thorn Trust. It also saw the beginning, after lengthy and tortuous intercollegiate negotiations, of acceptance in principle of the College's proposals for reform of the Fellowship examinations. This owed much to James Fraser's steadfastness of purpose and diplomacy, and it was the start of the evolutionary process which led eventually to the introduction at the turn of the 21st century of the modern membership and Fellowship examinations.

This sculpture, which stands in the centre of the College's Jules Thorn Museum, is a replica in fibreglass of the original plaster cast of a dissected body. That original plaster cast was made by John Goodsir (see page 107) in 1845.

For his role as a medical statesman and his services to surgical education he received many honours, including the honorary Fellowships of four sister Colleges, but the two that gave him particular pride were his appointment as a Regent of the College in 1990 and his designation just before leaving Southampton as Emeritus Consultant Surgeon to the Royal Navy.

James Fraser's courtesy, modesty and integrity combined with his warm personality to inspire the respect and affection of colleagues, students, patients and of the College's Fellows worldwide.

His portrait in the College is a good likeness but the expression depicted by the artist is thought by some to be too severe. To others it suggests determination, and this is a quality of which James Fraser had a super abundance. Above all, he was determined to be a worthy son of his illustrious father and to be true to those high traditions of Edinburgh surgery which were his heritage.

Roll number: 5940

David Watt (1918–2000)

David Watt (1918–2000).

A pioneer of prosthetic dentistry in Edinburgh, David Watt went on to international acclaim in that specialty.

David Mackie Watt was born in Aberdeen and educated at Daniel Stewart's College, Edinburgh, and Edinburgh University. He became a Licentiate in Dental Surgery of the College (LDS RCSEd) in 1940.

After graduation, he served in the Royal Navy from 1941 to 1946. His naval service took him to the Sicily landings, Australia and the USA.

On his demobilisation, he spent some two years in general dental practice and, in 1948, he was appointed an assistant lecturer in the prosthodontic department at Edinburgh Dental School; in the same year, he was awarded the Higher Diploma in Dentistry from the College (HDD RCSEd). In 1953, he gained FDS RCS Ed by examination and, in 1960, he was awarded a PhD by the University of Edinburgh for studies into morphological changes in the maxilla following tooth loss.

David Watt was a founder member of the British Society for the Study of Prosthetic Dentistry (BSSPD) and the European Prosthodontic Association (EPA). In 1960–1, he was the eighth President of the BSSPD and in 1981 he was awarded the Gold Medal Award of that Society for his contribution to prosthodontics. A year previously, he had been awarded the Prosthodontic Research Prize by the International Association for Dental Research.

He spent a year from 1966 to 1967 as visiting Professor at the University of New York at Buffalo. In 1969, he became Professor in Restorative Dentistry, at the University of Edinburgh.

David Watt's research interests lay in occlusion, particularly gnathosonics, in addition to establishing an evidence-based rationale for the design of complete dentures. Professor Watt served the College loyally in several capacities. He was first elected on to Dental Council in 1964 and was re-elected until 1974. He was subsequently elected again from 1977 to 1982. Professor Watt was one of the initiators of the Diploma in Restorative Dentistry (DRD RCSEd) and he was awarded this diploma in 1978. He was a formidable examiner, but most candidates left appreciating that he had tested them fairly.

Away from dentistry, David Watt was a devoted family man, an active churchgoer, a keen fisherman and an accomplished amateur wood-carver.

The cheerful stoicism with which he bore the physical tribulations of his last illness made a profound impression upon all who knew him.

Author: Fraser McCord

Dental roll number: 70

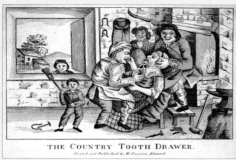

THE COUNTRY TOOTH DRAWER.
Printed and Published by W. Davison Alnwick

John Menzies Campbell (1887–1984)

Collecting, it is said, combines gnawing obsessions, stealthy pursuits, crushing disappointments and intoxicating triumphs. John Menzies Campbell would have experienced all of these as he amassed over a working lifetime a collection of dental memorabilia and ephemera, including books, paintings, instruments and advertisements, which was unique. 'Every collector, sooner or later,' he wrote, 'is confronted with deciding the destiny of his collection.' Fortunately for the British Surgical Colleges, he bequeathed the books and dental advertisements to the Royal College of Surgeons of England and the paintings and dental instruments to the Royal College of Surgeons of Edinburgh, where it forms the core of the Menzies Campbell Dental Museum, on display to this day both for the profession and the public.

John Menzies Campbell was born in Paisley and educated at George Watson's College in Edinburgh. On leaving school, he was apprenticed, as an articled pupil, to a dentist, Dr John Angus, whom he later described as 'a talented and enlightened craftsman imbued with considerable artistry and inventive ability'. After three years he was awarded the Licentiate in Dental Surgery (LDS) and, before setting up in practice, went to Toronto, where after a year's study he was awarded the degree of Doctor of Dental Surgery with honours. It was here that his interest in dental history was born, inspired by the teaching of Dr G. M. Hermiston, the lecturer on dental history. Returning to Glasgow, he established a dental practice in 1912 and continued in practice until his retiral in 1953.

His qualities as a historian and a writer were recognised early on and he was appointed in 1917 a Fellow of the Royal Society of Edinburgh, an unusual distinction for a 30-year-old.

He was a life-long advocate of preventive dentistry and gave the first talk on BBC radio on the topic of oral hygiene in 1923. His publications on dental history won him national acclaim and he came to be regarded as the foremost British dental historian of his generation. His book *Dental Biography, British and American, from 1682 to 1880,* published in 1949, is regarded as a seminal work. *Dentistry, Then and Now* (1963), which ran to three editions, was a series of vignettes of aspects of dental history.

It was as a dental historian and a writer that he established an international reputation but as a collector he was unique. From his earliest years in practice, he set out to acquire and collect anything related to the history of dentistry. This would include books, paintings and etchings, some of which dated from the 17th century, and dental instruments. Blessed with the energy and commitment necessary for successful collecting and with a penchant for writing letters, he soon established a wide circle of contacts around the world. Regular advertisements in *Exchange and Mart* soon established him among antique-dealers and book-sellers as a reputable collector and, in this way, he amassed and preserved items for his collection which might otherwise have been destroyed.

By the time of his death, he had contributed around 250 articles and letters to the dental literature, but he, himself, reckoned that his best book was the catalogue of the Menzies Campbell Collection, housed in the Royal College of Surgeons of Edinburgh. This describes, in detail, the history behind each of the items in the collection. In addition to all kinds of dental instruments, the collection includes artificial dentures, some of which have been fashioned from animal ivory and some from human teeth obtained from battlefield casualties. The pictures in the collection include paintings, cartoons and engravings, some dating from the 17th century and many providing insights into the history of dentistry not obtainable from other sources.

His eminence as a dental historian was recognised by the American Academy and the French Society of the History of Dentistry. In 1952 he was awarded an honorary Doctorate of Laws from the University of Toronto, but was prevented by ill health from receiving this honour in person. His passion for dental history was shared by his wife, Margaret, who had qualified in medicine and was the first woman to receive the honorary Fellowship in Dental Surgery of the Royal College of Surgeons of Edinburgh.

He died aged 87. His was a unique contribution to the history of dentistry, which he has shared through the legacy of his collection, and this continues to be enjoyed and appreciated in the Museum which bears his name in the Edinburgh College.

Authors: Paul Geissler and Iain Macintyre

Dental roll number: 81

John Menzies Campbell (1887–1984).

Thomas J. McNair (1927–94)

It is at least arguable that the ultimate accolade which a surgeon can receive is to be entrusted with the surgical care of a colleague or of a member of a colleague's family. This happened many times to Tom McNair, who throughout his distinguished professional career was inspired by the teaching and practice of his 'Chief' Mr T. McW. Millar (q.v.).

Thomas Jaffrey McNair was born in Edinburgh and educated at George Watson's College, and at Edinburgh University, from which he graduated MB ChB in 1949.

After six months as House Surgeon to Sir James Learmonth (q.v.), he spent some time in West Africa as a doctor to a mining company, where he acquired his first experience of sole responsibility for the care of surgical emergencies. This was followed by National Service as a medical officer in the Royal Air Force. On his return to civilian life, he underwent a period of training in anaesthesia before deciding to make surgery his career. At this stage he returned to Edinburgh Royal Infirmary as a surgical registrar and in 1955 and 1956 he obtained the Fellowships of the College and of the Royal College of Surgeons of England. It was during his time as a registrar that he was most profoundly influenced by Mr Millar, from whom he derived his long-standing interest in colorectal surgery.

In 1958 he became Senior Registrar to the Regius Professor of Clinical Surgery, Sir John Bruce (q.v.), and it was at this stage that he was invited by the celebrated surgical author and teacher, Hamilton Bailey, to be one of his proof-readers. Theirs was a happy relationship and after Hamilton Bailey's death in 1961, his widow invited Tom McNair to become editor of the world-famous textbook *Emergency Surgery*, her late husband's single-handed masterpiece, which had run to six editions. Having accepted this invitation, Tom McNair was determined that although the new *Emergency Surgery* would necessarily be written by a small team of expert contributors, the clear trenchant style of its original author would be maintained in every chapter. His aim was handsomely achieved and the success of the seventh and eighth editions of this surgical classic was a notable testimony to his editorial skills.

Thomas J. McNair (1927–94).

In 1960, having obtained the MD degree, Tom McNair went to Chicago, where he spent a year in the surgery department of the University of Illinois under the tutelage of one of the College's most distinguished honorary Fellows, Dr Warren H. Cole.

Shortly before his return to Edinburgh, he was appointed Consultant Surgeon to the newly established general surgical unit at the Eastern General Hospital, where his senior colleague was James A. Ross (q.v.). Together, they formed an admirable team which gave the best possible start to the new unit and, from the outset of his consultant career, Tom McNair imposed the highest standards upon himself and on his juniors. During the next 20 years, he moved to Chalmers Hospital and then back to the Royal Infirmary, where he became Consultant in administrative charge of one of the general surgical units. By this time he had largely committed himself to colorectal surgery, in which he acquired an impressive reputation, but not to the exclusion of other activities. His all-round professional distinction was appropriately recognised in 1977 when he was appointed Surgeon to HM the Queen in Scotland.

He became a Fellowship examiner in 1963 and over the next two decades gave diligent and devoted service to the College as a member of Council (to which he was elected three times) and as Vice President from 1980 to 1983. His energy, enthusiasm, clarity of thought and soundness of judgement made him an obvious presidential candidate and his election to the highest office in 1985 was universally regarded as a just reward for his contributions to the College.

The success of Tom McNair's presidency stemmed largely from his hugely effective chairmanship of the Council, the deliberations of which he controlled with a perfect blend of firmness and kindly good humour. In medico-political negotiations he could be as conciliatory, or as gently persuasive, or as sternly obdurate, as the situation might demand and although the latter attitude was foreign to his nature, he would brook no compromise on matters of principle. He always strove for consensus but certainly not at any price. Indeed, he was a fierce and implacable opponent of anything that he perceived as a threat to the prestige and influence of the College.

As a member of Council in the 1970s he had been a strong advocate of reform of the Fellowship examinations and it was fitting that the ideas originally promulgated by the College in 1977 should have eventually gained complete intercollegiate acceptance during his presidency. For his contributions to examination reform and to the enhancement of co-operation and mutual understanding between the surgical Royal Colleges, the Silver Medal of the Royal College of Surgeons of England was bestowed upon him. He was further honoured by the award of four honorary Fellowships. National recognition came with his appointment in 1988 as a Commander of the Order of the British Empire (CBE).

Tom McNair richly deserved a long and happy retirement and it would have given him immense joy to participate in the College's Quincentennial celebrations but his life was cruelly cut short in 1994. His untimely death deprived the College of an illustrious Fellow who had rendered it great service and who, as an elder statesman and wise counsellor, could and assuredly would have made many other valuable contributions to its affairs.

Roll number: 6195

Sir Michael Woodruff (1911–2001)

There were few greater tests of character in the 20th century than those imposed on the thousands of men who found themselves captives in Japanese prisoner-of-war camps during the Second World War. Even to survive such hardship showed a triumph of will, yet some individuals in that most hostile environment were able to learn new skills which would benefit their fellow prisoners, and ultimately their fellow men and women. Michael Woodruff joined the Australian forces fighting in Malaya and was taken prisoner on the fall of Singapore. His introduction to the phenomenon of graft rejection dated from this time, and subsequent research in this field led to the first successful renal transplant in Britain, which he performed while Professor of Systematic Surgery at Edinburgh.

Michael Francis Addison Woodruff was born in London, the son of a veterinary surgeon. Within two years, his father had accepted the Chair of Veterinary Pathology at the University of Melbourne. At the outbreak of the First World War, his father volunteered for the army. Since many of their relatives still lived in England, it was judged best that, in 1915, Woodruff, his mother, brother and sister should return to England. Soon after their arrival, Michael developed staphylococcal otitis media. His mother contracted the infection and died from septicaemia. With their father, the whole family returned to Australia in 1917.

Entering the Queen's College of the University of Melbourne, Michael Woodruff displayed musical talent and became organist to the College. The influence of well-loved and respected teachers led him first to mathematics, then to engineering. He achieved first-class honours in both subjects. However, a career in medicine offered better hopes of employment and Woodruff therefore became a medical student, graduating with honours in 1938.

At the outbreak of the Second World War, Woodruff was allowed to complete his Mastership in Surgery before sailing with the Australian forces for Malaysia. When Singapore surrendered, Woodruff, with 12,000 of his Australian compatriots and 38,000 British troops, was imprisoned. Soon, he was moved to Changi Camp, where the survival of disease-ridden, starving patients was threatened by vitamin and other deficiencies. A man of great practical skill, Woodruff devised a grinding machine that allowed the simple Malaysian grasses to be turned into an evil-tasting but life-saving powder. This work, in collaboration with James Burgess, was recognised as soon as the war ended and culminated in the publication of an influential governmental report.

While a prisoner, during a time when he learned surgery from his fellow prisoner Julian Taylor and benefited from the anaesthetic skills of David Middleton, Woodruff chanced upon that part of Rodney Maingot's surgical text that dealt with skin grafting. He determined to investigate the strange phenomenon of graft rejection. The opportunity for such work arose after the war when he returned to England as Tutor in Surgery at the University of Sheffield, where he began to investigate the response of mouse corneas to the implantation of foreign cells. He quickly found that his ideas had been anticipated by the Glasgow surgeon Tom Gibson (q.v.) and by the brilliant biologist and future Nobel Prize-winner Peter Medawar. Woodruff and Medawar became collaborators, then friends. An appointment as Senior Lecturer in

Sir Michael Woodruff (1911–2001).

Michael Woodruff with his father.

Surgeons' Lives: An Anthology of Biographies of College Fellows over 500 Years

Surgery at the University of Aberdeen, under the wise guidance of Professor W. C. Wilson (q.v.), provided the opportunity for foreign travel to centres such as the Mayo Clinic, New York and Boston, where experiments on transplantation were in active progress. He made many friends and established contacts that proved invaluable in his later work.

Returning to Britain, Woodruff applied successfully for the Chair of Surgery of the University of Otago, New Zealand. He soon discovered the limitations of working in the relatively small city of Dunedin, and proposed radical plans for the reform of clinical teaching in New Zealand. One benefit of this period was the opportunity of inviting guests to his department. None made a greater impact than Medawar.

In 1957 Woodruff was appointed to the newly designated Chair of Systematic Surgery in Edinburgh and became a Fellow of the College that year. He soon established a team of investigators which achieved renown in the new fields of graft rejection, cancer immunity and immunosuppression.

Royal Infirmary Edinburgh, Wards 13 and 14. Professor Woodruff's clinic, summer term 1957.

The concept of transplanting tissues and organs to take the place of those damaged by disease was crucially important. It was, therefore, no surprise that Woodruff should risk the entire future of his surgical career by deciding to attempt the first British renal transplant. At that time the best chance of success was a transplant between identical twins. In 1960 Lewis Abbot from Leith was successfully transplanted with the kidney of his identical twin brother, Martin. Both the patient and his twin brother survived for six years, the first successful renal transplant in Britain.

As a consequence of this achievement, Woodruff found national and international recognition. He became one of the best-known figures of the Edinburgh University medical school. He was elected a Fellow of the Royal Society of London in 1967, and was knighted in 1969. Honorary membership of the British Society for Immunology (1982) and honorary Fellowship of the Royal College of Physicians of Edinburgh (1982) followed and he was showered with national and international awards and medals.

Woodruff continued his research long into retirement, working at the Western General Hospital, Edinburgh, in his chosen field of cancer immunology. He wrote widely and for much of his life. His text *Transplantation Immunity* was published in 1970, his autobiography in 1994.

Michael Woodruff at the helm of his yacht.

Yet behind the façade of confident, worldly success, lay the inner resources of a scholarly, deeply religious Wesleyian Methodist with great insight into human life and its miracles and tragedies, and unexpected warmth as friend and colleague. There were moments of anger and frustration, provoked by a denial of access to beds in the Edinburgh Royal Infirmary, delay in occupancy of the Wilkie Surgical Research Laboratory, the incompetence of examination candidates, or the failure of a surgical procedure. But these were episodes tolerated in a character who, larger than life, had survived imprisonment and risen to the highest pinnacles of surgical achievement. Woodruff found great pleasure in sailing, in music and in foreign languages. Above all, he cherished the warmth of a close family life and worldwide respect as a benefactor of the human race.

Author: Dugald Gardner

Roll number: 6452

J. I. P. James (1913–2001)

J. I. P. James made his major contributions to orthopaedic surgery while holding the Chair of Orthopaedic Surgery at Edinburgh University from 1958 to 1979. During this period, Edinburgh became recognised as a world-class orthopaedic centre. He will be chiefly remembered for his seminal contributions to the introduction of organised specialty training, and for implementing ideas which have since been adopted by many other specialties.

J. I. P. James (1913–2001).

One of a large family, brought up in rather straitened circumstances, 'Jip', as John Ivor Pulsford James was universally known, obtained a scholarship which enabled him to study medicine at University College Hospital in London, qualifying in 1938. After some surgical training, he joined the Royal Army Medical Corps and, being of an adventurous spirit, volunteered for the Special Operations Executive, the SOE. He was parachuted into Yugoslavia to give medical assistance to Tito's guerrillas. His graphic account of his wartime experiences records operating with minimal equipment by the light of candles or burning sticks in caves or mountain huts and trying to cope with an epidemic of typhus without any effective medicines. He concluded, 'Were my services of value? I suspect that, apart from some limb wounds where I was able to … prevent infection, I did no good. However, the effect on morale was everything. To guerrilla soldiers who had had no medical care, a surgeon from the West had a magical effect.' His services were certainly appreciated by a grateful Yugoslav nation, for he was later awarded the Golden Star of Service by the Yugoslav Republic.

After the war, he trained in orthopaedics and in 1948 he was appointed as a consultant orthopaedic surgeon to the Royal National Orthopaedic Hospital in London. There he became Assistant Director to Herbert (later Sir Herbert) Seddon and the two men made a formidable partnership which contributed greatly to establishing the national and international reputation of that hospital.

In 1958 he was appointed to the Chair of Orthopaedic Surgery in Edinburgh and became a Fellow of the College. At that time there was an excellent orthopaedic service for the long-term care of children at the Princess Margaret Rose Hospital, but adult orthopaedic surgery was still regarded as an offshoot of general surgery. Jip's predecessor, the eminent Sir Walter Mercer (q.v.), had been a general surgeon, albeit with a major interest in orthopaedics, and much of the care of orthopaedic patients, including trauma, was still in the hands of the general surgeons.

Jip's appointment included a brief to organise the orthopaedic services in the south-east region of Scotland and within a short time his advice was accepted and a regional service established. The general surgeons gladly relinquished their residual orthopaedic interests, and under Jip's dynamic leadership orthopaedics in Edinburgh flourished. An academic department was built, specialist units were established and research was encouraged. His own special interests were in spinal deformity and the surgery of the hand, in which fields he published extensively and made many original contributions. The pre-eminence of Edinburgh as an orthopaedic centre attracted trainees from all over the world. Several of his trainees became professors in Britain and in Commonwealth countries, and at least 10 became presidents of their countries' orthopaedic associations. Jip followed the careers of his old trainees with great interest.

During Jip's early career, specialist training left much to be desired, being based largely on a haphazard drawn-out apprenticeship system without a definable endpoint. His own training, disrupted as it had been by the war, made him acutely aware of the inadequacies of the existing arrangements. Sir Frank Holdsworth had been instrumental in persuading the Surgical Colleges of the need for change, and following his death, Jip, as Chairman of the Specialist Advisory Committee in Orthopaedics and of the Orthopaedic Education Sub-Committee, was instrumental in establishing an ordered training programme and the Specialty Exit Examination, the FRCSEd Orth. Jip's contributions to orthopaedic training remain as a lasting memorial, for which subsequent generations of trainees must be grateful.

Collage of orthopaedic surgeons at Princess Margaret Rose Hospital in 1975.
Back row (left to right) George Fulford, William J. Gillespie, James Christie and Harley Gray.
Front row (left to right) George Mitchell, Peter Abernethy, J. H. S. Scott, J. I. P. James, Willie Soutar, John Chalmers, Bill McQuillan and Douglas Lamb.

There were two sides to Jip's character. At work he set and demanded high standards. When he had decided on a course of action he pursued his objective relentlessly. His determination and single-mindedness made him an effective organiser and influential in committee. This quality was recognised in his appointment to many national and international committees and councils. As a teacher he could be inspiring and did his utmost to promote the careers of those who applied themselves, but he could be unforgiving to those whom he considered uninterested. Away from work, he was relaxed and sociable, a great host and a loyal friend.

When he retired from Edinburgh in 1979, Jip was still full of energy and worked for several years in the Middle East, as Director of Orthopaedic Services in Kuwait and in Saudi Arabia. He had many interests outside medicine. His love of adventure led him in his student days before the war to motorcycle the length of Africa and in his eighties to go white water rafting in northern India. During his time in London, he narrowly escaped drowning when his yacht foundered in the Channel in a gale in 1957. Wherever he lived, he created a beautiful garden and in his eventual retirement he kept himself occupied tending his garden, in the village of Slad in the Cotswolds and caring for his bees.

Jip received many honours but none gave him greater pleasure than the award of honorary Fellowship of the British Orthopaedic Association, an association to which he had given sterling service as Secretary and President.

Author: John Chalmers

Roll number: 6648

Geoffrey Chisholm (1931–94)

A New Zealander of Scottish descent, Geoff Chisholm trained in urology and renal transplantation in London, where he established himself as a leading academic in his specialty. He went on to become Professor of Surgery in Edinburgh, Director of the Nuffield Transplant Unit and President of the College in 1988. His intellect, his energy and his charm marked him out as an effective and popular academic and collegiate leader.

Geoff Chisholm's ancestors had left Perthshire for New Zealand in the early 19th century. Born in Hawera, Taranaki, New Zealand, he was educated at the Scots College in Wellington, Malvern College in Worcestershire and qualified in medicine from St Andrews University. He trained in urology at the Hammersmith Hospital in London, where his prestigious research output began. He was a pioneer of vascular access for haemodialysis, which he always regarded as an integral part of urological practice. In 1961 he was awarded a Travelling Fellowship, which he spent at Johns Hopkins Hospital in Baltimore researching the effects of obstructive uropathy. Returning to the Hammersmith Hospital, he developed expertise in the new sub-specialty of renal transplantation, working with W. J. Dempster and Ralph Shackman. He became Director of Transplantation and in 1977 was the obvious choice to succeed Professor Michael Woodruff (q.v.) in the Chair of Surgery in Edinburgh, moving from the unit where the second renal transplant in Britain had been performed, to the unit which had performed the first. The clinical department, including the Nuffield Surgical Transplant Unit of which he was made Director, was at the Western General Hospital, while the research facilities were at the Wilkie Memorial Research Laboratory in the medical school. Here, he continued to publish widely on every facet of urological practice. *The Scientific Foundations of Urology* (1976), which he jointly edited, was destined to become the standard textbook of its day in the specialty and for 16 years he edited the *British Journal of Urology*.

He became President of the College in 1988. In the years following his presidency he became Chairman of the Joint Committee on Higher Surgical Training and of the Lister Postgraduate Institute, fitting appointments for one who had inspired a generation of urological trainees from Britain and around the world. The British Association of Urological Surgeons, of which he had been President (1986–8) awarded him the St Peter's Medal. The Danish Surgical Society honoured him with its Silver Medal and he received honorary Fellowships from Surgical Colleges in America and South Africa and was awarded the CBE in 1992.

A combination of intellectual rigour, boundless energy and persuasive charm were the attributes on which his achievements were founded.

Roll number: 7006

Geoffrey Chisholm (1931–94).

Robert Tinning (1925–2001).

Robert Tinning (1925–2001)

Bob Tinning, an Australian, did his orthopaedic training in Scotland and retained many links and fond memories dating from that period.

Robert Noel Tinning, on leaving school, saw active service in the Royal Australian Navy during the Second World War and was on HMAS *Shropshire* in Tokyo Bay when General Douglas MacArthur received the Japanese surrender on the USS *Missouri*. As a student, he was a keen oarsman and rowed bow in the Australian eight that won a gold medal in the Auckland Empire Games in 1950 and a bronze medal in the Helsinki Olympics of 1952.

After studying medicine at Sydney University, he graduated in 1953 and then spent eight years in Edinburgh from 1956 to 1964 acquiring his FRCSEd and working in the orthopaedic department, where he progressed from Registrar to Consultant. During his time in Edinburgh, he was much influenced by the teaching of Jip James (q.v.) and Douglas Savill, from whom he acquired his interest in the surgery of rheumatoid arthritis. While in Edinburgh he helped to train the Scottish rowing IV that competed in the 1958 Commonwealth Games.

On his return to his homeland, he was appointed to the Royal North Shore and Mater Hospitals in Sydney, where he specialised in rheumatoid surgery, establishing combined clinics with the rheumatoid physicians after the pattern which had been developed in Edinburgh. He was one of the early pioneers of joint replacement in Australia. One of his patients observed that, 'He operated … with great skill and equally importantly proved to possess rare virtues of compassion, modesty and … absence of interest in monetary aspects.' Despite a heavy clinical practice, he was much involved in teaching not only of orthopaedic trainees but of physio- and occupational therapists. He paid a prominent part in the establishment of the Cumberland College of Health Sciences in Sydney and was its Chairman for many years. He served the Australian Orthopaedic Association as committee member and treasurer. For his services to Australian medicine, he was awarded the Order of Australia in 1980.

Both he and his family retained a love of Scotland and returned frequently to visit their many friends in the orthopaedic fraternity and in the Border farming community where they felt particularly at home.

Yachting was his major recreation. He enjoyed nothing more than sailing his yacht *Basilisk* in Sydney Harbour and beyond, and he helmed the boat which won the regatta at the British Orthopaedic Association meeting in Torquay in 1993.

He was fiercely competitive, even in his later years when he suffered from severe asthma and peripheral vascular disease which resulted in bilateral below-knee amputations. His courage in coping with his disabilities was an inspiration to all who knew him and to many other disabled individuals whom he helped to overcome their problems. He bravely ran 400 metres on his artificial limbs carrying the Olympic torch to the Sydney Olympics in 2000. He died at the helm of his yacht while participating in a race in Sydney Harbour.

Author: John Chalmers

Roll number: 7051

W. M. Oliver (1925–2003)

A dental graduate of the University of St Andrews who became Professor and Director of Dental Education at the University of Liverpool, 'Montie' Oliver, as he was universally known, will be remembered for his contribution to periodontol research and to dental education internationally.

William Montgomerie Oliver was educated at Dundee High School and served in the Fleet Air Arm during the Second World War. In 1946, on his demobilisation, he became a dental student at the University of St Andrews, proving an outstandingly able member of a year full of ex-servicemen, many with distinguished war records.

After graduation, his first post was as a Senior House Officer to Professor Aylwin Hitchin (q.v.) in the Department of Oral Surgery in Dundee. Scotland exports many of its best graduates, and in 1957, after a happy period in general dental practice in Dundee, he was appointed Lecturer in Periodontology at the University of Liverpool, going on to become Senior Lecturer and, in 1978, Professor of Dental Health. In 1980 he became Head of the Department of Operative Dental Surgery, and Director of Dental Education at the University of Liverpool. He ultimately became Emeritus Professor in 1987, at the University of Liverpool.

W. M. Oliver (1925–2003).

Having served as a member of the Dental Council of the Royal College of Surgeons of Edinburgh, member of the Dental Examinations Committee and Convenor of the Dental Examinations Committee, he was elected Dean of the Faculty of Dental Surgery in 1987. During this period, he was actively involved in collaboration with overseas countries, which produced the first Memorandum of Understanding for dental examinations held jointly by the Singapore Academy of Medicine and the Edinburgh College. He was also energetic in the deliberations on Europe on behalf of the dental faculty of the College, and served on the European Economic Community Advisory Committee on the Training of Dental Practitioners.

In Liverpool his main research focused on the pathogenesis of periodontal disease, and his team contributed much to the understanding of the causes and early diagnostic markers of those diseases, work which gained international recognition. He was also widely admired and respected for his sterling personal qualities, and his teaching and administrative skills. He cared about people and they responded and respected him for it.

His statesman-like qualities resulted in his membership of national and international bodies. He was a valued member of the General Dental Council representing the United Kingdom on European Committees concerned with the training of dentists and specialists.

He continued his wartime association with the Royal Navy, serving as a dental officer in the Royal Naval Volunteer Reserve and Royal Naval Reserve from 1951 to 1970 – service which gained him a Volunteer Reserve Decoration.

Montie will be remembered with gratitude and affection for his contribution to dental surgery and his example will live on in the hearts and minds, lives and works, of those who were privileged to have known him.

Author: Sir David Mason CBE

Dental roll number: 214

Dorothy Geddes (1936–98)

Dorothy Geddes (1936–98).

In a remarkable career Dorothy Geddes achieved a 'triple first' in becoming the first woman to 'take her seat' as a Fellow in Dental Surgery of the Royal College of Surgeons of Edinburgh, the first woman to be appointed to a professorial chair in dentistry in the United Kingdom and the first woman to become the Dean of a Faculty of Dental Surgery of a Royal Surgical College in the United Kingdom. For these and many other achievements, she was appointed an Officer of the Order of the British Empire.

Dorothy Ann Malcolm Geddes was born in Alloa and educated at Brechin High School, where her father, James Geddes, was Rector. At an early age she decided on a career in dentistry because of its combination of scientific and artistic skills. She graduated from Edinburgh University in 1959, having demonstrated at an early stage her capacity for hard work and tenacity in overcoming the practical problems of being both left handed and dyslexic.

After graduation, under the guidance of the innovative Professor A. C. W. Hutchinson and the inspirational Dr (later Professor) W. D. MacLennan (q.v.), she specialised in oral surgery and in 1963 was elected Fellow in Dental Surgery. This was followed by a move to Birmingham, where she worked as a senior registrar in oral surgery, but pragmatic as always, she realised the dearth of consultant posts in that speciality and in 1964 undertook a career change. She went to the Eastman Dental Centre in Rochester, New York, and began what was to become her life-long research into dental caries. After five years' research in New York, she returned to Britain and funded by the Medical Research Council, she worked with Professor Neil Jenkins' Oral Research Group at Newcastle University. Her final career move was to Glasgow in 1975, where she was appointed Lecturer at the University of Glasgow Dental Hospital and one year later promoted to Senior Lecturer and Honorary Consultant in Periodontology and Preventive Dentistry.

It was after her move to Glasgow that Dorothy began to have a national influence on the development of dentistry. Her appointment in 1981 for five years as the Chairman of the Central Committee of the British Dental Association for University Teachers and Research Workers gave her the opportunity to highlight the particular problems of this group and their essential contribution to both undergraduate and postgraduate education and research. She brought together laboratory workers and clinicians to advance research in dental disease and salivary function, and, despite all the demands made upon her, continued to be research active all her life. Her last paper, received in January 1998, two months before her death, was published posthumously in 1999.

Her research contributions were marked by quality as well as quantity, in recognition of which she was awarded the highly prestigious European Organisation for Caries Research – Rolex Prize shortly before her death. But Dorothy was far from being an anaemic academic. She had a quick wit and a mischievous sense of humour and it was therefore perhaps not surprising that she became a prime mover in introducing behavioural sciences to the undergraduate curriculum both in Glasgow and nationally.

She was a wise and warm-hearted counsellor, readily approachable by colleagues and students alike, who knew that confidentiality would be respected and no opinion offered without much careful thought. Her appointment to a chair in 1990, while no surprise and universally acclaimed, did not separate her from the profession at large and she continued to be a valuable member of the Royal Odonto-Chirurgical Society of Scotland and the West of Scotland Branch of the British Dental Association, of both of which organisations she had been President.

While enthusiastically committed and loyal to the Glasgow Dental Hospital and its parent University, there was no disguising her pride and delight when in 1992 she was elected Dean of the Faculty of Dental Surgery of the Royal College of Surgeons of Edinburgh. In this capacity she was instrumental in driving forward many initiatives predominantly concerned with specialty qualifications. She did much to improve relations with sister dental faculties and strengthen ties with overseas dental centres.

Dorothy Geddes was indomitable. As well as overcoming her dyslexia, she overcame the early deaths of both her parents and her much-loved younger brother. She knew how hard it was for career women in dentistry when she graduated, but she never flinched and, while not a feminist, derived pleasure in being elected honorary President of Women in Dentistry. She loved her country cottage, gardening, painting and opera but especially cats, one of which appears in the background to her portrait.

Author: G. H. Moody

Dental roll number: 240

William Houston (1938–91)

Orthodontics is recognised as dentistry's oldest specialty originating at the start of the 20th century. Formal training in orthodontics evolved from the middle years of the century replacing the *ad hoc* system of apprenticeship. The establishment of formal postgraduate training programmes allowed the specialty to develop and evolve, and Bill Houston was in the vanguard of that evolution.

William Houston was born and educated in Edinburgh. After undergraduate training at Edinburgh Dental School, he went on to become a lecturer in orthodontics and obtained his Fellowship in Dental Surgery from the Edinburgh College. In London he studied orthodontics at the Royal Dental Hospital under Professor Philip Walther, who at once recognised his potential. After Walther's sudden death, he became Senior Lecturer in Orthodontics and in 1974 he was appointed Professor and Head of the Department of Orthodontics. During this time he emerged as an outstanding research worker and co-ordinator of the orthodontic postgraduate programme. Here, too, his clarity of thought and his vision marked him out as a future leader of the profession.

From his earliest days in London, postgraduate education in orthodontics began to occupy his attention, and to this he devoted much of his time and effort. It was his foresight that encouraged the development of the three-year postgraduate course in orthodontics and brought intercollegiate postgraduate training in orthodontics in London University to its present highly rated position as a clinical discipline firmly based on sound academic foundations.

William Houston (1938–91).

Bill was quiet, modest and unassuming, always ready to help and encourage anyone who came to him. His contribution to the advancement of orthodontics in the United Kingdom was enormous, as Chairman of the Specialist Advisory Committee in Orthodontics and later as Chairman of the MSc in orthodontics of London University. With characteristic vision, he realised early on that the formation of the European Community would have considerable implications for orthodontics. He was able to convince British orthodontics of the need to work for a unified training programme for postgraduate orthodontic students throughout Europe. It was appropriate that he should become Honorary Secretary of the European Orthodontic Society, a post which he held for 10 years. During this time he was also the editor of the *British Journal of Orthodontics*, where his knowledge of the orthodontic literature was almost proverbial. One had only to ask about a particular reference and he would provide not only the date and journal but would go on to suggest a number of others – often much more appropriate. When the editorship of the *European Journal of Orthodontics* became vacant, he relinquished the post of Honorary Secretary and took over as the editor. Under his leadership this became the foremost scientific orthodontic journal in the world.

He became a member of the Dental Council of the Edinburgh College, and it was here that he could be guaranteed to express his views with enviable eloquence, profound wisdom and neat precision. Whenever a discussion became difficult or confused he could be depended upon to summarise the issue with great clarity, leaving very little need for further discussion. His capacity for work was enormous – if you wanted to talk to him without interruption the best time to catch him was at his desk at 6 a.m.!

As a teacher he had the ability to make difficult topics easy, a virtue not always found in one of such great intellect. He was in demand as a lecturer throughout the world and became well known for his research into the prediction of growth and craniofacial development, particularly in studies in Ecuador and Sri Lanka on patients with craniofacial anomalies. Yet perhaps it is as a teacher that he will be most remembered, especially by those for whom he made time early in the morning, when he seemed to make the most difficult subjects simple and clear.

Like many Scots, he never forgot his allegiance to the land of his birth, and particularly to the Royal College of Surgeons of Edinburgh. His wisdom and advice were always greatly valued by the College and he was instrumental in developing its examinations, particularly the Membership in Orthodontics, which has become the recognised exit examination for specialist orthodontists in the United Kingdom.

The various compartments of his life were not allowed to mix and few of his students knew of his great love of music, mountain walking and skiing. He prided himself on his physical fitness and from an early age he had enjoyed walking and climbing in the mountains, liking nothing better than to enjoy the peace of nature. It was both fitting and tragic that he should die on a climbing holiday in the Swiss Alps at the early age of 53.

Author: Jonathan Sandy

Dental roll number: 263

The 21st Century

The start of the 21st century saw the College continuing its campus development as part of the Quincentennial celebration. The College acquired the large office building in Hill Street, which after refurbishment became the Adamson Centre, housing most of the College's administrative staff. Major redevelopment of the Symposium Hall has given the College a larger auditorium with modern audio-visual facilities. A refurbishment of and extension to the postgraduate residence will transform it into a modern hotel. Most ambitious of all a modern skills centre will be built on the site of the former Forbes Laboratory to provide better training facilities for the doctors and dentists of the 21st century and a new innovative public education facility to encourage public engagement with and understanding of medicine in society. Rarely in its proud 500-year history can the College have been in better heart.

Artist's impression of the clinical skills building
on the north side of the College campus.
The former Royal College's School of
Medicine building is on the right.

General Bibliography

Beaton, J., R. Millar and I. T. Boyle (eds) (1998),
Treasures of the College, Glasgow: Royal College of Physicians and Surgeons of Glasgow.

Comrie, J. D. (1932),
History of Scottish Medicine, London: Balliere, Tindel and Cox.

Creswell, C. H. (1926),
The Royal College of Surgeons of Edinburgh: Historical Notes from 1505 to 1905,
Edinburgh: Oliver and Boyd.

Dingwall, Helen (2003),
A History of Scottish Medicine, Edinburgh: Edinburgh University Press.

Dingwall, Helen (1995),
Physicians, Surgeons and Apothecaries: Medical Practice in 17th Century Edinburgh,
East Linton: Turkwell Press.

Dow, D. A. (ed.) (1988),
The Influence of Scottish Medicine, Carnforth, England: Parthonon.

Gairdner, J. (1860),
Historical Sketch of the Royal College of Surgeons of Edinburgh,
Edinburgh: Sutherland and Knox.

Guthrie, Douglas (1965),
Extramural Medical Education in Edinburgh, Edinburgh: E. & S. Livingstone.

Hamilton, David (1981),
The Healers: A History of Medicine in Scotland, Edinburgh: Canongate.

Kaufman, M. H. (2003),
Medical Teaching in Edinburgh during the 18th and 19th Centuries,
Edinburgh: The Royal College of Surgeons of Edinburgh.

Logan Turner, A. (1937),
The Story of a Great Hospital: The Royal Infirmary of Edinburgh, 1729–1929,
Edinburgh: Oliver and Boyd.

Masson, A. H. B. (2001),
A College Miscellany: Some Treasured Possessions of the Royal College of Surgeons of Edinburgh,
Edinburgh: Royal College of Surgeons of Edinburgh.

Masson, A. H. B. (1995),
Portraits, Paintings and Busts in the Royal College of Surgeons of Edinburgh,
Edinburgh: Royal College of Surgeons of Edinburgh.

Miles, A. (1918),
The Edinburgh School of Surgery before Lister. Edinburgh: A. & C. Black.

Plarr, V. (ed.) (1912–96),
Plarr's Lives of the Fellows of the Royal College of Surgeons of England, revised by D'Arcy
Power, vols 1–8, London: Royal College of Surgeons of England.

Porter, Roy (ed.) (1986),
Cambridge Illustrated History of Medicine, Cambridge: Cambridge University Press.

Ross, J. A. (1978),
The Edinburgh School of Surgery after Lister, Edinburgh: Churchill Livingstone.

Rutkow, I. M. (1993),
Surgery: An Illustrated History, St, Louis: Mosby.

Chronological List of the College Presidents

Between 1505 and 1580 there are no Minutes of the Incorporation to provide the names of the early Deacons and other officer-bearers. However, from the records of the Edinburgh Town Council during this period it has been possible to obtain some of the names of those holding the position of Deacon between 1535 and 1580, but the list is incomplete. From 1580 to the present day the list is continuous and complete.

Before the Charter of 1778, the Head of the Incorporation was referred to as Deacon and after this as President.

1535	Lancellot Barbour	1591	James Craig	1648	James Borthwick*
1536	Anthony Brussat	1592	Hendrie Lumisden	1651	David Kennedy
1539	George Leithe	1594	James Rig	1652	William Burnet
1543	William Quhite	1595	John Naysmyth*	1655	Thomas Kincaid*
1555	Alexander Bruce	1596	Hendrie Lumisden	1657	James Cleilland
1556	Alexander Bruce	1598	Andro Scott	1659	James Borthwick
1557	Nowie Brussat	1600	James Henrysoun	1661	William Burnet
1558	Alexander Bruce	1601	Henrie Aikman	1663	Walter Trumble
1559	Patrick Lindesay	1602	Gilbert Primrose	1665	Arthur Temple
1560	Robert Hendersoun	1603	James Skaithmure	1667	Thomas Carter
1561	Robert Hendersoun	1605	Hendrie Lumisden	1669	Arthur Temple
1562	James Lindesay	1606	James Kinloch	1671	Samwell Cheislie
1563	James Lindesay	1606	Andro Scott	1673	John Jossie
1564	James Lindesay	1608	James Kinloch	1675	William Borthwick
1565	John Chalmer	1610	Henrie Aikman	1677	George Stirling
1566	Nowie Bruis	1612	David Pringle	1679	James Nisbet
1567	Alexander Bruce	1614	James Henrysoun	1681	William Borthwick
1568	Nowie Brussat	1616	Andro Scott	1683	David Turnbull
1569	Alexander Bruce	1618	James Henrysoun	1684	David Pringle
1570	Alexander Bruce	1619	James Kinloch	1685	Thomas Edgar
1571	Records missing	1620	Andro Scott	1687	John Baillie
1572	Robert Hendersoun	1622	David Pringle	1689	George Stirling
1573	Nowie Brussat	1624	Henry Aikman	1691	John Raynolds
1574	Gilbert Primrose*	1626	John Pringill	1692	James Crawford
1575	Gilbert Primrose	1627	Andro Scott	1693	Gideon Eliot*
1576	Gilbert Primrose	1629	Laurence Cockburne	1695	Alexander Monteath*
1577	Gilbert Primrose	1631	John Ker	1697	Thomas Dunlop
1578	Robert Hendersoun	1632	John Spang	1699	Alexander Monteath
1579	Robert Hendersoun	1633	James Rig	1699	Gideon Eliot
1580	Gilbert Primrose	1635	John Pringill	1701	Alexander Monteath acts in place of Robert Clerk, who refuses to accept office
1581	Gilbert Primrose	1637	David Douglas		
1583	Robert Hendersoun	1639	John Pringle		
1584	Henrie Blyth	1640	David Douglas	1702	James Hamilton
1586	James Craig	1641	James Rig	1704	Henry Hamilton
1587	James Henrysoun	1642	John Scott		
1588	James Lindsay	1644	Alexander Pennycuik*		
1589	James Henrysoun	1646	David Douglas		

*Biography included in this book

1706	John Mirrie	
1708	Alexander Nesbet	
1710	Henry Hamilton	
1712	John Monro*	
1714	John Lauder	
1716	John McGill*	
1718	John Lauder	
1720	Robert Hope	
1722	John Knox	
1724	John Kirkwood	
1725	John Kennedy	
1726	John Kirkwood	
1728	John Kennedy	
1730	John Lawder	
1732	John McGill	
1734	John Kennedy	
1736	John Lawder	
1737	William Mitchel	
1739	George Cunninghame	
1740	Alexander Nesbet	
1742	George Langlands	
1744	George Lauder	
1746	George Cunninghame	
1748	Adam Drummond*	
1750	George Cunninghame	
1752	James Russel	
1754	Robert Walker	
1756	Thomas Young	
1758	William Chalmer	
1760	John Balfour	
1762	Alexander Wood*	
1764	James Rae*	
1766	James Brodie	
1768	Robert Smith	
1770	David Wardrobe	
1772	William Inglis*	
1774	Andrew Wood	
1776	Alexander Hamilton	
1778	James Gibson	
1780	William Chalmer	
1782	William Inglis	
1784	Thomas Hay	
1786	Forrest Dewar	
1788	Andrew Wardrop	
1790	William Inglis	
1792	Thomas Wood	
1794	Thomas Hay	
1796	James Russell*	
1798	Andrew Wood	
1800	James Law	
1802	John Bennet*	
1804	John Rae	

1806	William Farquharson	
1808	Andrew Inglis	
1810	Alexander Gillespie*	
1812	James Law	
1814	Sir William Newbigging	
1816	James Bryce	
1818	Alexander Gillespie	
1820	John Henry Wishart*	
1822	William Wood	
1824	David Hay	
1826	David Maclagan*	
1828	William Wood	
1830	John Gairdner*	
1832	John Campbell	
1834	William Brown	
1836	Sir George Ballingall*	
1838	Andam Hunter	
1840	Richard Huie	
1842	Andrew Fyffe	
1844	James Simson	
1846	Samuel Alexander Pagan	
1848	John Argyll Robertson*	
1849	James Syme*	
1851	James Scarth Combe*	
1853	Archibald Inglis	
1855	Andrew Wood	
1857	Robert Omond	
1859	Sir Andrew Douglas Maclagan*	
1861	Patrick Small Keir Newbigging*	
1863	Benjamin Bell*	
1865	James Dunsmure	
1867	James Spence*	
1869	James Donaldson Gillespie	
1871	William Walker*	
1873	James Simson	
1875	Sir Henry Duncan Littlejohn*	
1877	Sir Patrick Heron Watson*	
1879	Francis Brodie Imlach*	
1882	Sir William Turner, KCB*	
1883	John Smith	
1885	Douglas Moray Cooper Lamb Argyll Robertson*	
1887	Joseph Bell*	
1889	John Duncan*	
1891	Robert James Blair Cunynghame	
1893	Peter Hume Maclaren	
1895	Sir John Struthers*	
1897	John Chiene, CB*	
1899	James Dunsmure	
1901	Sir John Halliday Croom*	
1903	Sir Patrick Heron Watson	
1905	Charles Watson MacGillivray	

1907	Sir Joseph Montagu Cotterill, CMG*
1910	Sir George Andreas Berry*
1912	Francis Mitchell Caird*
1914	Sir James William Beeman Hodsdon, KBE
1917	Robert McKenzie Johnston
1919	George Mackay
1921	Sir David Wallace, KBE, CMG*
1923	Sir Harold Jalland Stiles, KBE*
1925	Arthur Logan Turner*
1927	Alexander Miles*
1929	James Haig Ferguson*
1931	John Wheeler Dowden
1933	Arthur Henry Havens Sinclair*
1935	Sir Henry Wade, CMG, DSO*
1937	William James Stuart*
1939	Harry Moss Traquair*
1941	John William Struthers, LLD
1943	Robert William Johnstone, CBE
1945	James Methuen Graham, LLD*
1947	Francis Evelyn Jardine
1949	Walter Quarry Wood
1951	Sir Walter Mercer*
1957	Sir John Bruce, CBE*
1962	James Johnston Mason Brown, OBE*
1964	George Ian Scott, CBE*
1967	James Roderick Johnston Cameron*
1970	Sir Donald Douglas, MBE*
1973	James Alexander Ross, MBE*
1976	Andrew Wood Wilkinson, CBE*
1979	Francis John Gillingham, CBE
1982	Sir James David Fraser, Bt*
1985	Thomas Jaffrey McNair, CBE*
1988	Geoffrey Duncan Chisholm, CBE*
1991	Patrick Stewart Boulter
1994	Sir Robert Shields
1997	Arnold George Dominic Maran
2000	Sir John Temple
2003	John A. R. Smith

*Biography included in this book

Abbreviations

BA (Bachelor of Arts)

BDS (Bachelor of Dental Surgery)

BSc (Bachelor of Science)

CB (Companion of the Order of the Bath)

CBE (Commander of the Order of the British Empire)

ChM (Master of Surgery)

CIE (Commander of the Order of the Indian Empire)

CMG (Companion of the Order of St Michael and St George)

DM (Doctor of Medicine)

DSc (Doctor of Science)

DSO (Distinguished Service Order)

FDS RCSEd (Fellow of Dental Surgery of the Royal College of Surgeons of Edinburgh)

FRCOG (Fellow of the Royal College of Obstetricians and Gynaecologists)

FRCS (Fellow of the Royal College of Surgeons)

FRCSEd (Fellow of the Royal College of Surgeons of Edinburgh)

FRCSEng (Fellow of the Royal College of Surgeons of England)

FRFPSG (Fellow of the Royal Faculty of Physicians and Surgeons of Glasgow)

FRS (Fellow of the Royal Society)

FRSE (Fellow of the Royal Society of Edinburgh)

HDD RCSEd (Higher Diploma in Dentistry of the Royal College of Surgeons of Edinburgh)

Hon FRCSEd (Honorary Fellow of the Royal College of Surgeons of Edinburgh)

KBE (Knight Commander of the Order of the British Empire)

KCB (Knight Commander of the Order of the Bath)

KCVO (Knight Commander of the (Royal) Victorian Order)

LDS (Licentiate in Dental Surgery)

LDS RCSEd (Licentiate of the Royal College of Surgeons)

LLD (Doctor of Laws)

LRCS (Licentiate of the Royal College of Surgeons)

LRCSEd (Licentiate of the Royal College of Surgeons of Edinburgh)

MA (Master of Arts)

MB BCh (Bachelor of Medicine, Bachelor of Surgery)

MB ChB (Bachelor of Medicine, Bachelor of Surgery)

MB CM (Bachelor of Medicine, Bachelor of Surgery)

MBE (Member of the Order of the British Empire)

MCh (Master of Surgery)

MD (Doctor of Medicine)

MDS (Master of Dental Surgery)

MRCOG (Member of the Royal College of Obstetricians and Gynaecologists)

MRCP (Member of the Royal College of Physicians)

MRCS (Member of the Royal College of Surgeons)

MSc (Master of Science)

OBE (Officer of the Order of the British Empire)

OM (Order of Merit)

PRSA (President of the Royal Scottish Academy)

RCOG (Royal College of Obstetricians and Gynaecologists)

RCSEd (Royal College of Surgeons of Edinburgh)

VRD (Volunteer Reserve Decoration)

Illustration List

Illustration List

Illustration List

p. 274 Major General J. M. Matheson. Photograph. (Courtesy of the Army Medical Services Museum)

p. 275 David Waterston. Photograph. (RCSEd)

p. 275 David Waterston. Photographs. (Courtesy of the Friends of the Children of Great Ormond Street Library, London)

p. 277 Sir Robert Wright. Photograph. (Courtesy of the Royal College of Physicians and Surgeons of Glasgow)

p. 279 Douglas Clark. Photograph by Elliot Robertson, 1982. (Courtesy of the Royal College of Physicians and Surgeons of Glasgow)

p. 281 Sir Donald Douglas. Photograph. (RCSEd)

p. 283 Arthur Hodgson. Photograph. (Courtesy of British Medical Journal Publishing Group)

p. 284 Walter Galbraith. Photograph. (Courtesy of the Royal College of Physicians and Surgeons of Glasgow)

p. 285 Patrick Steptoe. Chalk drawing. Peter Wardle. (Courtesy of the National Portrait Gallery, London)

p. 287 Aylwin Hitchin. Photograph. (RCSEd)

p. 288 Douglas Roy. Photograph. (Courtesy of Professor George Parks)

p. 290 William MacLennan. Photograph. (RCSEd)

p. 291 G. B. Ong. Photograph. (RCSEd)

p. 292 G. B. Ong. Photograph. (Courtesy of the Department of Surgery, University of Hong Kong)

p. 292 Examining team in Hong Kong. Photograph. (Courtesy of Mr I. F. MacLaren)

p. 293 Sir James Fraser Bt. Oil painting. Alan Sutherland, 1992. (RCSEd)

p. 294 Cast sculpture in College Museum. (Photograph by Max McKenzie)

p. 295 David Watt. Photograph. (RCSEd)

p. 296 Images from the Menzies Campbell Collection. (RCSEd)

p. 297 John Menzies Campbell. Photograph. (RCSEd)

p. 297 T. J. McNair. Oil painting. Alan Sutherland, 1992. (RCSEd)

p. 298 Images from the Menzies Campbell Collection. (RCSEd)

p. 299 Sir Michael Woodruff. Photograph. (RCSEd)

p. 299 Michael Woodruff with his father. Photograph. (RCSEd)

p. 300 Professor Woodruff with staff wards 13 and 14 and undergraduate clinics, summer term 1957. Photograph. (RCSEd)

p. 300 Michael Woodruff at the helm of his yacht. Photograph. (Courtesy of Lady Woodruff)

p. 301 J. I. P. James. Photograph. (Courtesy of Mr John Chalmers)

p. 302 Collage of orthopaedic surgeons, Princess Margaret Rose Hospital, Edinburgh. Illustration. Mark Proctor, 1975. (Courtesy of Mr Peter Abernethy)

p. 303 Geoffrey Chisholm. Oil painting. Victoria Crowe, 1992. (RCSEd)

p. 304 Robert Tinning. Photograph. (Courtesy of Mr John Chalmers)

p. 305 W. M. Oliver. Photograph. (RCSEd)

p. 306 Dorothy Geddes. Oil painting. Jane Allison, 1998. (Courtesy of the Faculty of Dental Surgery, RCSEd)

p. 308 William Houston. Oil painting. Jane Allison, 1992 (Courtesy of the Faculty of Dental Surgery, RCSEd)

p. 309 Artist's impression of the clinical skills building. Photograph. (RCSEd)

Index

Index

Index

Index

Index